POLYTECHNIC INSTITUTE OF BROOKLYN

MICROWAVE RESEARCH INSTITUTE

SYMPOSIA SERIES

I	Modern Network Synthesis	April 1952
II	Nonlinear Circuit Analysis	April 1953
III	Information Networks	April 1954
IV	Modern Advances in Microwave Techniques	November 1954
V	Modern Network Synthesis II	April 1955
VI	Nonlinear Circuit Analysis II	April 1956
VII	The Role of Solid State Phenomena in Electric Circuits	April 1957
VIII	Electronic Waveguides	April 1958
IX	Millimeter Waves	March–April 1959
X	Active Networks and Feedback Systems	April 1960
XI	Electromagnetics and Fluid Dynamics of Gaseous Plasma	April 1961
XII	Mathematical Theory of Automata	April 1962
XIII	Optical Masers	April 1963
XIV	Quasi-Optics	June 1964
XV	System Theory	April 1965
XVI	Generalized Networks	April 1966
XVII	Modern Optics	March 1967

Organized by
The Polytechnic Institute of Brooklyn
Microwave Research Institute
Department of Electrical Engineering

In Cooperation with
The Institute of Electrical and Electronics Engineers
Automatic Control Group
Circuit Theory Group
Information Theory Group
The Society for Industrial and Applied Mathematics

Co-Sponsored by
The Air Force Office of Scientific Research
The Office of Naval Research
The U.S. Army Research Office

Arrangements for this Symposium were sponsored in part by the Joint Services Electronics Program under Contract Number AF-49(638)-1402.

DISTRIBUTORS: **INTERSCIENCE PUBLISHERS, A DIVISION OF JOHN WILEY & SONS, INC. • NEW YORK • LONDON**

Symposium on System Theory, New York, 1965

PROCEEDINGS OF THE SYMPOSIUM ON

SYSTEM THEORY

NEW YORK, N. Y., APRIL 20, 21, 22, 1965

Microwave Research Institute Symposia Series

VOLUME XV

POLYTECHNIC PRESS
OF THE
POLYTECHNIC INSTITUTE OF BROOKLYN, BROOKLYN, N. Y.

Edited by
Jerome Fox

Associate Editor
Martha Crowell

Assistant Editor
Rose Krieger

Library of Congress Catalog Card Number 65-28522

TABLE OF CONTENTS

FOREWORD

WELCOMING ADDRESS

by

DR. ERNST WEBER
President, Polytechnic Institute of Brooklyn

I am very happy, indeed, to welcome this large gathering to the 15th Symposium in a series that started in 1952 and that has become a hallmark of Polytechnic. The selection of topics and of participants has set such a high level of discourse and publication that we can rightly be proud of the longevity and the general expectance of the series. It is certainly less difficult to choose a topic of current interest than it is to promise unusual treatment and to keep that promise.

There has been so much discussion as to the meaning and substance of System Theory that the selection of this topic could well be a real test of such promise. And perhaps it is unusual that we should find among the 26 authors, 12 representing engineering disciplines, 11 representing mathematics, and, in addition, one each from social sciences, from economics and from biomathematics. This could express, perchance, the conviction of our faculty, which approved three years ago a B.S. program and this last fall an M.S. and a Ph.D. program in System Science under the guidance of an interdepartmental committee composed of members of engineering departments and of mathematics. Some of the discussions in the faculty meeting, when the first proposal came before it, might have made interesting reading here.

Actually, the organizations that cooperated in the organization of this Symposium are indicative of the breadth of scope that the topic covers, namely Circuit Theory, Information Theory, Automatic Control, and Industrial and Applied Mathematics. In a sense, we could argue that a good deal of this symposium series has provided an intensifying preparation for this program; the very first symposium and the fifth were devoted to Modern Network Synthesis, the second and sixth to Nonlinear Circuit Analysis, the third to Information Networks, the tenth to Active Networks and Feedback Systems, and the twelfth to Mathematical Theory of Automata. Indeed, this is a progression in an integrative sense that provides many of the building blocks for an evolving structure of System Theory.

And, it is an evolving and not a finished structure that we are dealing with. Again looking at the list of authors, we should notice that 21 of the total number of 26 are associated with academic institutions, four come from large industrial organizations, and one from a nonprofit government-sponsored corporation. Clearly this emphasizes the creative role that universities can and should play in the systematization of concepts and methods of analysis and synthesis. And clearly, too, the leading faculty members in this effort will be the ones who have kept close to the pulse of our scientific and technological advances. It is indispensable for the strong schools of science and engineering to provide an atmosphere in which teaching and research go hand in hand and reinforce each other. In order to nourish the creative abilities adequately to their full unfoldment, large scale government support of university research has become a national necessity. The cosponsorship of this symposium by the research offices of the three services is a clear and most significant expression of a fruitful partnership which contributes so outstandingly to scientific advance.

Permit me to make one further observation. System Theory, particularly as it might be extrapolated to population problems, to economic and biological systems, and others, indicates the penetration of quantitative thought into areas to which engineering has already contributed such basic concepts as feedback, information content, realizability, modeling, etc. Modern technological society demands, moreover, increasing participation by engineers in the responsibilities of government, be it local, state or federal. It is therefore of great importance to provide all possible forums for interchange between all sectors of society. Realizing that science and engineering manpower represents a very small fraction of our total academically trained manpower, it will be imperative that we enlarge the scope of engineering education to include increasingly stronger programs in social and political science, in history and economics, in philosophy and in humanities. We must give to the engineering graduates the awareness of society's structure, of the interdependence of technological advances and social changes, of the irrepressible cravings of man, so as to equip them to discharge responsibilities to society that they will be expected to assume. The broadly ranging concepts and tools of System Theory may serve to accelerate the trends discernible now but still shrouded in early morning mist.

I should like to repeat the most cordial welcome on behalf of Polytechnic Institute of Brooklyn, and to call now upon the representatives of the cosponsors who so graciously joined us this morning.

GREETINGS FROM THE COSPONSORING AGENCIES

MAJOR GENERAL DON R. OSTRANDER
Commander, Office of Aerospace Research

Dr. Weber, ladies and gentlemen: I am delighted to be able to participate once again in the opening ceremonies of a Brooklyn Polytechnic Symposium. This fifteenth of the series, which is devoted to "System Theory," actually is the second in this same general field to be hosted here. The earlier one, you may recall, was entitled "Mathematical Theory of Automata" and was held here in April 1962, exactly three years ago. So much has happened in this field since then, not the least of which are the rather spectacular advances in computer theory and technology, that I feel we can now, with some clarity, recognize the emergence of a new sub-discipline of engineering science called "System Science." It is an area of science in which we of the Air Force have had a most vital interest for some time, dating at least from the design of the first airborne central fire control system of our World War II B-29's. Our reliance upon this developing body of science will inevitably increase as our systems become more and more complex and sophisticated.

We might ask: what is a system? Simply speaking, of course, it is a collection of objects interacting in some way. But for the study of systems to warrant being accepted as a science, the interaction must be accurately describable by mathematical relationships. And for system engineering these relationships must be tractable, at least to the degree that practicable applications can be found. As you know, most of the past advances in system theory have until recently been due to successful manipulations of linearized relations. Hopefully, modern computational techniques, and some successful inroads into the mathematics of nonlinear systems, will expand the applicability of the theory. Historically, early system science grew largely out of studies of electrical network theory and mechanical analogues. The science of system analysis, however, can now be extended to include applications to biological and chemical systems, and even, I suspect, to certain cases of individual and group social behavior. In this latter connection, I think one might even conceive of a contribution of system science to the solution of some of the problems of research management which arise in organizations such as you and I are associated with.

One such problem which is of continuing interest to *us* concerns the proper balance of research funding between management mechanisms such as the tri-services-supported Joint Services Electronics Program (which is cosponsoring this symposium), single-service-supported group research, and individual unsolicited research projects. It is a problem which all of us in organizations such as mine, which support basic research, constantly grapple with. Unfortunately, the resolution of this problem cannot await the extension of system science for an answer. We have to make decisions daily which affect this balance, and have to rely largely upon judgment or instinct.

Analyses of research programs conducted in universities throughout the country, including your own, indicate a continuing trend of the programs, as they grow, to coalesce in such a way that an institutional multi-disciplinary laboratory is born. Each such birth results in a decrease of dependence upon individual support by government research funds and a greater need for support of the total laboratory or group. There are many advantages to this latter method of funding and, in fact, the Air Force supports a number of group efforts this way. There are also disadvantages, both administrative and scientific. We are constantly trying to balance the advantages against the disadvantages and arrive at a proper ratio for the allocation of our available funds between this method of group support, and support of individual scientific investigators.

I haven't been able to find any magic, or even any very objective method of arriving at the optimum ratio. Certainly all basic research cannot and should not be supported solely by large group-effort type funding. I am also sure that the proportion will always have to be flexible from one funding cycle to the next. Whatever the ratio, however, I feel that it will depend strongly upon the same criteria that we have used in the past: namely, the quality of the scientific work and, in our case, its potential relevance to Air Force problems.

One factor which complicates our decisions on these matters is the fact that so much of modern science overlaps traditional scientific disciplinary boundaries. As an example, although the program which supports this symposium is called the Joint Services *Electronics* Program, it involves a number of investigations that a few years ago could hardly have been called electronics.

The result is that we are finding it increasingly important to perform continuing analyses of our programs in order to seek reasonably accurate descriptions of our work. In doing this, we are finding it increasingly difficult to retain the classical partitions between scientific disciplines. This in itself should neither surprise nor disturb us, for it merely reflects changes in the observable pattern of science which are the result of enormous expansions in our knowledge. It does mean, however, that as these partitions dissolve and as new disciplines and subdisciplines emerge, we must insure that our internal organizational structure and management philosophies keep pace. I am sure that this problem is not unique to those of us in government, but exists equally at university and research laboratory management levels. I am reminded of a recent remark by Professor Katchalsky which amused me, but which I thought was singularly appropriate. He said that modern electronics was like his wife, that while he could recognize her, he couldn't define her.

The emergence of "System Science" as a recognizable scientific-discipline, as an outgrowth of studies in electrical engineering, is another step in the progress of science which illustrates the changes that are taking place. It is a step, together with many others, that I hope we in the Air Force can continue to help make possible with moral and financial help to both individual research investigators and large group efforts.

In closing, I would like to comment upon the excellent cooperation we in the Air Force have experienced in our association with the laboratories of the Joint Services Electronics Program. The degree of coupling between the research accomplishments of these laboratories and the solution of practical Air Force scientific and engineering problems has been outstanding. We are confident that the future will be even more productive.

May I wish all of you here a most interesting and profitable meeting, and again express our pleasure to be able to assist as a cosponsor for this symposium.

CAPTAIN E. J. HOFFMAN, USN
Deputy and Assistant Chief of Naval Research

I am very happy to represent the Office of Naval Research as one of the cosponsors of this symposium. For many years we have enjoyed our association with this important series of symposia entrepreneured by the Microwave Research Institute of the Polytechnic Institute of Brooklyn.

ONR is a full participant in system theory research through a number of basic and applied research programs which are supported at universities and in industrial laboratories. We have also long been aware of the need to bring coherence to the mass of technical data that has been steadily accumulated and which may hopefully be interpreted and used by the methods of systems theory.

Certainly we can point to progress in the development and wider use of systems. In the postwar years the Navy has taken giant strides forward from the day when our most complicated system was fire control for a gun-battery. Today the speed, deadly accuracy and variety of weapons that can be employed against us require systems of great complexity and reliability to provide advance warning, and to enable us to defend ourselves and respond effectively.

Our ships are now equipped with the Naval Tactical Data System (NTDS) which joins together an entire task force into a single coherent fighting unit. We are designing new ships from the keel up, each as an integrated whole, matching weapon systems electronics equipment with hull design and crew composition, so that all these factors are viewed as components of a fighting system.

We can see increases in the sophistication of Naval command and control mechanisms. Integrated control is rapidly being achieved in individual combat vehicles through research conducted under such programs as the Joint Army-Navy Aircraft Instrumentation Research Program (JANAIR), where the objective is to achieve a simplified and unified cockpit display. There is also a related program known as Submarine Integrated Control (SUBIC), which is currently feeding into Navy's FRISCO system (Fast Reaction Integrated Submarine Control) now under development. Here involved are techniques for collecting data from all subsystems, such as ship control, propulsion, surveillance and communications, and for analytically selecting the best arrangements and combinations for accomplishment of intended missions. Presentation in unified displays results in greatly reduced delays in decisions and choices of action on the part of officers in command. In addition, integration of the communications circuits, which weave the individual Navy units into the broad pattern of national military deployment, permits increasing flexibility and rapidity of response to evolving situations.

Many of our efforts have been largely empirical. Thus, it is timely and appropriate that we devote the next few days to system theory. I have used the term system several times today; yet, fundamentally, few people can adequately define a system, and I am not one of them.

Sound theory can only come from carefully planned long-range programs of basic research. When ONR was established nearly 20 years ago, its primary mission was to support basic research in a variety of scientific areas. That is still our major mission today, although we include an appropriate mix of applied research and exploratory development.

We recognize, however, that providing for research is not enough; it also is important to insure that research results are widely disseminated. Toward this end, we continually sponor, either by ourselves or in partnership with other branches of the service and agencies, workshops and research symposia such as this one. This not only contributes to speeding up the process of dissemination, but also provides a platform for the investigator to clarify aspects of his work which may raise questions in the minds of his colleagues.

We like to bring together in these meetings representatives from government laboratories, industry and the campus, as well as scientists from abroad. I am pleased to note, for example, that this symposium includes papers by scientists from Germany and Argentina. This broad representation is likely to win a wider and more immediate acceptance of new ideas but, more important than that, stimulates an exchange of ideas that goes well beyond the formal papers presented.

I am sure that the impact and influence of this symposium will be significant. Simply focusing on system theory as an organized body of material will itself accomplish a great deal. I know that the Navy, as well as the other services, will greatly benefit from what is discussed here this week in ways we may not now anticipate.

DR. RICHARD A. WEISS

Deputy and Scientific Director, Army Research Office

It is a pleasure to participate again in an annual Polytechnic Symposium. This, the fifteenth, should provide a real service in assisting each of us in gaining a better understanding of "System Theory" and the many interrelated aspects of this problem. The Army is pleased to join with its sister services in cosponsoring these symposia. I would like to express my appreciation to those at the Microwave Research Institute and others who have assisted in making arrangements for this meeting.

In the tradition of these symposia, the subject of "System Theory" is a timely one. Later on this morning we will be addressed on the subject of "What is System Theory?" The Institute of Electronic and Electrical Engineers has defined an electronic system as "a complex assembly of primarily electronic subsystems and components designed comprehensively to accomplish a major end function or functions." I note that here, as is the case in other definitions, a system may range from a single discrete component to an entire complex of components such as a weapons, surveillance, or command and control systems.

The military expert, however, tends to evaluate the system or the subsystem as a totality and is likely to give more wholehearted acceptance to that research product which may be expressed in terms of actual or potential payoff. The Army supports many research programs directed toward the acquisition of new knowledge which may have application to a variety of system requirements. As the emphasis on the system approach to the solution of many of our problems increases, we are becoming ever more aware of the need to consider the relevancy of the human in the system. The Army Research Office actively pursues solutions to problems relating to operations research and the man-machine relationship. One area of particular interest is the military requirement for timely, accurate and complete intelligence. Work is currently progressing on the development of reconnaissance and surveillance systems and image interpretation facilities to meet this need. Effective system engineering and design, however, depend on data that define the capabilities of both the machine and human components.

Fullest exploitation of available resources is inhibited by lack of experience and traditional concepts which inhibit innovation. Freedom for innovation and improvisation, though very much desired, is restricted because innovation by intuition is not trusted. An analysis of intuition shows that it relies to a large extent on experience and the ability to relate experiences to meet sudden new demands by improvisation from resources at hand. In order to overcome, in part, the limitations imposed by the risk associated with lack of experience when defining new systems, the military must be provided with readily understandable data. This data should express the fundamental relationships between the quantities and basic qualities of parts and the structures and configurations composing the properties of the desired system. In order to replace dependence upon intuition and at the same time facilitate successful improvisation, data must be provided in conventional format, such as handbooks of tables, monographs, graphs and simple rugged special purpose computation devices to include slide rules and mechanized charts.

In recent years, Army demands for assured man-machine compatibility in all weapons and equipment systems have expanded human factors engineering and engineering psychology from simple studies concerning knobs and dials and after-the-fact retrofit modifications of equipment to a concept of system design. This includes the balancing off of the human operator against machine functions to optimize the efficiency and effectiveness of the entire system. In this expansion of its concern in engineering psychology, the Army has entered the stage in which it seeks to capitalize on the unique capabilities which the human being can contribute to the system. It is now increasingly necessary to evaluate the place of the human in the system as well as the ability of the human to utilize the system. In designing a new item, it is required at the earliest conceptual stages that the military mission of the item be reviewed with reference to the human factors affecting the design concepts. This leads to the need for identification of the man-machine-environment relationship and the interactions among these which will be critical to the success of the entire system. It is evident, as we review the work in our university laboratories and research institutions, that there is a strong shift of effort in this direction. Programs that support electronics research, for example, find more and more emphasis on tasks that instrument the study of the complex man in the design of input and output devices to his machines. Information science and systems theory are perhaps the fastest growing areas on the technological front today.

The answers to some of our questions related to systems theory will undoubtedly be revealed during the course of this symposium. The Army is pleased to participate, and on behalf of General Lotz, the Director of Army Research, I extend best wishes for a very successful conference.

DR. DONALD L. THOMSEN, JR.

Chairman of the Board, Society of Industrial and Applied Mathematics

On behalf of the Society for Industrial and Applied Mathematics (SIAM), we are very happy to present greetings to you on this occasion of the fifteenth Polytechnic Institute of Brooklyn International Symposium, and at the same time express our gratitude for your invitation to participate formally as a cooperating professional society. SIAM owes a great deal to the general support it has received over the years from members of the faculty and staff at the Polytechnic Institute of Brooklyn, and I think it appropriate to take this occasion to acknowledge that active interest and support. There has been a close and pleasant affiliation with some of those who are directly associated with organizing this symposium. This is only natural, since the activities of SIAM have to a considerable extent centered around the mathematics germane to system theory.

In the emergence of any new discipline, it is most helpful for a sympathetic atmosphere or medium to exist in which that discipline can grow. SIAM was founded in 1952 as a result of a need for a professional home for applied mathematics and, in particular, that kind of mathematics which finds its expression in problems in "control, communication, information processing, and economic forecasting." The mathematical theory of control is one excellent example of a subset of system theory which has received special attention within SIAM in recent years. No less important are the contributions of mathematics to the other aforementioned areas of system theory, and we are very gratified to see many presenting papers on your program who have made significant contributions to SIAM meetings and publications.

With the increased presence of mathematics in all fields of science and engineering, including such fields as system theory, one very important question should be constantly kept in mind. Namely, how to cope with the resulting demands on people and facilities at all levels for mathematics education, and especially applied mathematics education. I realize this may appear to be something of a digression, but the problems are so great and so unique to mathematics, particularly in the minds of some of those who are individual members of our Society from industry, that I cannot help making brief mention of them here. As an illustration of why demands are being placed upon existing resources for mathematics education, consider the fact that during the 60's, on the basis of conservative estimates, the number of bachelors' degrees in mathematics is expected to quadruple—a phenomenon not to be even approached by any other field of science or engineering. Along with this educational demand which is being created, the teaching loads of many mathematicians are steadily diminishing. There are numerous other contributing factors which add to this educational problem but, even so, one can begin to see measurable steps being taken by many groups, including a number of professional organizations, to correct the situation. Hence, with respect to every field of science and engineering which mathematics invades, one cannot help but be conscious of extraordinary educational requirements being generated. All I am suggesting is that we bear in mind at times this obvious need produced, in part, by the emergence of system theory, as we listen to the important papers to be presented during the next three days.

Again, let me thank you on behalf of SIAM for your invitation. We are very pleased to cooperate and we look forward with you to these excellent sessions on system theory..

DR. W. G. SHEPHERD
Vice President, Institute of Electrical and Electronic Engineers

It is a pleasure for me to represent the Institute of Electrical and Electronic Engineers at this Symposium. President Oliver was unfortunately unable to join with you and has asked that I bring you his greetings and best wishes for a successful conference.

The Institute has many reasons for welcoming this opportunity to cooperate with the Microwave Institute of the Polytechnic Institute of Brooklyn, and the Society for Industrial Mathematics, in organizing this Symposium. The IEEE, as a non-national organization, is particularly attracted to the international character of the significant series of symposia which the Polytechnic Institute has presented over the years. The topic System Theory is of interest to a major segment of the IEEE membership, exemplified by the fact that three of our professional groups, Automatic Control, Circuit Theory, and Information Theory, have participated in the formulation of the program. The Institute is happy to be able to reciprocate in some measure the interest which the faculty of Polytechnic Institute has shown in promoting the welfare of the Institute. In particular, Ernst Weber served as President of the IEEE at a critical point in its history when its predecessor societies, the IRE and the AIEE were merging. That process has been brought organizationally to a successful conclusion, and we are now pressing forward vigorously to serve the professional interests of the joined membership. We are particularly interested in serving this membership without regard to national boundaries in the best tradition of science. Joining in the sponsorship of a symposium such as this is therefore an opportunity the IEEE welcomes.

A symposium on "System Theory" to provide for a review of its status is timely. The accomplishments of our space program have brought, even to the general lay public, an increasing awareness of the complex systems necessary for the successful launching and control of space vehicles. The remarkable success of the Ranger shots, and particularly Ranger IX, gave a television audience the opportunity to participate vicariously in the experiment and to sense the extraordinary technology which made it possible.

This achievement exemplifies many others, less well heralded, which make possible the enormously complex technological civilization in which we live. Our ability to press forward will increasingly demand an organized disciplinary attack. World War II alerted the technological world to the needs for systems capability. The initial system efforts of that time were largely ad hoc and fragmented. Considerable progress has been made in the last two decades, but the emergent state of the discipline is perhaps best exemplified by the fact that it is thought necessary at a symposium on system theory to have as an opener a session bearing the title "What Is System Theory?" I make this comment in no invidious way. No one who has a technological background can fail to appreciate the enormous analytical complexities involved in the systems which produce goods and services for a modern society. One can only respect the courage and intellect of those who undertake to develop the scientific tools which will make possible a more orderly attack on the design of systems and improved predictions of their performance. It is encouraging that curricular efforts in system theory are beginning to appear at a number of institutions, and that symposia on the subject are occurring. Electrical and electronics engineers have a major stake in the success of these efforts, and it is for this reason that the Institute is happy to join in this symposium. On behalf of the membership of the Society I am happy to bring you greetings and our most cordial best wishes for a successful conference.

IS SYSTEM SCIENCE A DISCIPLINE?*

DR. EMMANUEL PIORE
Vice President and Chief Scientist, IBM

I am not going to define system theory, but system theory has become a respectable academic subject, and now that it has attained this great position, it is in search of a real curriculum, one that will stand on its own feet and not be derived from other disciplines. In IBM we pioneer in a lot of things, and five years ago we created, under a vice president, John McPherson, a Systems Research Institute.

We take in a group of about seventy-five people at a time and try to teach them something about systems in about three or four months. These people have to pass an exam. They have to have some ability to read and write. It is interesting, as one reviews that curriculum, to note that it reflects very much the program of this symposium. There's a very heavy emphasis on mathematics, on statistics, on analysis, and then one starts doing case studies pretty much as the lawyers do, of various systems that IBM has sold as services to customers. This characterizes, basically, the problem of trying to teach systems engineering or systems theory or something of that character. After you have done some mathematical analysis, then it is necessary to deal with real-life problems and it becomes a case-by-case analysis. It is difficult to get generalization, although we in IBM tried to generalize after our experience with the SABRE System, which is used by American Airlines for reservations and all the other problems in airlines. In approaching other systems, you look for the people who are involved in some system to get into a new system. They have experience. There is no formalism that can get passed on, and this is the state of affairs.

Another indication of whether a technology or science has reached maturity is whether it has a certain style and a certain taste. It is very difficult to be a great engineer or a great scientist; you have to have taste in your field. I don't know how to describe it any other way. In addition to taste, you have a certain approach to the problem. A great deal has been written about scientific method, and let's leave that alone. But if one reads some of the things that Conant has written on scientific methods, he always stresses the fact that scientific method is something that comes along to try to understand, to systematize, how a problem was done. Scientific method is not a procedure that is used in getting at a solution. But a scientist doesn't use scientific methods, or an engineer doesn't use scientific methods. He just lives. He tackles the problem. Then some sociologist or someone like that comes around and embroiders on the scientific method. Why do I state this? Because you look at a mathematician and he tackles a problem a certain way. You look at a physicist and he tackles a problem a certain way. A biologist tackles it a certain way. A mechanical engineer tackles a problem a certain way. The system engineer is yet to evolve this sort of concept. He

*Address presented by Dr. Piore at the banquet following the opening day of the Symposium on System Theory, Polytechnic Institute of Brooklyn, April 20, 1965.

does draw a bunch of little boxes and connects them with lines. I'll even go further. A physicist goes in the lab, he takes off his coat and if he wears a vest he takes off his vest. He rolls up his sleeves and takes his tie off. He gets to work. A biologist goes in the lab. The first thing he does is he puts on a white coat. Now they both do valid work but this characterizes the differences in sciences, the difference in various disciplines. The systems people have to evolve a style. Maybe bow ties or sandals will characterize them. I'm not trying to be humorous. These are the realities of the world and the laboratory.

Now I've talked about or mentioned the fact that people would like to consider systems and the relation of man and systems, and my spies tell me that the gentlemen from Washington were unhappy with the management of this symposium, because no consideration has been given to the man and machine environment. I understand the problem that one faces, that a pilot faces, an astronaut faces, etc. However, we are trying to make progress in a very tough, complicated technological area, systems design, systems engineering—whatever you want to call it—and you can only make progress if you can digest the problem. I propose to state tonight that the development of this whole systems area still requires further simplification to be able to digest the problem and we should not complicate it by putting man into it. It is a tough problem in its own right, just to take a look at a very simple computing mechanism. Let me try to supersimplify. A computer without man is a memory with some logic elements, arithmetic elements, control elements. This problem alone is tough to analyze. You design these computers—and I'm discounting all the peripheral gear—in terms of an art, in terms of a feeling. You don't know how well a computer works until it's put together and you try a specific problem. You're still trying to look for some generalizations. You're trying to acquire some kind of structure. This is a problem of first order of magnitude. We still must evolve methods of measuring and knowing what to measure. Putting man into it, although this may be an immediate problem that faces a lot of systems people, will not advance the state of the art until we understand simpler problems, of just trying to predict performance with a lot of logic elements, a lot of memories, etc. People invent algorithms and try to deal with them. But all algorithms are highly specific, and I have yet to see algorithms that have generalities in this general area. So I feel that, as far as the systems people are concerned, if you can deal with this highly simplified problem, tremendous progress has been made.

I have a notion where one can start dealing with man in the systems area, and again one goes into something that can be simplified. At the moment there is a great deal of activity going on in several schools and companies, in an area which we in IBM would like to call "computer-assisted instruction," where you try to use a computer in one way or another to program-instruct people who want to learn. There is a direct, meaningful relation that possibly can be built up. There's the whole history of using the direct approach of teacher and student to teach the multiplication table, and this may have a greater significance in understanding man/machine relations than worrying what do you do with an astronaut with all that machinery in the capsule. That's a super-complex problem—a completely artificial atmosphere physiologically, psychologically, and all that. Tackling a global problem is not the way to get clarity and thoughtfulness or progress in a real science, in spite of the pressures from Washington.

I raise these points because we are now in a perpetual revolution in revising our curriculum. You've got this whole problem of revising the curriculum, for the electrical engineer and for the mechanical engineer. There's a very nice paper from a Stanford group in the December 1964 issue of the *Proceedings of the IEEE* (J. G. Linvill, et al., Vol. 52, No. 12, pp. 1425-1429), which tries to deal with the integrated electronics vs. electrical engineering education. They have the standard block diagrams, but this deals with education. On one end they have systems; on the other end is "technology," with "devices," and "circuits," the other blocks coupled to systems. They are trying to decide what an undergraduate should be taught. It is obvious that he ought to be taught something about systems. At this point the only thing you can teach him about systems is the case method used at the Harvard Law School, or the philosophical method used at the Yale Law School, which is basically a case method with a little whipped cream on top of it.

This is one end of the spectrum, and at the other end, technology, you can start with solid state physics, with quantum mechanics, Maxwell's field equations, even Kirchhoff's laws. You must find a discipline and you must set a style—whether a person wears a bow tie or white coat, etc., as I alluded to earlier.

I know that technological advance in the future will depend on some very fundamental solutions in the systems area. Let me try to cite some examples. In the last twenty years we've been able to increase, through gadgetry, the speed of addition in the computer by a magnitude of 7. That's ten million times. We've been able to increase the size of memories, and it is just astronomical, the speed at which you can get at memories. We talk now of the billion bit store—its access is slow. But we can get a million bits and we start talking about nanoseconds. These very powerful tools have their own internal, intellectual dynamics to go faster and faster. You have transistors that switch in nanoseconds—silicon transistors. You have germanium that will switch faster. You dunk them in liquid air and they'll switch still faster. You've got the whole similar technological development in memories, etc. Now we face the problem of what to do with them systems-wise and we get stuck. That's why I'm trying to get man out of the picture. We've got just enough headaches without man in it to complicate it. When we understand this much, then let's bring man into it. How do we make use of all this wonderful technology in the system? This is tough. It's an artistic endeavor to do it.

Now where are we going? You know industry will sort of roll up its sleeves and move ahead. It always does, whether it understands something or not. The marketplace will determine whether a thing works, whether it is viable or not. There is a great opportunity in our academic institutions to get understanding with leisure. With leisure you have great opportunity to have brilliance, because brilliance just takes a great deal of leisure. This is really the challenge to the academic institutions in the system area—to make it an engineering discipline, a scientific discipline, to give it sort of an intellectual structure, to get almost order out of chaos or order out of an art. Brooklyn Poly, in running this symposium, and in being dedicated to starting a curriculum in this area, has a wonderful opportunity to be creative, to provide leadership, and I want to wish them good luck and God speed.

PROGRAM

SYMPOSIUM ON SYSTEM THEORY
April 20, 21, 22, 1965

TUESDAY, APRIL 20, 1965

Morning Session

WELCOMING ADDRESS
Dr. Ernst Weber, *President, Polytechnic Institute of Brooklyn*

OPENING REMARKS
Major General D. R. Ostrander, U. S. A. F., *Commander, Office of Aerospace Research*
Captain E. J. Hoffman, U. S. N., *Deputy and Assistant Chief of Naval Research*
Dr. Richard A. Weiss, *Scientific Director, Army Research Office*
Dr. Donald L. Thomsen, Jr., *Chairman of the Board, Society of Industrial and Applied Mathematics*
Dr. William G. Shepherd, *Vice President, Institute of Electrical and Electronics Engineers*

WHAT IS SYSTEM THEORY?
Chairman: E. Weber
Polytechnic Institute of Brooklyn

AN APPRAISAL OF THE STATUS AND FUTURE OF SYSTEM THEORY
R. F. Drenick, *Polytechnic Institute of Brooklyn (on leave at Technische Hochschule, Munich, Germany)*

MATHEMATICAL ASPECTS OF SYSTEM THEORY
R. Bellman, *The RAND Corporation, Santa Monica, Calif.*

A NEW VIEW OF SYSTEM THEORY
L. A. Zadeh, *University of California, Berkeley, Calif.*

TUESDAY, APRIL 20, 1965

Afternoon Session

REPRESENTATIONS OF SYSTEMS

Chairman: H. Hochstadt
Polytechnic Institute of Brooklyn

MONOTONIC OPERATORS AND CERTAIN SYSTEMS OF DIFFERENTIAL EQUATIONS
G. J. Minty, *University of Michigan, Ann Arbor, Mich., and Courant Institute of Mathematical Sciences, New York University, New York, N. Y.*

NONLINEAR NETWORKS
R. K. Brayton, *IBM Thomas J. Watson Research Center, Yorktown Heights, N. Y.*

A THEORY OF LINEAR SYSTEMS WITH STATE SPACES OF NON-FINITE DIMENSIONS
A. V. Balakrishnan, *University of California, Los Angeles, Calif.*

PARTITIONING AND TEARING LARGE SYSTEMS OF EQUATIONS
D. V. Steward, *University of Wisconsin, Madison, Wisc.*

TUESDAY EVENING—SYMPOSIUM BANQUET

IS SYSTEM SCIENCE A DISCIPLINE?
Guest Speaker: Dr. Emmanuel R. Piore
Vice President and Chief Scientist, IBM

WEDNESDAY, APRIL 21, 1965

Morning Session

SYSTEM DYNAMICS

Chairman: P. Mendelson
Polytechnic Institute of Brooklyn

CONCEPTS AND PROBLEMS OF MODERN DYNAMICS
L. A. MacColl, *Polytechnic Institute of Brooklyn*

DYNAMICAL SYSTEMS WITH INPUTS
E. O. Roxin, *University of Buenos Aires, Argentina*

SOME NOTIONS OF STABILITY AND RECURRENCE IN DYNAMICAL SYSTEMS
J. Auslander, *Yale University, New Haven, Conn.*

INSTRUCTION-CONTROLLED MACHINES
C. C. Elgot, *IBM Thomas J. Watson Research Center, Yorktown Heights, N. Y.*

COMPUTABILITY
M. Davis, *Yeshiva University, New York, N. Y.*

WEDNESDAY, APRIL 21, 1965

Afternoon Session

NON-DETERMINISTIC SYSTEMS

Chairman: M. Rosenblatt
University of California, San Diego, Calif.

ON SYSTEM MEASUREMENT AND IDENTIFICATION
W. L. Root, *University of Michigan, Ann Arbor, Mich.*

THE WOLD DECOMPOSITION PROBLEM
D. L. Hanson, *University of Missouri, Columbia, Mo.*

A GROUP-THEORETIC APPROACH TO CAUSAL SYSTEMS
R. Goodman, *Massachusetts Institute of Technology, Cambridge, Mass.*

APPLICATIONS OF FUNCTION SPACE INTEGRALS TO NONLINEAR DIFFERENTIAL EQUATIONS
M. D. Donsker, *Courant Institute of Mathematical Sciences, New York University, New York, N. Y.*

STOCHASTIC STABILITY AND THE DESIGN OF FEEDBACK CONTROLS
H. J. Kushner, *Brown University, Providence, R. I.*

THURSDAY, APRIL 22, 1965

Morning Session

OPTIMAL SYSTEMS

Chairman: D. Slepian
Bell Telephone Laboratories, Murray Hill, N. J.

PREDICTION AND FILTERING THEORY
R. E. Kalman, *Stanford University, Stanford, Calif.*

INFORMATION THEORY AND REAL INFORMATION
N. M. Abramson, *University of California, Berkeley, Calif.*

A SURVEY OF DETERMINISTIC OPTIMAL CONTROL THEORY
L. W. Neustadt, *University of Southern California, Los Angeles, Calif.*

OPTIMUM DEMODULATION OF SIGNALS THROUGH RANDOMLY FADING MEDIA
M. Schwartz, *Polytechnic Institute of Brooklyn*

LINEAR MEAN SQUARE FILTERING AND SMOOTHING WHEN PROCESS STATISTICS ARE UNDEFINED
D. E. Johansen, *Sylvania Electronic Systems, Waltham, Mass.*

THURSDAY, APRIL 22, 1965

Afternoon Session

APPLICATIONS OF SYSTEM THEORY

Chairman: H. W. Kuhn
Princeton University, and Mathematica, Inc., Princeton, N. J.

SYSTEM ENGINEERING
J. G. Truxal, *Polytechnic Institute of Brooklyn*

A FEEDBACK REALIZATION OF A CONTINUOUS-TIME OPTIMAL FILTER
S. L. Fagin, *Sperry Gyroscope Co., Great Neck, N. Y.*

CERTAIN PROBLEMS IN THE APPLICATION OF MATHEMATICAL ECONOMICS
M. D. Godfrey, *Princeton University, Princeton, N. J.*

MATHEMATICS IN BIOLOGY
H. Cohen and S. I. Rubinow, *Cornell School of Medicine, New York, N. Y.*

POLYTECHNIC INSTITUTE OF BROOKLYN
MICROWAVE RESEARCH INSTITUTE

Ernst Weber, *President*
F. B. Llewellyn, *Director of Research*
C. G. Overberger, *Dean of Sciences*
J. G. Truxal, *Dean of Engineering*

SYSTEM THEORY SYMPOSIUM COMMITTEE

R. F. Drenick, *Co-Chairman*
L. Shaw, *Co-Chairman*

H. Hochstadt
A. E. Laemmel
W. A. Lynch
E. J. Smith
J. G. Truxal
D. C. Youla

J. Fox, *Secretary*

THE JOINT SERVICES TECHNICAL ADVISORY COMMITTEE

R. O. Parker, *Executive Secretary*

THE AIR FORCE OFFICE OF SCIENTIFIC RESEARCH
J. F. Masi
E. P. Gaines

THE OFFICE OF NAVAL RESEARCH
I. Rowe
A. Shostak

THE U. S. ARMY RESEARCH OFFICE
H. Robl
S. B. Levin

COOPERATING PROFESSIONAL SOCIETIES

THE INSTITUTE OF ELECTRICAL AND ELECTRONICS ENGINEERS
O. Hugo Schuck, *Chairman, G-AC*
R. J. Schwarz, *Chairman, G-CT*
M. Schwartz, *Chairman, G-IT*

THE SOCIETY FOR INDUSTRIAL AND APPLIED MATHEMATICS
J. B. Rosser, *President*

The committee wishes at this time to acknowledge gratefully the encouraging support and assistance of Mrs. Gene Bond, of the Institute of Electrical and Electronics Engineers, throughout all fifteen of this series of symposia.

AN APPRAISAL OF THE STATUS AND FUTURE OF SYSTEM THEORY

R. F. Drenick

*Department of Electrical Engineering, Polytechnic Institute of Brooklyn, Brooklyn, N. Y.**

The idea of a general theory of physical systems, man-made or not, is of quite recent origin. It was suggested by the observation that the various theories which have grown out of engineering in the last two decades seemed to invite a unification in a common conceptual framework. Yet only portions of the framework exist at the present time. It is the purpose of this paper to review the portions that exist, to speculate on how they might be fitted together, on how they might have to be supplemented, and on what the main features of the resulting theory might be. In a sense, this paper is also a brief for the symposium and for its make-up. As the symposium is constituted, it is intended as a review of those theories which are likely to impinge on system theory, or which are likely to be affected by it, if it is ultimately successful.

There is a suspicion in many minds that "system theory" is merely another of the several concepts which have come out of engineering, especially out of electrical engineering, in recent years, which have defied all attempts at definition, and which in the end perhaps did not seem to have been really worth defining in the first place. The present symposium is intended to dispel this suspicion. It is devoted to the proposition that a mathematical theory of physical systems is a meaningful and important field of study, and the papers to be presented here, whether invited or contributed, were selected with this aim in mind. It is hoped that the proposition will be borne out.

The program should, more specifically, be indicative of the scope of system theory as a field of applied mathematics and, to a lesser extent, it should suggest and review fields of possible application (for, as is well known, not all of applied mathematics is also applicable). It is quite possible, however, that the program will leave yet another impression, namely, that a theory of systems in its own right does not really exist. This impression is also not quite unintended. For it is a fact that no general theorems have been proven and no general results obtained which were consciously derived with the idea of being applicable to all physical systems or even to large classes of such systems. There has been very fundamental work done, for instance, on dynamical systems (especially the linear ones), on random processes, on discrete-state machines, and in other fields, all of it bound to have important bearing on a theory of systems, but all of it more specialized in scope and intent than the theory. Nevertheless, it is this kind of work that is most strongly represented in this program. It may thus be indicative

*On leave at Technische Hochschule, Munich, Germany.

Presented at the Symposium on System Theory
Polytechnic Institute of Brooklyn, April 20, 21, 22, 1965

more of the scope of a future system theory than of an existing one, and it may point up its deficiencies rather than its achievements. If the program does this it could only be to the good in the long run.

Typical, in this respect, are the three important theories of optimal systems which have come out of engineering in the last two decades, namely, the theories of filtering, of control, and of communication. They can be arranged in a hierarchy of conceptual difficulty which shows up some curious and intriguing inconsistencies among them. It is most tempting to ask whether or not these inconsistencies cannot be removed and whether it might not be one of the first tasks of system theorists to try and remove them.

The simplest of the three is filtering theory. Its central problem, in rough terms, is shown in Fig. 1.

Two inputs x and z are fed into a system and an output y is generated from them. The input x is often called the "signal" in the vernacular of the communications engineer, z the "noise," and the system is called the "channel." The problem is this: It is desired to operate on the output y (which is a combination of signal and noise) with a second system called a "filter" and to choose the latter in such a way that its output v is as close as possible at all times to the original signal x. It is customary to insist further that the filter be a causal device.

This formulation of the filtering problem is incomplete in many respects. One must establish certain ground rules under which the various possible filters are judged relative to each other and the best one among them selected. In the form in which it was posed and solved by N. Wiener in 1941, signal and noise were taken to be random processes with meaningful second-order statistics, the channel was linear, and the criterion of optimality was taken to be the mean square error. Professor Kalman in his talk will discuss the filtering problem and certain related ones, as well as some of the more recent developments that have taken place in its treatment.

The papers by Professor Schwartz, Mr. Fagin, and Mr. Johansen fall into this area, also. Professor Schwartz in particular brings to bear the machinery of functional analysis on the problem of demodulating a signal which has been distorted by a passage through a randomly varying medium. The term "demodulating" is here in effect a synonym for "filtering," and "medium" one for "channel."

Mr. Johansen's paper is more specialized. It deals with the filtering of a signal from noise if it is deterministic, but otherwise largely unknown. Mr. Fagin in his paper describes a realization of a continuous-time filter which employs feedback.

The formulation of the filtering problem given above is fairly generally ac-

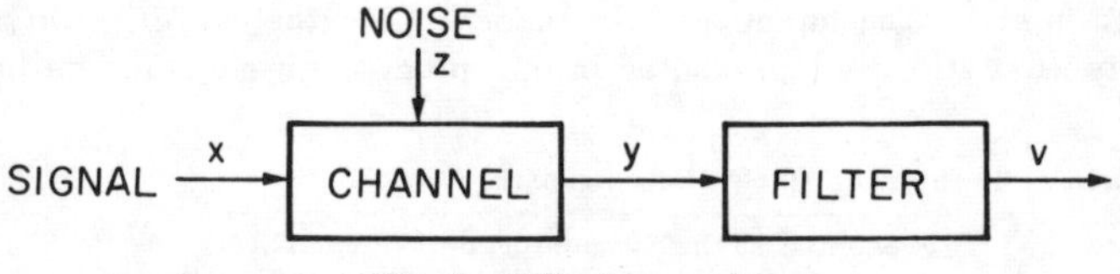

Fig. 1. Filtering problem.

cepted, in the writer's opinion, and will probably recur in roughly this form in Professor Kalman's paper. There is much less agreement on what constitutes the basic problem of control theory. One formulation which seems to come fairly close to the heart of the matter is the following.

Given, as in the filtering problem, is a system with two inputs *x* and *z* (see Fig. 2). The terminology is a little different here, however; *x* is called the "control signal" and *z* goes under various names such as "noise" or "disturbance" or also "uncertainty." The system used to be called the "load," more recently, the "plant" or the "object," and, most recently (and most unfortunately because of various possible confusions), the "process." The problem is this: The plant (as we shall call it here) is to be preceded by yet another system, now fairly universally referred to as the "controller" whose input is a signal *u* (the "reference"). The controller is to be so chosen that the plant output *y* is as close as possible at all times to the reference *u*. It is again usually required that the controller be a causal device.

This formulation, just as that of the filtering problem above, is incomplete but can be supplemented and extended by adding similar information. The two problems are evidently quite symmetrical in the formulation we have given them here, a fact which is perhaps worth remarking because it is not often noted. The reason for this oversight is simple: the distinctions which lie beneath the symmetry are more striking than the symmetry. Three of them are quite relevant here:

1) Firstly, it is quite possible to assume in the control context that there is no noise (or disturbance or uncertainty) allowed in the plant. The so-called "deterministic" theory which results from that is far from trivial. On the contrary, the most thoroughly studied portion of control theory deals with just this case and Professor Neustadt will describe it in his paper. The reason for the nontriviality lies essentially in the constraints which are often placed on the choice of the controller: the more restricted the choice, the more difficult it tends to be mathematically. (In the filtering problem, comparable restrictions

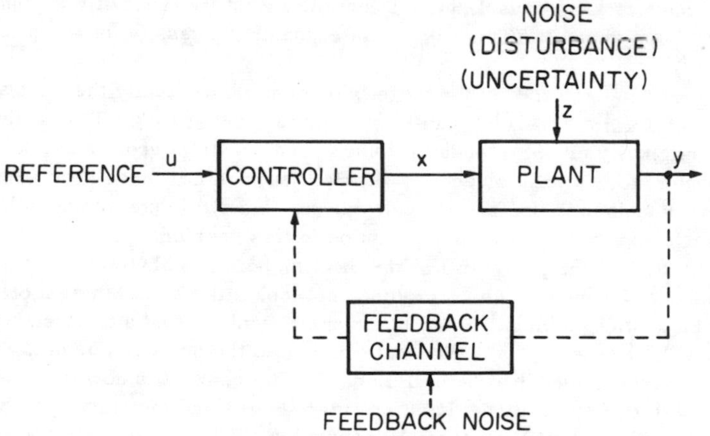

Fig. 2. Control problem.

have never been considered, perhaps because they have never been suggested by practice, and nothing is known of what difficulties may be introduced by them).

It should not go entirely unreported here, however, that the control problem formulation with noise-free plants is questioned on occasion, its mathematical interest notwithstanding. One can argue that control rarely makes much sense in practice, and is rarely even considered, unless there is some uncertainty in the plant. The deterministic theory, from this point of view, unavoidably suffers from an air of unreality. It is easier, however, to raise this objection than to remove it, the main problem being that of how to formulate mathematically the notion of "uncertainty." Some like to equate it with probability, an idea which has no doubt contributed to the development of the stochastic counterpart of deterministic control theory, a field with which Dr. Kushner's paper is concerned. The equation between "uncertainty" and "probability" is not really satisfying, however, in the opinion of many, yet no one has come up with a generally accepted alternative, not even the statisticians who have been struggling with this problem for some time. Professor Zadeh will direct much of his talk at this question of the fuzziness (as he calls it) of systems, and will in fact propose an altogether novel approach to it.

2) A second feature which distinguishes a control system from a filtering system is that it is very often permissible and advisable to introduce "feedback," that is, a channel along which the signal y can be fed back and utilized by the controller (see Fig. 2). This channel may or may not be noisy. (A symmetrical assumption can also be made in the filtering problem. There, however, the parallel channel is a feed-forward path whose inclusion does not lead to any interesting questions and in fact may make the problem vacuous).

3) The deepest-seated distinction between filtering and control problems, however, is the following: the plant in a control system is typically a device with what is often called "inertia." By this one means that the value of the control signal x injected into the plant at any one time will cause after-effects which will be present in the output for considerable time, possibly even infinitely long, thereafter, and which must therefore be taken into account in the optimal choice of that value of x. A causal optimal controller must, in terms of the popular slogan, "plan ahead." (There is no corresponding necessity for an optimal filter to do so.)

The most natural and, in the writer's opinion, conceptually the most appealing way of drawing up such plans is by dynamic programming. This method, although originally (1946) intended for use in mathematical economics, has been first applied to control problems by Dr. Bellman, and has since been widely used and proven eminently useful. He will discuss this procedure, along with other topics relevant to our symposium, later on in this session.

Information theory, the third of the theories born and abstracted out of engineering, deals basically with a problem that looks like a combination of a filtering and a control problem. Given is a system, again called a channel, with two inputs x and z (see Fig. 3). The latter is called the noise, as before, and the former sometimes the "transmitted signal." The channel is now to be supplemented with two auxiliary devices, one preceding it and the other following it. These could be called the "controller" and the "filter," and probably would be if information theory had developed from the control and filtering theories. But it

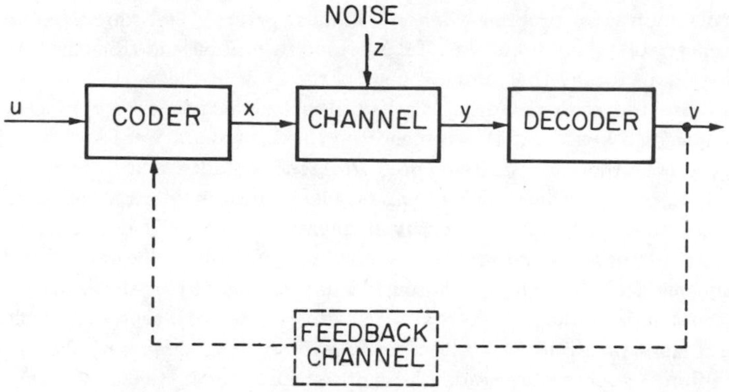

Fig. 3. Communications problem.

has not. It developed from communication problems and the terms most appropriate there seemed to be "coder" and "decoder," and this is what the devices are generally called. These two are to be so chosen that the original signal u and the terminal signal v are as close as possible to each other at all times.

One might expect that, regardless of terminology, the methods that proved useful in control and filtering theories might also be useful in information theory, and vice versa. Similarly, one might expect that results obtained in one field might at least resemble those obtained in the others. But, as will no doubt become apparent from Professor Abramson's talk, this is hardly the case. The most fundamental results of information theory are not so much conditions under which optimum coders and decoders exist, nor methods by which they can be found. They are, instead, conditions under which a prescribed performance can be achieved in the first place, optimally or otherwise. These are summarized in Shannon's famous coding theorems. These conditions do not involve any consideration of causality in its coders and decoders. On the contrary, noncausal devices are admitted as freely as causal ones, and are in fact necessary if the performance is to be achieved which is achievable according to the coding theorems. Dynamic programming which one might expect to be appropriate to at least the coder design has never been used for this purpose. Nor does there exist a deterministic information theory which would correspond to deterministic control theory.

Conversely, the concept of entropy and those related to it which play such a strikingly central role in information theory have, for some puzzling reason, never turned up in control or filtering theory. In fact, there are no theorems known in filtering or in control theory of a breadth and depth comparable to those of the coding theorems. Perhaps all this is as it should be but, at least to the writer's knowledge, no evidence has been produced whether or not it is.

The three theories discussed here deal in one way or another with system performance and, in fact, most often with optimal performance. It seems unlikely, however, that the most basic properties of systems in general should be related in any very intimate way with an optimality concept. On the other hand, it is not quite obvious what properties of systems should be considered the most basic and which problems concerning systems the most pressing.

The ideas on what problems deserve highest priority and which features are the most noteworthy no doubt vary from person to person and from time to time. It is probably safe to say that, until recently, the bulk of the work on physical systems was directed at the calculation, or at least at an adequate characterization, of the output of a system if the system itself and its input were known. It is interesting to note that, by contrast, both Professors Zadeh and Root give high priority in their papers to the problems of system representation and system identification, neither of which has received much attention until recently.

The first of these is the problem of how to represent in the language of mathematics a completely known and thoroughly understood physical system. A closely related problem is perhaps also that of how to convert one representation into another, if more than one exists, and of how to do this adequately and efficiently. The solution to such problems can be quite simple, for instance, if the system is simple or if one can be satisfied with a summary representation, but it can be most difficult if the system is very complex. The paper by Mr. Steward describes a case in point here.

The problem of identification, by contrast, concerns systems which are not completely known and understood. In such cases, one asks what tests to apply to the system to establish its nature (in terms of some chosen representation) or at least some particular relevant feature.

A system, in recent parlance, is a device which accepts one or more inputs and generates from them one or more outputs. No discussion of the subject would be complete without at least mentioning that a system is the same thing as a

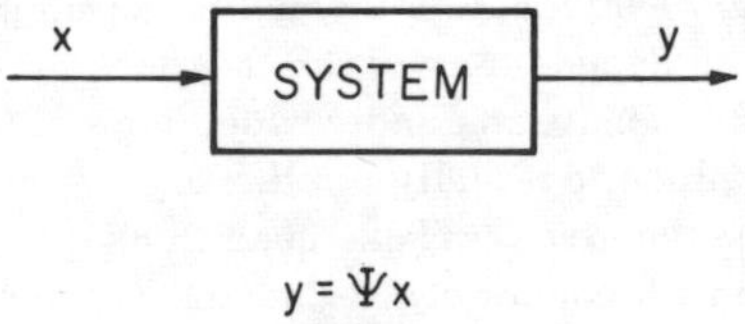

Fig. 4. The "black box."

"black box" and that it is usually pictured as shown in Fig. 4. Mathematically, a system is typically represented by an operator, Ψ, say, and the input-output transformation which it induces by

$$y = \Psi(x). \tag{1}$$

The input x is an element in the domain X of Ψ (also often called the input-space) and it is a function of a parameter t, the time:

$$x = \{x_t;\ t \in T\}.$$

Time is always a real parameter. It may vary over an interval (proper or improper), in which case x is called a "continuous-time" input, or it may vary over some set of consecutive integers, in which case x is a discrete-time input. The components x_t of x are drawn from component spaces X_t which are always taken to be identical. Each may contain a finite number of points, or countably many, or it may be a continuum. It may be one-dimensional, more generally finite-dimensional, or infinite-dimensional, or even abstract. In any case, the domain X is a product space

$$X = \prod_{t \in T} X_t .$$

The range Y of Ψ is a similar space. It too, is a product of coordinate spaces Y_t.

The representation problem may be thought of as the problem of finding expressions for the operator Ψ in terms of others which are considered more manageable or more clearly indicative of certain properties of the system. One step in this direction almost suggests itself. The special nature of the range and domain of the operator Ψ allows a special representation: in this, each of the coordinates y_t of y is written as a function (or, more generally, as a functional) of x. That is,

$$y_t = \psi_t(x) = \psi_t(x_\tau;\ \tau \in T), \quad (t \in T). \tag{2}$$

The representation (2) is equivalent to (1). It is, however, more explicit, and has been used as a starting point for other and yet more detailed representations. Thus, in cases of continuous component spaces X_t and Y_t, series expansions have been proposed for the functionals ψ_t along the lines of the Taylor and orthogonal series. For finite coordinate spaces, matrix representations and graphs have been proposed. It is possible that Professors Root and Zadeh will describe some of these in their papers. For systems with a countable X_t, Professor Davis has introduced a special and, by now, quite well-known formalism.

The functional representation (2) is also useful in another respect. It allows the definitions of some of the most important properties of systems in general. For example, systems with the property that all functions ψ_t are identical are those most often considered in physics and engineering. They are called "stationary" or "time-invariant."

More important, however, than stationarity is the concept of system causality which has already been mentioned repeatedly here. The term is applied to systems whose output at any one time depends on the inputs only up to that time, at most, but not beyond it. It is a most important concept for it is a quite generally accepted assumption that no physical device, man-made or natural, can react to inputs otherwise. The property of causality in a system can be defined by a direct translation into mathematical language: one specifies that

$$y_t = \psi_t(x_\tau;\ \tau \in T,\ \tau \leq t), \quad (t \in T). \tag{3}$$

The distinction between causal and noncausal systems is evidently most significant and it is difficult to envisage a system theory in which it does not play an important part. This prospect is reflected in several topics discussed at this symposium into which the concept of causality enters, explicitly or implicitly.

The notion is, of course, hardly new to the natural sciences. On the contrary, it has had the loving attention of philosophers for a long time already, with the result of a gigantic literature on the subject which can only be done justice to by yet another philosopher. It is the writer's impression, however, that the traditional sense of the term is not quite that expressed by eq. (3). Rather, it is one which has been given its mathematical form essentially by Leibnitz, and according to which the state of a system at any time is completely determined by its initial state. This version does not concern itself with the response to an input as does (3). It is, on the other hand, the causality concept which underlies classical physics and dynamical theory, and it is also the one which has had to be reviewed under the impact of quantum and relativity theory.

The definition of causality by (3) seems to be the more general one, at least potentially. Unfortunately, it is not altogether satisfactory for at least one (but probably more than one) reason. This is the fact that the operator Ψ need not be, and in most cases in practice actually is not, single-valued. (According to recent mathematical usage, one should therefore avoid the term "operator" altogether and say "relation" instead; however, the latter seems too nondescript and insipid a term to be appropriate in a theory of systems). The nonuniqueness of Ψ is of course transmitted to the functionals ψ_t as well. Instead of (2) and (3), one must accordingly write

$$y_t = \psi_t(x, p_0) = \psi_t(x_\tau,\ p_0;\ \tau \in T), \quad (t \in T) \tag{4}$$

and

$$y_t = \psi_t(x_\tau,\ p_0;\ \ \tau \in T,\ \tau \leq t), \quad (t \in T) \tag{5}$$

where p_0 is a parameter which indexes the multiplicity of y_t for a given x, and which is often called the "initial state" of a system.

The phenomenon of nonuniqueness of y, and also the terminology for p_0, come about in the following way.

It is admittedly highly desirable for a system to be given in one of the forms (1) to (5) but, unfortunately, it is a rare case indeed for this to be so in practice. Much more often than not, it is the inverse operator Ψ^{-1} that is given rather than Ψ, and in fact not even Ψ^{-1} but certain functional representations related to Ψ^{-1}. To be more specific, in practice, Ψ^{-1} is typically both causal and single-valued. It therefore has a functional representation of the form (3), say,

$$x_t = \psi_t(y_\tau,\ \tau \leq t).$$

(For the sake of brevity, the notation $t \in T$ is omitted). On occasion, systems are actually stated in terms of the functionals ψ_t themselves, or else are easily converted to them. More frequently, however, it is another set of functionals, ϕ_t, that is given. In the case of discrete time, they are of the form

$$y_t = \phi_t(x_t;\ y_{t-1},\ y_{t-2}, \ldots), \tag{6}$$

which differs from the ψ_t only in that y_t is expressed in terms of x_t and $y_{t-1}, \ldots$ rather than x_t in terms of $y_t,\ y_{t-1}, \ldots$. If the ϕ_t are functions of only a finite number of $y_{t-\nu}$, n, say, (6) is a difference equation order n. When time is continuous, one has sometimes as a counterpart to (6):

$$y_t = \phi_t(x_\lambda,\ t - \Delta t < \lambda \leq t;\ y_\tau,\ \tau \leq t - \Delta t), \quad (\Delta t > 0). \tag{7}$$

More often, a differential, or differential-difference, equation is given which can be thought of as being derived from (7) by letting $\Delta t \longrightarrow 0$ in a suitable way. Needless to say, this transition is not always possible and, even if it is, it need not lead to an expression that contains differential or difference operators of only finite orders. In other words, there are many continuous-time systems that are not representable by differential or differential-difference equations. Nevertheless, those that are, are the ones that occur most often in practice or at least are those that have been studied the most.

There exists a terminology of quite long standing which applies to representations such as (6) or (7). It is customary to combine the output variables y_τ and ϕ_t into a vector p_t and to call it the "state" or "phase" vector of the system. Thus, in (6) the state vector would be denoted with

$$p_t = \{y_{t-1}, \, y_{t-2}, \ldots\}$$

and it would be finite- or infinite-dimensional depending on how many of the variables $y_{t-1}, y_{t-2}, \ldots$ entered ϕ_t. (It is customary to assume that this dimensionality does not vary with t.) In (7) the corresponding vector would be

$$p_{t-\triangle t} = \{y_\tau; \; \tau \le t - \triangle t\}.$$

In those cases, in which ϕ_t contains derivatives of y_t, those, too, are included in the state vector.

The set of states (phases) of a system is called its state (phase) space. In many cases, it is simply a product of the output (coordinate) spaces Y_t. It may then consist of a finite number of points, or of a countable infinity, or it may be a continuum, depending on the nature of the spaces Y_t. In any case, the functionals ϕ_t induce on it a family of transformations whose members carry the state space into itself. In the case of discrete-time systems, those members can be indexed by t and x_t. The same is true for systems described by differential equations. For those described by equations of the form (7), the transformations are indexed by t, $\triangle t$, and by input segments $\{x_\lambda, \, t - \triangle t < \lambda \le t\}$.

A system which is characterized by the functionals ϕ_t can evidently be characterized as well by the state transformations which they induce. The latter have been almost universally preferred so far.

The problem which suggests itself immediately in connection with systems given in terms of their operator Ψ^{-1} (or of some version of the functionals ϕ_t) is the inversion of the operator, i.e., the determination of the functionals ψ_t. At least until recently, this inversion has been interpreted as follows. It was assumed that the initial state of the system, p_0, is known at the time t_0. It was further assumed that the system was driven by one well-defined input x. An effort was then made at determining the evolution of the state p_t for $t > t_0$. Once this was found, the evolution of the output y_t was known also, as a matter of course, and so were the functionals ψ_t. Each of these was thus indexed by the initial state p_0, thence their nonuniqueness and the expressions (4) and (5). The determination of p_t (or of y_t or ψ_t) was then called the "solution" of the functional (i.e., differential or difference or other) eq. (6) or (7). The problem of finding a solution in this sense has been of primary concern for many years.

It soon became evident, however, that the systems and inputs for which solutions in accepted forms could be determined were extremely rare. An effort was accordingly made to search for properties of these solutions which could be found under fairly general conditions even if the solutions themselves were unattainable. This effort led to a large and handsome body of theory, usually called "dynamical theory." The conditions that underlie it are essentially threefold. It is required that

i) the input be fixed,

ii) the state space transformations be continuous, and

iii) they form a group.

Dynamical theory is discussed in two papers at this symposium, one by Professor MacColl, who plans to give a broad review of the theory, and the other by Professor Auslander, who will report on some more recent developments in which he himself has had a hand. In addition, the paper by Dr. Brayton will discuss a recent and very interesting application of some of these notions to the theory of nonlinear electrical networks.

It is probably correct to say that dynamical theory has its origin in the nineteenth-century study of celestial mechanics, and that one can still recognize that origin in many of its concepts and issues. The concept of stability is a rather typical example. Originally, by all indications, it arose from the question of whether or not the solar system, in its present configuration, is stable. Or, to put the question a little more precisely: is the present configuration of the solar system permanent, disregarding perturbations from the outside, or is it merely the initial state to another, perhaps altogether different configuration? To this, one can add a second supplementary question: if the present configuration is in fact permanent, from what initial states of sun and planets could it have been reached in the first place?

The concept of stability has had a good deal of attention lately, especially in control theory, but basically, it seems, for an essentially different reason. In many modern man-made systems it is important that the output of the system be, at least in the long run, independent of the initial state. (It would not be acceptable, for instance, to have a television receiver whose output on one channel depended on the state induced in it at switch-over from another). This requirement of the irrelevance of the initial state is a stability requirement of a kind and, at least in certain cases (for instance, in linear systems), equivalent to the classical concept.

Some of the notions and problems of dynamical theory, such as that of stability, will thus carry over, with or without modifications, to system theory while others will have to be quite substantially extended. The most serious restriction that, from this point of view, overlies dynamical theory is the single-input requirement. Historically, the restriction is eminently understandable. In celestial mechanics one dealt with unpleasantly nonlinear differential equations, but always with single and, for that matter with extremely simple, inputs. Typical were constants and sine waves. The input x, all of whose components x_t vanished, was particularly often employed because it represented, in many cases, the input-free or "autonomous" (as it was called) operation of the system. The example of the solar system is a case in point. (The term "nonautonomous" used to denote the opposite of this, but has more recently, and quite unfelicitously, been applied also to autonomous but nonstationary, i.e., time-varying, systems.)

From the viewpoint of system theory, however, the restriction to a single input, and especially to one with a simple analytic expression, is highly undesirable. The desideratum here is the search for properties which hold for the outputs generated in a system by inputs arbitrarily drawn from some fairly large sets of possible inputs. There are several papers at this symposium which report successful efforts in this direction.

The effort which seems closest related in spirit to dynamical theory is Professor Roxin's. This work has been inspired by deterministic control theory, a field in which the consideration of sets of inputs is almost a necessity. In this paper, interesting stability concepts are developed, among others, which are applicable under these conditions.

In his paper, Professor Balakrishnan reports on some of his recent work on linear systems with infinite-dimensional state spaces. Linear systems with finite-dimensional state spaces are rather thoroughly understood but it will be of interest to hear whether or not the extensions reported in this paper have lead to unexpected developments.

Prof. Minty's paper, by contrast, deals with a class of systems which can be nonlinear but which exhibits a certain monotonicity property. It points out by way of examples that many physical systems do indeed have that property. The main objective is to obtain theorems for the invertibility of operators characterizing such systems.

Second in the line of priority for removal among the basic assumptions of dynamical theory is that of continuity. This assumption was again evidently reasonable from the viewpoint of celestial mechanics but it is totally inappropriate, for instance, to systems whose state spaces are countable. Such systems however have become highly relevant in recent years. It is probably unnecessary to mention digital computers and relay networks as examples.

These kinds of systems have of course been studied also but by methods and with aims quite unlike those of dynamical theory. There are two papers on discrete-state systems, by Profs. Davis and Elgot, scheduled for the same session as those on dynamical theory. This was done intentionally, in order to emphasize the contrast between these theories.

Prof. Davis has introduced a formalism and an axiomatic treatment of systems with a countable infinity of states which seem to be particularly appropriate to computers or at any rate to machines very similar to computers. To say only this, however, would be to sell his formalism short. For it is equally appropriate to the study of problems of decidability and computability, that is, to questions in the foundations of mathematics. In fact, there is no reason why it should not also be appropriate to the closely related field of finite-state machines, that is, to systems with a finite number of states. Nevertheless, it has not been very widely used in the latter, nor do the problems which are of prime interest in one field have obvious counterparts in the other, as far as the writer knows. It is possible that some of this will become evident from Professor Elgot's paper, which deals with what he calls "instruction-controlled machines."

Not only are the concepts which dominate the field of discrete-state machines, finite or infinite, quite different from those emphasized by dynamical theory; the same seems to be true also of the problems which occupy the workers in these fields. The concept of stability, for instance, which has been quite important in the latter, has not cropped up in any recognizable shape in the former. The converse is true, for instance, for computability problems. One is tempted to wonder whether this need be so, that is, whether systems with discrete and with continuous state spaces really have as little in common as their present treatments indicate.

The removal of the assumptions underlying dynamical theory has also, in a way, been carried out in the probabilistic treatment of systems. In this treatment, sets of inputs are considered at a time, instead of single inputs as in most of dynamical theory; moreover, the continuity assumption is replaced with a measurability assumption. On the other hand, a probability measure is always defined on the input space. This assumption does not seem to be quite essential but it has proven extremely useful. The papers in the session "Non-Deterministic Systems" are intended to show this.

Professor Root's paper will introduce the topic and then discuss the identification problem which has already been mentioned above. In the probabilistic context, this concerns the question of whether or not (or better, to what extent) a system can be determined from the probability measure which it induces on the output space from a known measure on the input space. In this connection, the question arises as to when a system should be considered identified in the first place or, in other words, what representation of the operator Ψ should be considered acceptable. Professor Root will discuss several such representations for systems that carry nonatomic measures into nonatomic measures.

It may be worth adding here that, at least to the writer's knowledge, identification problems have been attacked with nonprobabilistic techniques only for discrete-state systems. In fact, it may not be stretching the point too far when one says that it was an identification problem of a kind which led to Turing's famous noncomputability deadlock. One can wonder therefore whether identification problems in the probabilistic formulation should not lead to a similar deadlock. So far, nothing has been uncovered that is clearly indicative of trouble in this direction. It is tempting to speculate on whether or not this issue has been avoided so far by the restriction to nonatomic measures, how it might show up in the probabilistic formulation of the identification problem, and whether that is the only problem in which it can show up.

Professor Hanson's paper on the Wold decomposition problems is concerned with a very many-sided topic, in the sense that it can be given many equivalent interpretations. One way of viewing it is the following. It is assumed, as in Professor Root's paper, that the statistics of input and output are known. Wanted are the conditions under which one can be converted into the other by a causal single-valued system. The answer to this and similar questions, it stands to reason, should be most fundamental to system theory, and Professor Hanson's work goes further than any other (known to the writer) toward such an answer. In this work, a rather striking distinction shows up between systems with discrete and continuous state spaces, a distinction which may have a bearing also on the compatibility between dynamical theory and discrete state machine theory. There also may be a connection between the problem discussed by Professor Hanson and stability theory.

Dr. Goodman's paper on causal systems deals with a topic in the same conceptual region as Professor Hanson's. It is restricted to linear operators but to a type of particular interest because the systems discussed in it are drawn from physics, classical as well as modern. Dr. Goodman will deduce the surprising result that systems of massless particles are nondeterministic while those with particles of nonzero mass are deterministic.

Professor Donsker's talk deals with the solution of certain differential equations, for instance, the equations describing the flow of a viscous liquid, in terms of function space integrals.

The paper by Dr. Kushner defines a stability concept which seems quite appropriate to control problems which are probabilistically formulated. He will show that systems that are stable in this sense exhibit desirable and, under circumstances, even optimal behavior.

Professor Truxal will underscore the indebtedness of system theory to engineering by reviewing the particular branch of engineering that shares the word "system" with the theory. The term "system engineering" was coined, to the writer's knowledge, around 1950 at the Bell Telephone Laboratories, to describe what was apparently a new kind of engineering effort, or at least one which had not been consciously practiced before. This was the effort of organizing machines of various kinds and men into efficiently operating units, a task which typically transcended the traditional boundaries of electrical, mechanical, and other engineering specialties. A new term, accordingly, was indicated. System engineering, despite the many misunderstandings and misuses of the concept, is widely practiced today and will presumably be fertile field for system theory, as a producer of new ideas as well as of new applications.

But not only system engineering, or for that matter, engineering in the large, will be fertile for system theory in these respects. Of those other fields, which might contribute to and profit from system theory, two were chosen to be reviewed at this symposium, namely, mathematical economics and mathematical biology. Professor Godfrey will discuss problems in the application of mathematics to economics. Economic systems, he will point out, have several important and unique features which engineering systems lack or at least do not exhibit to the same degree. They are, first of all, surrounded by uncertainty to an extent unknown in engineering. In Professor Zadeh's terminology, economic systems are extremely fuzzy. To complicate matters further, interdependence, growth (i.e., nonstationarity), and misinformation (including deceit) are often present, all of which pose considerable challenge to the theorist.

Doctors Cohen and Rubinow will take a similarly cautious view and will point out that the application of mathematics to biology has so far always been based not on an underlying general theory, but on mathematical models.

It is hoped, as mentioned earlier in this talk, that the papers which are to be given at the symposium will be indicative not only of the scope of system theory as it may develop in the near future, but also of the open problems which must be solved in order for it to deserve even the name of a theory. We further hope that they are indicative also of the potential value of the theory, value not so much, or at least not only, in the sense that it may lead to new devices and bolder machinery, but rather, one may hope, that it will lead to new and surprising recognitions concerning the world we live in, not only the world as we find it and as physics has been studying it, but also the part of the world which is our own making. This, it is felt, should be the really new thing that can be hoped for from system theory.

MATHEMATICAL ASPECTS OF THE THEORY OF SYSTEMS

Richard Bellman*
The RAND Corporation, Santa Monica, California

The study of large systems has become of increasing importance in all parts of science. For this reason, it is appropriate to begin a taxonomy of systems and their associated problems. There is a variety of problems of description, design and control, and identification, as well as many types of inverse problems. New categories of systems have developed as a consequence of the study of biological entities, and new concepts have entered via quantum mechanics and relativity. Of particular significance are semi-group properties in time, space, and structure. The analytic techniques of dynamic programming, invariant imbedding, and quasi-linearization will be discussed.

1. INTRODUCTION

In attempting to formulate a mathematical theory of systems, various intuitive principles can furnish useful guidance and counsel. A first heuristic principle is that a meaningful theory must be closely related and correlated, in several different ways, with our ideas concerning the roles and general objectives of mathematical model-making in science. A second maxim is that the terms "problem" and "solution" are most fruitfully regarded as relative, time-varying concepts to be interpreted in terms of the current ability to provide qualitative and quantitative answers. A third, and perhaps most important, principle is a meta-principle which permits, and indeed urges, us to rise above principles if the situation demands. By this we mean that in any type of research it is occasionally important to follow one's intuition and to pursue intriguing leads regardless of immediacy or relevance.

From the foregoing precepts, we are led via familiar syllogisms to several conclusions. The first is that the most important sources of stimuli for a mathematical theory of systems will be found in the study of real systems: economic, engineering, physical, military, biological, medical, and so forth. It is certainly conceivable that the armchair philosopher, aided only by the power of pure reason, can conjure up all kinds of meaningful systems as objects of study. In actuality, as the history of mathematics so clearly shows, this has not been the case. It is the consensus of opinion, as well as history, that the imagination of the mathematician intermittently requires the spur of reality. Without this, as in other in-

*Any views expressed in this paper are those of the author. They should not be interpreted as reflecting the views of The RAND Corporation or the official opinion or policy of any of its governmental or private research sponsors.

Presented at the Symposium on System Theory
Polytechnic Institute of Brooklyn, April 20, 21, 22, 1965

tellectual areas, what ultimately results is esotericism, sterility, and finally boredom.

Secondly, it is essential to acknowledge that the development of computers—analog, digital, and hybrid types—has significantly, and irrevocably, altered the art of conceiving and using mathematical descriptions of physical phenomena. This, in turn, is merely one aspect of the fact that in the study of systems it is necessary to take account of the manner in which the actual process unfolds in time.

Thirdly, it is important to explore and develop systematically a number of new mathematical theories whose origins lie in the real systems of the world without premature attempts at either application, axiomatization, or confrontation with established methodology. Of particular significance are many nonnumerical theories of algebraic and topological structure.

Taking what has been said into account, we feel that a most appropriate way to inaugurate a mathematical theory of systems is by way of a graduated set of questions (for a general discussion of problems and problem-solving, see reference 1). The first major problem towards which we point is that of the identification of systems. Informally, it may be posed in the following terms:

> "Given some information concerning the structure of a system, and some observations of inputs, outputs, and internal behavior over time, deduce all of the missing information concerning structure, inputs, and outputs."

With some justice, we may consider it to be a fundamental problem on which many others hinge. As we shall mention again below, the foregoing is part of an attempt to construct a general theory of experimentation. We shall present below a series of questions which indicate a feasible path to the treatment of this general question.

A second problem of major concern involves the simultaneous identification and control of systems. This is a far more complex type of problem than might be imagined, and it requires a certain amount of preliminary discussion before one can obtain a proper perspective. These matters will be discussed below, and a number of references for further reading will be provided.

2. WHAT IS A SYSTEM?

Although this may appear to be a natural first question, it is probably best, at this time, to bypass it and avoid any direct answer. It appears to be far more profitable to begin with the study of a number of important processes and systems in detail, and in this way both to obtain an intuitive feel for the nature and structure of systems and to gain some familiarity with the various means available for treating systems. With experience and understanding, we can undertake axiomatization in a meaningful manner. We must avoid any preliminary "rigor mortis." For a detailed discussion of many of the basic ideas, let us refer to Zadeh and Desoer.[2]

3. HOW DO WE DESCRIBE A SYSTEM?

We are so accustomed to a number of powerful traditional techniques that may be used to describe systems that it is easy to overlook the fact that these are only a few of infinitely many ways of superimposing a mathematical structure on a physical process.

Ideally, the choice of state variables should depend upon our analytic and computational expertise, the type of data that is available, and upon the over-all goals. Often, questions of storage, processing, and retrieval of information dominate the more sophisticated analytic techniques when a global view is taken.

We are resigned by now to the fact that in many areas the classical views of space and time and cause and effect must be replaced by the less familiar concepts of relativistic mechanics and quantum mechanics. It is perhaps not so well-known that even within the conventional domains of mathematical physics there is a great deal of freedom as far as analytic formulation is concerned. We shall return to this point below, particularly in connection with the uses of dynamic programming[3,4,5] and invariant imbedding.[6,7,8]

Another choice that must be carefully made is that of a deterministic or a stochastic formulation. Furthermore, there is no reason why both versions should not be combined. In general, flexibility and versatility is the goal, a goal that is much more realizable these days with modern computers and other technological devices. It is usually the case that different formulations will be useful for different purposes.

It cannot be sufficiently emphasized that the initial mathematical model determines all of the analytic and computational effort that follows. Once we have replaced the original physical system by its necessarily condensed mathematical image, we have automatically restricted our efforts. So many of the serious difficulties encountered by mathematicians in their efforts in mathematical physics are of their own making, inevitable consequences of a lack of understanding of what is both required and desired by engineers, scientists, and others who must use the language of mathematics for their own purposes. As a game, the difficulties are intriguing; as a tool for scientific research, they are distracting.

4. HOW DO WE PREDICT THE FUTURE BEHAVIOR OF A SYSTEM?

Let us suppose that we have finally decided upon a means of describing a system. It is natural then to ask if we can use the information available concerning the present state to predict its future behavior. This is almost a circular question, since our tendency would be to reject a description which did not, in principle, permit this foretelling of the future. However, we appreciate the fact that there is a vast difference between theoretical and effective prediction. Much of classical analysis is devoted to this problem of cause and effect, of existence and uniqueness of solutions of functional equations. Its importance cannot be over-estimated, since the answers to all of our subsequent questions depend upon our ability to treat the problem of obtaining numerical algorithms for solving functional equations of the form

$$\frac{dx}{dt} = g(x(\cdot)), \tag{4.1}$$

where $x(\cdot)$ denotes a dependence upon the present and past history of the system. Leaving aside the numerical aspects, it is essential to possess criteria for determining whether questions are well-posed or not.

The most familiar version of (4.1) is the vector differential equation

$$\frac{dx}{dt} = g(x), \quad x(0) = c. \tag{4.2}$$

Here $x = (x_1, x_2, \ldots, x_N)$, $g(x) = (g_1(x), g_2(x), \ldots, g_N(x))$. Equations of this type can be numerically resolved at the present time in a reasonably routine fashion, provided the dimension of x does not exceed one thousand or so. With the computers available in a year or so, this number will be upped to five thousand; with the computers of ten years hence, we can conservatively think in terms of ten thousand or twenty-five thousand.

Formerly, many ingenious devices were used to circumvent the use of large systems of nonlinear differential equations. They represented formidable, and often insuperable, barriers to progress in understanding. Now, they represent *solutions*, if by "solution" we mean a simple algorithm for providing numerical answers. This change in viewpoint must reflect itself in the choice and formulation of problems.

In many cases, (4.1) represents a system with an infinite-dimensional state vector. The most common version of this is a partial differential equation, such as

$$u_t = u_{xx} + e^u, \tag{4.3}$$

or

$$\begin{aligned} u_t + uu_x + vu_y &= p_1, \\ v_t + uv_x + vv_y &= p_2. \end{aligned} \tag{4.4}$$

Formerly, partial differential equations required for their solution a great deal of analytic ingenuity, sophistication, and experience. Now, however, we can use very simple and direct methods. Suppose that we write, in (4.1),

$$u = \sum_n u_n(t)\, e^{inx}. \tag{4.5}$$

Then, (4.3) becomes an infinite system of nonlinear ordinary differential equations,

$$u_n' = n^2 u_n + g_n(u_0, u_1, u_{-1}, \ldots). \tag{4.6}$$

Suppose we truncate by taking $u_n \equiv 0$ for $|n| > N$. We then have a finite system of the form appearing in (4.2). Taking $N = 100$, 200, or 1000, it is reasonable to expect that we can obtain a numerical solution of (4.3) in a very simple and direct fashion; cf. reference 9.

There is certainly nothing elegant about this approach, and some mathematicians might complain about this sledge-hammer method. It has one merit: it enables people with very little training in mathematics to solve scientific problems of significance. Moreover, it indicates the strong possibility that the computer may cause an unexpected schism between science and mathematics in many classical areas. Scientists in these areas will no longer require high-powered analytic methods for the treatment of their problems. Let us hasten to add that this does not mean that there will be less over-all need for mathematicians. There will, however, be a considerable shift in their efforts. It is another facet of automation.

Particularly in mathematical biology, we encounter processes involving a dependence upon past history, which is to say, hereditary effects. Then, (4.1) is replaced by differential-difference equations,

$$\frac{dx}{dt} = g(x(t), x(t - \tau_1), \ldots, x(t - \tau_N)), \tag{4.7}$$

where the delays may be constant, or functions of time, or, more generally, themselves be dependent on the state x,

$$\tau_i = \tau_i(x(t), t), \tag{4.8}$$

cf. references 10 and 11.

Finally, let us mention the theory of branching processes, a natural outgrowth of the classical theories of iteration and semigroups, cf. Harris.[12] The concept of "point of regeneration" considerably extends the ideas behind (4.1).

It is easy to see that there are unlimited opportunities for mathematical research in the areas we have so briefly examined. Precisely for this reason is it so necessary to examine over-all objectives in order to make sure that the usual clustering phenomenon of science does not occur. We do not want to funnel all of our talent and effort into certain currently fashionable areas at the expense of other, usually more important, areas. This is harmful to science, and particularly destructive to young researchers.

One further point is worth mentioning. Sometimes, in an investigation, we require numerical values in connection with the design and construction of a physical system. In many other cases, only qualitative behavior is needed, information which will culminate in a "yes" or "no." For example, we may want to know whether a system is stable, whether a certain type of steady-state behavior exists, whether there is periodicity or almost-periodicity, and so on. In some situations, this information can be obtained purely by means of analytic techniques. In general, in dealing with complex processes, the only way to obtain the qualitative information is by means of suitably chosen quantitative data.

For this reason, it is extremely important to correlate the choice of state variables and the analytic formulation with the numerical capability and the type and accuracy of input data. All of this explains in part the statement made above concerning the effect of the computer upon mathematics. The quality of computational algorithms available must influence the analytic tools used. This is "impedance matching."

5. HOW DO WE DEDUCE THE PAST HISTORY OF A SYSTEM?

So far, we have considered various parts of the problem of determining the future behavior of a system. Let us now consider the case where we catch glimpses of a system from time to time and are then required on that basis to deduce its past, present, and future behavior. By the term "glimpse," we mean that it is not possible at any particular time to obtain values of all of the components of the state vector. A typical example of this occurs in orbit determination, where it is relatively easy to observe the position of an object at any time, but not at all easy to obtain an accurate estimate of its velocity.

Processes of this type give rise to two-point, or in general multipoint, boundary-value problems. These are several levels of difficulty above initial-value problems, and in no sense of the word can we regard their analytic or computational solution as routine.

A variety of boundary-value problems arise in mathematical physics. Consider, for example, a transport process associated with a plane-parallel slab.

Given the nature of the flux incident at both boundaries, we wish to determine the reflected fluxes and the internal fluxes.

In connection with the minimization of a functional such as

$$J(u) = \int_0^T g(u, u')\, dt, \tag{5.1}$$

we obtain, via the calculus of variations, a differential equation subject to two-point conditions,

$$\frac{d}{dt}\left(\frac{\partial g}{\partial u'}\right) - \frac{\partial g}{\partial u} = 0. \tag{5.2}$$

What is interesting to point out, and relevant to our principal theme of versatility and flexibility, is that in both of the foregoing cases, there are alternate analytic formulations which avoid the intricacies of two-point boundary-values. In the first case, we can employ invariant imbedding;[6,7,8] in the second case, dynamic programming.[3,4,5]

This illustrates the point previously stressed: there is nothing intrinsic about any analytic representation of a physical process. At the risk of being repetitious, let us note that the classical formulations of mathematical physics are of eighteenth and nineteenth century vintage. Even quantum mechanics and relativity theory, of early twentieth century origin, are, expectedly, nineteenth-century in their analytic formulation.

It is reasonable to suspect that many different mathematical interpretations of physical processes exist. This should be the case well within the classical framework, and particularly so (our familiar refrain) when digital computers are available. Mathematics and science alike are determined by the ability to do arithmetic.

From here on out, we are engaged in a perpetual scientific revolution. Unlike the relatively peaceful scientific era of 1700–1950, we can expect that the formulations of theories will constantly change over time to keep parallel with the increase in experimental techniques, the development of computers, and the varying objectives of society.

At the present time we can, without flinching, contemplate the integration of systems of ordinary differential equations of order 1000. In the next few years, this number will be 5000; in ten years or so, 10,000 to 100,000. What happens to so much of classical mathematical physics when these formerly formidable operations become exercises? This question cannot be overstressed, since the answers to it should determine the curriculum in the undergraduate and graduate schools.

6. WHAT ARE THE DUAL SYSTEMS?

We are all familiar with the power and versatility of the geometric concept of duality. One of the advantages of the abstract mathematical point of view is that it permits a ready geometricization of processes far removed from the study of points and lines, and thus a simple transference and translation of existing techniques. Much has been done in the area of duality, but very much remains.

7. HOW DO WE APPROXIMATE A SYSTEM?

The student in school is trained to furnish precise answers to precise questions. This is hardly adequate training for a real world in which the essence of success is that of obtaining reasonable answers to reasonable questions in areas which are vague and imprecise. Even in the academic world, success depends more upon the choice of one's own questions than the supplying of answers to the questions of others. In other words, it is the art of approximation to reality that counts throughout.

A basic part of this is the construction of the original mathematical model. We have discussed some aspects of this above. Let us consider here the simpler matter of obtaining an analytic approximation to an already existing analytic structure. Suppose, for example, that a system is described by an N-dimensional vector nonlinear differential equation

$$\frac{dx}{dt} = g(x), \quad x(0) = c. \tag{7.1}$$

How do we find a linear equation

$$\frac{dy}{dt} = Ay, \quad y(0) = c, \tag{7.2}$$

with the property $x \cong y$ in some prescribed sense. For example, we may wish to minimize $\int_0^T (x - y, x - y)\, dt$.

Or suppose that a system is governed by the equation

$$\begin{aligned} k(x)\,u_t &= u_{xx}, \quad 0 < x < 1, \quad t > 0, \\ u(x,0) &= g(x), \\ u(0,t) &= u(1,t) = 0, \end{aligned} \tag{7.3}$$

and it is desired to find a finite-dimensional system of the type appearing in (7.1) with the property that $x \cong z$ where

$$z = \begin{bmatrix} u(x_1, t) \\ u(x_2, t) \\ \cdot \\ \cdot \\ \cdot \\ u(x_N, t) \end{bmatrix}$$

Many other problems of this nature can be posed, and very little has been done in this area; see, however, reference 13.

These, however, represent only a small part of the questions that arise in connection with the mathematical theory of the approximation of systems. There is the question of what is meant by the approximation of one process by another; the approximation of one set of state variables by another; matters of "lumping" of variables, and of closure and truncation; the mode of calculation of variables. All of these, in turn, are aspects of the choices: discrete versus continuous, stochastic versus deterministic, finite versus infinite, linear versus nonlinear, Markovian versus non-Markovian, static versus dynamic, numerical versus non-numerical, and variational versus descriptive.

As we shall see below in connection with control processes, this by no means exhausts the decisions which must be made.

8. HOW DO WE DEDUCE THE STRUCTURE OF A SYSTEM?

Let us now consider what are often called "inverse problems." In Section 1, we have called them identification problems. Given input-output data, or asymptotic behavior, or, in general, what has usually been considered an answer, the problem is to determine the question. This may be the task of deducing a structure or deducing an equation. It is clear that we cannot expect unique answers to problems of this type, unless we restrict our attention to particular categories of systems. In other words, once we specify the general structure of a system, and reduce the unknown aspects to the determination of constants, then we can expect to determine the particular system within the category whose behavior best approximates the observed behavior.

For example, suppose that we know that $x(t)$, the state vector describing a system, satisfies an equation of the form

$$\frac{dx}{dt} = g(x, a), \quad x(0) = c, \tag{8.1}$$

where a and c are unknown vectors. We wish to determine them so as to minimize the expression

$$\sum_{i=1}^{M} ((x(t_i),\ b_i) - c_i)^2, \tag{8.2}$$

where the scalars c_i correspond to "observations" at the times t_i. A large number of scientific problems fall in this area.[13]

We see from this simple example that the identification problem is again a relative matter, a matter of knowing and parametrizing the set of systems under consideration. We see then the need for a taxonomy of systems which will furnish us a wide variety of choices. Let us repeat the point made before that the solution of identification problems depends on our ability to treat descriptive processes.

9. DISCUSSION

Up to now, we have been taking quite a detached view of system theory, in the sense that we have engaged in the pretense that our only goal was to understand the structure and behavior of systems. In actuality, in the majority of cases, we want to use this understanding for a variety of purposes. It is plausible that greater understanding will enable us to accomplish these purposes in more efficient fashion. Since, however, in many cases we cannot wait for complete understanding (e.g., cancer, inflation, traffic), our objective is again one of approximation: partial control based upon partial understanding, improved control based upon improved understanding.

In what follows, we wish briefly to indicate what we mean by the term "control" and to point out some of the many new questions that have arisen in recent years.

10. HOW DO WE CONTROL A SYSTEM?

A fundamental problem in the world around us is that of making a particular system behave in an acceptable fashion. This ranges from keeping a space vehicle on course, or an economy expanding, to preventing the further growth of a cancerous tumor. Nothing can be more practical than a theory of systems.

One important aspect of control theory is the elucidation of what is meant by the terms "an acceptable fashion." It is not difficult to construct analytic versions of control processes, but these may not have much to do with what is really desired in practice. The price of the introduction of available mathematical techniques is often a strange mixture of oversimplification and overcomplication—oversimplification of the actual process and overcomplication in the application of analysis.

To illustrate these remarks, let us consider a type of mathematical problem which is quite fashionable now, and then, point-by-point, indicate the tacit assumptions that have been made, and how these assumptions weaken the validity of the model and limit its applicability.

Let x be an N-dimensional vector and y an M-dimensional vector related by means of the differential equation

$$\frac{dx}{dt} = g(x, y, t), \quad x(0) = c, \tag{10.1}$$

the local constraints

$$r_i(x, y, t) \leq 0, \quad i = 1, 2, \ldots, k, \tag{10.2}$$

and the global constraints

$$\int_0^T k_j(x, y, t)\, dt \leq 0, \quad j = 1, 2, \ldots, \ell. \tag{10.3}$$

It is required to determine x, the state vector, and y, the control vector, so as to minimize the functional

$$J(x, y) = \int_0^T h(x, y, t)\, dt + \phi(x(T)), \tag{10.4}$$

cf. references 14 and 15.

This is a very interesting and difficult problem which contains enough in its particularizations and generalizations to keep mathematicians busy for decades. This, of course, is at once its principal merit and demerit. The mathematician seeing a control process so precisely and neatly posed is apt to closet himself in his study and pay no attention to far more important, but less well-posed, questions. These ill-posed questions are, however, far more significant as far as the development of mathematics itself is concerned.

Let us now analyze the many assumptions adroitly hidden in the preceding. To begin with, there is the explicit criterion function in (10.4). The triple assumption here is first that an objective is known, secondly that it can be expressed in analytic terms, and thirdly that it is a scalar and not a vector criterion.

Let us bypass these exceedingly sticky matters, which can be treated by means of simulation techniques, and continue with our dissection.

Next, there is the assumption implicit in (10.1) that we understand cause and effect well enough to write down an equation of this type. In many important processes, this is not the case. There are several ways of meeting this difficulty, on several levels of sophistication.

The first is to replace a deterministic process by a stochastic process in which uncertainty is represented by stochastic functions with known distributions. It is not, however, sufficient to assume that this ingenious device disposes of uncertainty. On the contrary, it forces us to examine a number of problems which did not arise in classical control theory because of the low order of complexity of the systems considered. Essentially, these are the problems of the storage, processing, and retrieval of information.

In a deterministic process, it is inherent that knowledge of the state at one time determines the state at any time in the future. The analog of this for the usual stochastic process is that a knowledge of the probability distribution for current states determines the probability distribution at any subsequent time. Since this is seldom sufficient information for effective control of a system, we face the problem of observation of a system. In this way enter "feedback control," "on-line" control, and so on.

As the theory of dynamic programming shows, one can use the concept of feedback control to construct a theory of deterministic control processes.[3,4,5] The classical theory is dual to this, and each possesses its own analytic and computational advantages. In dealing with stochastic control processes, this duality breaks down. There is now a continuum of varieties of control processes between the two poles of complete information at each time, and of no information once the process has started. As mentioned above, the processes of the real world furnish us with important prototypes. The concepts of information and policy are now dominant.

In the preceding paragraph, we used the term "policy." A policy is a rule for decision-making. It determines what to do in terms of where one is and what one knows. It has several advantages over the usual prescription of a control vector as a function of time. Among these are its more intuitive flavor, its applicability in simulation processes where optimization may not be meaningful, its high degree of compatibility with the capabilities of computers, the many new types of approximation it makes available, and the uniform way in which deterministic, stochastic, and adaptive processes can be treated.

Furthermore, the emphasis upon feedback control concepts has the desirable effect of focussing attention on state variables, means of observing state variables, the accuracy of these observations, interruption of communication, and, in general, all aspects of the acquisition, processing, storing, and use of information.

It is important to point out that the recognition of the fact that time and other resources are required for data-processing leads to an analog of the classical uncertainty principles for quantum mechanics. We can obtain approximate information quickly and cheaply, or more accurate information slowly and expensively. In either case, we incur a cost of control. There are many interesting questions associated with the choice of variables to observe and the cost involved in obtaining information of various degrees of accuracy.

11. HOW DO WE IMPROVE AN OPERATING SYSTEM?

It is not sufficiently emphasized that the design and control of a new system is a different problem from that of improving the performance of a system which has been operating for some time. Leaving aside the inevitable psychological aspects of change, there is the standard problem of transient effects. How does one change from the current policy to an optimal policy without dangerous or costly side effects due to transients? The associated mathematical questions are quite difficult. For example, starting with a given policy, how does one improve monotonically?

All of this is connected with the vital problem of "on-line" control.

12. HOW DO WE LEARN ABOUT AND CONTROL A SYSTEM?

What has preceded is preliminary to the basic problem of controlling a system whose properties are not completely known. In order to do this, we must divide our energies between the tasks of observing, experimenting, and learning, and the tasks of exerting control influences. Although these matters are of paramount importance, only recently have problems in these areas been precisely formulated. They constitute part of the new field of adaptive control.

It is most likely the case that the current formulations are too complex for convenient analytic or applied use. What is needed is work in the direction of Monte Carlo methods, stochastic approximation, and particularly experimentation along the lines of simulation. What the most fruitful directions are is certainly not clear at this time.

13. CONCLUSION

There are, of course, no such things as objective questions. The choice of questions, and even their framing, consciously or unconsciously reflects the philosophical attitudes of the questioner. We have tried our best to keep the questions verbal and thus avoid any hardening of the analyses or ossification of the issues. Nonetheless, from time to time we have weakened and indicated possible analytic approaches.

We feel that a great deal of significant work can be done following conventional lines, and that it should be done. We also feel that it is worthwhile to spend a good deal of time and energy searching for new routes. It is probably best to mix strategies and to pursue both activities, not only within research groups but within the individual himself.

In any case, we hope that we have made it clear that the theory of systems is one of the most exciting of modern scientific fields, with application and inspiration everywhere. A young mathematician can hardly go astray in this domain.

REFERENCES

1. R. Bellman and P. Brock, "On the Concepts of a Problem and Problem-solving," *Amer. Math. Monthly*, **67**, pp. 119–134, (1960).

2. L. A. Zadeh and C. A. Desoer, *Linear System Theory, The State Space Approach* (New York: McGraw-Hill, 1963).

3. R. Bellman, *Dynamic Programming* (Princeton, N. J.: Princeton University Press, 1957).

4. R. Bellman, *Adaptive Control Processes: A Guided Tour* (Princeton, N. J.: Princeton University Press, 1961).

5. R. Bellman and S. Dreyfus, *Applied Dynamic Programming* (Princeton, N. J.: Princeton University Press, 1962).

6. R. Bellman, R. Kalaba, and M. Prestrud, *Invariant Imbedding and Radiative Transfer in Slabs of Finite Thickness* (New York: American Elsevier Publishing Co., 1963).

7. R. Bellman, H. Kagiwada, R. Kalaba, and M. Prestrud, *Invariant Imbedding and Time-dependent Processes* (New York: American Elsevier Publishing Co., 1964).

8. G. M. Wing, *An Introduction to Transport Theory* (New York: John Wiley & Sons, 1962).

9. R. Bellman, J. M. Richardson, and S. P. Azen, "On New and Direct Computational Approaches to Some Mathematical Models of Turbulence," *Q. Appl. Math.*, to appear.

10. R. Bellman and K. L. Cooke, *Differential-difference Equations* (New York: Academic Press, 1963).

11. A. D. Myskis, *Lineare Differentialgleichungen mit nacheilenden Argument* (Berlin, 1955).

12. T. E. Harris, *The Theory of Branching Processes* (Englewood Cliffs, N. J.: Prentice-Hall, 1963).

13. R. Bellman and R. Kalaba, *Quasilinearization and Boundary-value Problems* (New York: American Elsevier Publishing Co., to appear in 1965).

FUZZY SETS AND SYSTEMS*

L. A. Zadeh
Department of Electrical Engineering, University of California, Berkeley, California

The notion of fuzziness as defined in this paper relates to situations in which the source of imprecision is not a random variable or a stochastic process, but rather a class or classes which do not possess sharply defined boundaries, e.g., the "class of bald men," or the "class of numbers which are much greater than 10," or the "class of adaptive systems," etc.

A basic concept which makes it possible to treat fuzziness in a quantitative manner is that of a fuzzy set, that is, a class in which there may be grades of membership intermediate between full membership and non-membership. Thus, a fuzzy set is characterized by a membership function which assigns to each object its grade of membership (a number lying between 0 and 1) in the fuzzy set.

After a review of some of the relevant properties of fuzzy sets, the notions of a fuzzy system and a fuzzy class of systems are introduced and briefly analyzed. The paper closes with a section dealing with optimization under fuzzy constraints in which an approach to problems of this type is briefly sketched.

1. INTRODUCTION

This paper constitutes a very preliminary attempt at introducing into system theory several concepts which provide a way of treating fuzziness in a quantitative manner. Essentially, these concepts relate to situations in which the source of imprecision is not a random variable or a stochastic process but rather a class or classes which do not possess sharply defined boundaries. An example of such a "class" is the "class" of adaptive systems. A simpler example is the "class" of real numbers which are much larger than, say, 10. Still another example is the "class" of bald men. Clearly, such classes are not classes or sets in the usual mathematical sense of these terms, since they do not dichotomize all objects into those that belong to the class and those that do not.

One way of dealing with classes in which there may be intermediate grades of membership was described in a recent paper.[1] The approach in question is based on the use of the concept of a "fuzzy set," that is, a class in which there may be a continuous infinity of grades of membership, with the grade of membership of an object x in a fuzzy set A represented by a number $\mu_A(x)$ in the interval [0, 1]. Thus, a fuzzy set A in a space of objects $X = \{x\}$ is characterized by a membership function μ_A which is defined on X and takes values in the interval [0, 1],

*This text is an abbreviated version of a paper presented at the Symposium under the title of "A New View of System Theory." The work described here was supported in part by the National Science Foundation under Grant GP-2413.

Presented at the Symposium on System Theory
Polytechnic Institute of Brooklyn, April 20, 21, 22, 1965

such that the nearer the value of $\mu_A(x)$ to unity, the higher the grade of membership of x in A. As a simple example, let A be the fuzzy set of real numbers which are much greater than 10. In this case, a set of representative values of $\mu_A(x)$ may be: $\mu_A(10) = 0$; $\mu_A(50) = 0.6$; $\mu_A(100) = 0.9$; $\mu_A(500) = 1$; etc. In general, the values of $\mu_A(x)$ would be specified on a subjective rather than an objective basis.

2. CONCEPTS RELATING TO FUZZY SETS

As a preliminary to sketching a possible role for fuzzy sets in system theory, it will be helpful to summarize some of their main properties.* To begin with, it is clear that when there is no fuzziness in the definition of a class A, A is a set or a class in the ordinary sense of this term,** and its membership function reduces to the familiar two-valued characteristic (indicator) function for A, with $\mu_A(x)$ being one or zero according as x belongs or does not belong to A.

The notion of a fuzzy set provides a convenient way of defining *abstraction*—a process which plays a basic role in human thinking and communication. Specifically, suppose that A is a fuzzy set with an unknown membership function μ_A. Furthermore, suppose that one is given a set of n samples from A of the form $(x_1, \mu_A(x_1)), \ldots, (x_N, \mu_A(x_N))$, where x_i, $i = 1, \ldots, N$, is an object in X and $\mu_A(x_i)$ is its grade of membership in A. Then, by abstraction on these samples is meant the formation of an estimate, $\tilde{\mu}_A$, of the membership function of A in terms of the specified values of $\mu_A(x)$ at the points $x_1, \ldots, x_N$.

Many of the problems in pattern classification involve abstraction in the sense defined above. For example, suppose that we are concerned with devising a test for differentiating between handwritten letters O and D. One approach to this problem would be to give a set of handwritten letters and indicate their grades of membership in the fuzzy sets O and D. On performing abstraction on these samples, one obtains the estimates $\tilde{\mu}_O$ and $\tilde{\mu}_D$ of μ_O and μ_D, respectively. Then, given any letter x which is not one of the given samples, one can calculate its grades of membership in O and D, and, if O and D have no overlap, classify x in O or D.

To make abstraction mathematically meaningful, it is necessary to have enough a priori information about the membership function μ_A to make it possible to assess or at least place bounds on the error in the estimate of μ_A. As stated in reference 2, a disconcerting aspect of the problem of abstraction is that the human mind can perform abstraction very effectively even when the problems involved are not mathematically well defined. It is this lack of understanding of the way in which humans can abstract in mathematically ill-defined situations and our consequent inability to devise abstracting devices which can perform even remotely as well as the human mind, that lie at the root of many unresolved problems in heuristic programming, pattern recognition and related problem areas.

*A more detailed exposition of fuzzy sets and their properties is given in references 1 and 2.

**When it is necessary to emphasize the distinction between fuzzy sets and ordinary sets, T. Cover has suggested that the latter be referred to as *crisp* sets. We shall follow his suggestion in this paper.

There are several concepts relating to fuzzy sets which will be needed in later discussions. These are:

Equality. Two fuzzy sets A and B in a space X are *equal*, written $A = B$, if and only if $\mu_A(x) = \mu_B(x)$ for all x in X. (In the sequel, to simplify the notation we shall follow the convention of suppressing an argument to indicate that an equality or inequality holds for all values of that argument.)

Containment. A fuzzy set A is *contained* in a fuzzy set B, written as $A \subset B$, if and only if $\mu_A \leq \mu_B$. In this sense, the fuzzy set of "very tall men" is contained in the fuzzy set of "tall men." Similarly, the fuzzy set of real numbers which are "much greater than 10" is contained in the crisp set of real numbers which are "greater than 10."

Complementation. A fuzzy set A' is the *complement* of A if and only if $\mu_A' = 1 - \mu_A$.

Union. The *union* of two fuzzy sets A and B is denoted by $A \cup B$ and is defined as the smallest fuzzy set containing both A and B. An immediate consequence of this definition is that the membership function of $A \cup B$ is given by

$$\mu_{A \cup B}(x) = \text{Max}\,[\mu_A(x), \mu_B(x)]. \tag{1}$$

Thus, if at a point x, $\mu_A(x) = 0.8$, say, and $\mu_B(x) = 0.5$, then at that point, $\mu_{A \cup B}(x) = 0.8$.

Intersection. The intersection of two fuzzy sets A and B is denoted by $A \cap B$ and is defined as the largest fuzzy set contained in both A and B. The membership function of $A \cap B$ is given by

$$\mu_{A \cap B}(x) = \text{Min}\,[\mu_A(x), \mu_B(x)] \tag{2}$$

In this case, if $\mu_A(x) = 0.8$ and $\mu_B(x) = 0.5$, then $\mu_{A \cap B}(x) = 0.5$.

So far, we have not made any restrictive assumptions either about X or μ_A (other than $0 \leq \mu_A(x) \leq 1$ everywhere on X). In what follows, we shall assume for concreteness that $X = E^n$ (Euclidean n-space) and define a few more notions* relating to fuzzy sets which will be of use at later points.

Shadow. Consider a fuzzy set A in E^n which is characterized by a membership function $\mu_A(x_1, \ldots, x_n)$, with $x = (x_1, \ldots, x_n)$. Let H be a hyperplane in E^n. Then, the *orthogonal shadow* (or simply *shadow*) of A on H is a fuzzy set $S_H(A)$ in H which is related to A in the following manner.

Let L be a line orthogonal to H and let h be its point of intersection with H. Then,

$$\mu_{S_H(A)}(h) = \underset{x \in L}{\text{Sup}}\, \mu_A(x) \tag{3}$$

and

$$\mu_{S_H(A)}(x) = 0 \text{ for } x \notin H.$$

The fuzzy set $S_H(A)$ is called a shadow of A because it is suggestive of a shadow cast by a cloud on a plane.

If H_1 is a coordinate hyperplane $H_1 = \{x \mid x_1 = 0\}$, then the membership func-

*The notions of shadow, convexity, concavity, etc., can be defined, of course, in the context of more general spaces than E^n. For our purposes, however, it is sufficient to assume that $X = E^n$.

tion of the shadow of A on H_1 is given by

$$\mu_{S_{H_1}(A)}(x_2, \ldots, x_n) = \operatorname*{Sup}_{x_1} \mu_A(x_1, \ldots, x_n), \quad x_1 = 0$$
$$= 0, \quad x_1 \neq 0. \tag{4}$$

Note that $\mu_{S_{H_1}(A)}$ is analogous to a marginal distribution of a probability distribution in E^n. However, whereas in the case of a marginal distribution, an argument of a distribution is eliminated by integration, in the case of a shadow the elimination occurs through taking the supremum of the membership function.

Let $S_H^*(A)$ denote a cylindrical fuzzy set defined by

$$\mu_{S_{H_1}^*(A)}(x) = \mu_{S_{H_1}(A)}(x_2, \ldots, x_n), \quad x \in E^n. \tag{5}$$

Then, clearly, $A \subset S_{H_1}^*(A)$. Thus, if $H_i = \{x \mid x_i = 0\}, i = 1, \ldots, n$, then A is bounded from above by the intersection of $S_{H_1}^*(A), \ldots, S_{H_n}^*(A)$. In symbols,

$$A \subset \bigcap_{i=1}^{n} S_{H_i}^*(A). \tag{6}$$

Complementary shadow. The *complementary shadow* of A on H is denoted by $C_H(A)$ and is defined as the complement (on H) of the shadow of the complement of A. More specifically,

$$\mu_{C_H(A)}(h) = \operatorname*{Inf}_{x \in L} \mu_A(x), \quad x \in H \tag{7}$$
$$= 0, \quad x \notin H.$$

In terms of complementary shadow, A is bounded from below by the union ot the cylindrical fuzzy sets $C_{H_1}^*(A), \ldots, C_{H_n}^*(A)$. Thus,

$$\bigcup_{i=1}^{n} C_{H_i}^*(A) \subset A \subset \bigcap_{i=1}^{n} S_{H_i}^*(A) \tag{8}$$

As will be seen later, these bounds are of some use in problems involving optimization under fuzzy constraints.

Convexity. A fuzzy set A is *convex* if and only if the sets $\Gamma_\alpha = \{x \mid \mu_A(x) \geq \alpha\}$ are convex for all α in the interval (0, 1]. Equivalently, A is convex if and only if for any pair of points x_1 and x_2 in E^n and any λ in [0, 1], we have

$$\mu_A(\lambda x_1 + (1 - \lambda)x_2) \geq \operatorname{Min}[\mu_A(x_1), \mu_A(x_2)]. \tag{9}$$

For example, the fuzzy set of real numbers which are "approximately equal to 1" is a convex fuzzy set in E^1. The membership function of this set is depicted in Fig. 1. In the same figure, μ_B is the membership function of a non-convex fuzzy set in E^1.

Concavity. A fuzzy set A is *concave* if and only if its complement A' is convex. The notions of convexity and concavity are duals of one another, as are A and A', union and intersection, $\supset$ and $\subset$, shadow and complementary shadow, etc.

This concludes our brief introduction to some of the basic notions pertaining to fuzzy sets. In the following, we shall merely indicate a few of the possible applications of these notions in system theory, without any attempt at detailed analysis or exploration.

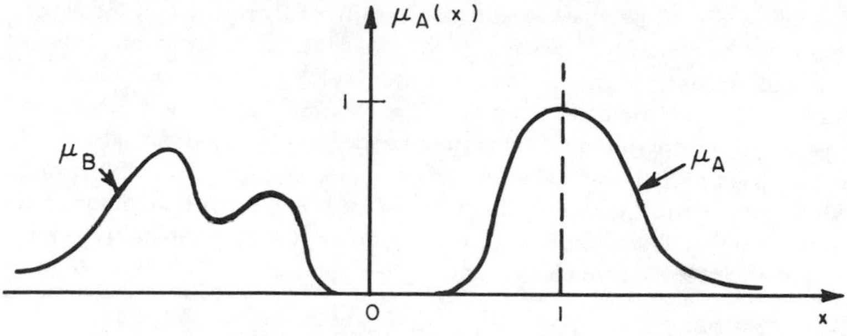

Fig. 1. Convex and non-convex sets in E^1.

3. FUZZY SYSTEMS

We begin with the notion of a fuzzy system, by which we mean the following. Let S be a system, with the input, output and state of S at time t denoted by $u(t)$, $y(t)$, and $x(t)$, respectively. Then S is a *fuzzy system* if $u(t)$ or $y(t)$ or $x(t)$ or any combination of them ranges over fuzzy sets. For example, if the input† to S at time t is specified to be "considerably in excess of 5," then this input is a fuzzy set and a system which can act on such imprecisely defined inputs is a fuzzy system. Similarly, if the states of S are described by such fuzzy adjectives as light, heavy, not very heavy, very light, etc., that is, if they are fuzzy sets, then S is a fuzzy system.

Assuming for simplicity that S is a discrete time system, with t ranging over the integers, we can characterize S by the usual state equations

$$x_{t+1} = f(x_t, u_t) \tag{10}$$

$$y_t = g(x_t, u_t) \tag{11}$$

where u_t, y_t and x_t denote, respectively, the input, output and state of S at time t, and f and g are functions of the indicated arguments. The difference between fuzzy and non-fuzzy systems, then, lies in the nature of the ranges of the variables, u_t, y_t and x_t. Thus, in the case of a fuzzy system, one or more of these variables range over spaces where elements are fuzzy sets. Since a fuzzy set is characterized by a scalar-valued membership function, that is, by a functional, this implies in effect that, in the case of a fuzzy system, the values of one or more of the variables u_t, y_t and x_t are functionals.

The situation described above is similar to that encountered in the case of stochastic systems which can be described as deterministic systems in terms of the probability distribution of the input, output and state variables.[3] In the case of such a system, a relation such as (10) would signify that the probability distribution of the states at time $t + 1$ is uniquely determined by the probability distribution of the states at time t and the probability distribution of the inputs at time t.

The difference between a stochastic and a fuzzy system is that in the latter the source of imprecision is nonstatistical in nature and has to do with the lack of

†It should be recognized, of course, that such inputs admit of precise definition in terms of fuzzy sets.

sharp boundaries of the classes entering into the descriptions of the input, output or state. Mathematically, however, these two types of systems are substantially similar and present comparable and, unfortunately, great difficulties in their analyses. These difficulties stem from the fact that, at present, we do not possess effective computational techniques for dealing with functionals, so that equations such as (10) and (11) are easy to write in symbolic form but difficult to translate into explicit computer programs when the variables involved in them are functionals rather than points in spaces of fairly low dimensionality—which is usually the case with conventional non-fuzzy systems.

4. FUZZY CLASSES OF SYSTEMS

A notion which is related to and yet distinct from that of a fuzzy system is that of a *fuzzy class* of systems. For instance, the "class" of systems which are "approximately equivalent" to a given system S is a fuzzy class of systems; so is the "class" of systems which are "approximately linear"; and so is the "class" of systems which are "adaptive." In fact, one may argue that most of the adjectives used in system theory to describe various types of systems, such as: linear, nonlinear, adaptive, time-invariant, stable, etc., are in reality names for fuzzy classes of systems. If one accepts this point of view, then one is freed from the necessity of defining these terms in a way that dichotomizes the class of all systems into two classes, e.g., systems that are linear and systems that are nonlinear. More realistically, then, one would regard, say, the "class" of adaptive systems as a fuzzy class, with each system having a grade of membership in it which may range from zero to one.

How can a fuzzy class of systems be characterized? The answer to this question depends on the mode of characterization of the systems which form a fuzzy class. More specifically, if one starts with the definition of a system as a set of input-output pairs— which is the point of departure in reference 4—then a fuzzy class of systems would be a fuzzy set in the product space $U \times Y$, where U is the space of inputs and Y is the space of outputs.

To illustrate this point, suppose that a system designer wishes to give a precise, albeit subjective, characterization of the fuzzy class, A, of time-invariant, approximately linear, systems. He could do this, at least in principle, by associating with each input-output pair (u, y) a number in the interval $[0, 1]$, representing its grade of membership in A. For example, he may assign the grade 0.8 to an input-output pair $(t, t + 0.001\, t^2)$, $0 \leq t \leq 100$; the grade 0.3 to $(t, 0.1 + t)$, $0 \leq t \leq 100$; and so forth. In this way, A would be characterized as a fuzzy set in the product space of input-output pairs. In practice, of course, the designer could assign grades of membership to only a finite number of input-output pairs (u, y). Thus, in general, one would have to estimate the membership function $\mu_A(u, y)$ from the values of this function over a finite set of sample input-output pairs $(u_1, y_1), (u_2, y_2), \ldots, (u_N, y_N)$. As was pointed out in the beginning of this paper, this is a problem in abstraction—a problem for which we do not possess as yet effective general methods of solution.

Alternatively, if one starts with a characterization of a system in terms of its input-output-state relation or state equations, and if each system is indexed by a parameter λ taking values in a space Λ, then a fuzzy class of systems may be characterized as a fuzzy set in Λ. For example, consider a family of discrete-time systems characterized by the state equations

$$x_{t+1} = f_{\lambda}(x_t, u_t) \tag{12}$$

$$y_t = g_{\lambda}(x_t, u_t) \tag{13}$$

in which λ is a real non-negative number. Then a fuzzy class, say A, of such systems would be defined by a fuzzy set, say B, in the parameter space $[0, \infty]$, with the grade of membership of the system with index λ in A being given by the grade of membership of λ in B, that is, by $\mu_B(\lambda)$.

One of the basic problems in the case of non-fuzzy (crisp) systems is that of deriving an input-output-state relation or, equivalently, state equations for a system which is defined by a set of input-output pairs. Recently, a solution to this problem in the context of finite-state automata was described by Tal.[5,6] The same basic, although much more difficult problem presents itself in the case of fuzzy classes of systems. More specifically, suppose that a fuzzy class of discrete-time systems, say A, is defined as a fuzzy set of input-output pairs (u, y) in the product space $U \times Y$. Then, the problem is to find a representation for this fuzzy class in the form of a family of state equations (12) and (13) and a fuzzy set B in the parameter Λ. It hardly needs saying that, in general, this would be an extremely difficult problem—a problem concerning which we know practically nothing at this time.

5. OPTIMIZATION UNDER FUZZY CONSTRAINTS

In the previous two sections, we focused our attention on ways in which fuzziness can enter into the definition of a system or a class of systems. In this section, we briefly touch on a different facet of fuzziness in system theory, namely, the optimization of crisp systems under fuzzy constraints.

Our consideration of this problem is motivated by the fact that in many practical optimization problems, particularly these involving man-machine systems, the constraints on variables are seldom sharply defined. Thus, in many instances the constraints are fuzzy or "soft," in the sense that the variables which they involve are only approximately—rather than precisely—constrained to fall within specified sets. For example, a constraint on a variable x may have fuzzy forms such as "x should not be significantly larger than 5," or "x should be close to 10," or "x should be approximately between 5 and 10," etc.

A standard approach to problems of this type is to idealize a fuzzy constraint by replacing it with an approximating "hard" (that is, crisp) constraint. For obvious reasons, this approach and its variants do not constitute a satisfactory way of handling problems in which the constraints are intrinsically fuzzy, and do not lend themselves to satisfactory approximation with hard constraints. In such cases, it is more natural—and perhaps more efficient computationwise—to deal with fuzzy constraints in the manner sketched below.

As a preliminary, consider the standard problem of maximizing a non-negative objective function $f(x_1, \ldots, x_n)$ over a crisp constraint set A in E^n, that is, subject to the condition that $x \in A$.

Let $\mu_A(x)$ denote the characteristic function of A ($\mu_A(x) = 1$ for $x \in A$ and $\mu_A(x) = 0$ for $x \notin A$). Then, it is clear that the above problem is equivalent to the maximization of the modified objective function†

$$f^*(x) = f(x)\,\mu_A(x) \tag{14}$$

without any side conditions. This suggests that, when A is a fuzzy set and hence it is not meaningful to speak of x being constrained to A, the maximization of f over a fuzzy constraint set A be interpreted to mean the maximization of the modified objective function (14) over E^n. In this way, the maximization of $f(x)$, subject to a fuzzy constraint represented by a fuzzy set A, reduces to an unconstrained maximization of the function,

$$f^*(x_1, \ldots, x_n) = f(x_1, \ldots, x_n)\,\mu_A(x_1, \ldots, x_n). \tag{15}$$

In many optimal control problems, the constraints on x have the form $x_1 \in A_1$, $x_2 \in A_2, \ldots, x_n \in A_n$, where $A_1, \ldots, A_n$ are specified crisp sets in E^n. In such cases, the constraints in question can be replaced by the single constraint on x: $x \in A$, where A is the direct product of $A_1, \ldots, A_n$, that is, $A = A_1 \times A_2 \ldots \times A_n$. Note that the crisp sets $A_1, \ldots, A_n$ may be regarded as the shadows of the crisp set A on the coordinate axes.‡

A natural question that suggests itself at this point is: what if $A_1, \ldots, A_n$ are fuzzy sets? How can we derive A from $A_1, \ldots, A_n$, if the latter are taken to be shadows of A on the coordinate axes?

In the case of fuzzy sets, these questions do not have a unique answer, since A is not uniquely determined by its shadows.§ However, as in (6), one can bound A from above by the intersection of the cylindrical fuzzy sets $A_1^*, \ldots, A_n^*$, where the membership function of A_i^*, $i = 1, \ldots, n$, is given by

$$\mu^*_{A_i}(x) = \operatorname*{Sup}_{x_2} \operatorname*{Sup}_{x_3} \ldots \operatorname*{Sup}_{x_n} \mu_A(x_1, \ldots, x_n) = \mu_i(x_i) \tag{16}$$

More specifically

$$A \subset \bigcap_{i=1}^{n} \mu_i(x_i) \tag{17}$$

or equivalently,

$$\mu_A(x) \leq \text{Min}\,[\mu_1(x_1), \ldots, \mu_n(x_n)]. \tag{18}$$

Then, if—as an approximation—$\mu_A(x)$ is identified with the right member of (18), the modified objective function becomes

$$f^*(x_1, \ldots, x_n) = f(x_1, \ldots, x_n)\,\text{Min}\,[\mu_1(x_1), \ldots, \mu_n(x_n)]. \tag{19}$$

†More generally, the modified objective function can be taken to be $f^*(x) = f(x)\,[\mu_A(x)]^k$, where k is any positive real number. For our purposes, it will suffice to let $k = 1$.

‡The membership functions of the shadow of A on the axis $0x_1$ is given by $\mu_{A_1}(x) = \operatorname*{Sup}_{x_2} \operatorname*{Sup}_{x_3} \ldots \operatorname*{Sup}_{x_n} \mu_A(x_1, \ldots, x_n)$ on the axis; $\mu_{A_1}(x) = 0$ elsewhere; and similarly for other axes.

§As shown in references 1 and 2, a convex fuzzy set is uniquely determined by the totality of its shadows on all hyperplanes in E^n. Dually, a concave fuzzy set is uniquely determined by the totality of its complementary shadows.

In many practical situations, this approximation may be quite adequate. Unfortunately, no sharper estimates of A can be made when all we know about A are its shadows on coordinate axes.

The subject of optimization under fuzzy constraints has numerous additional ramifications, a few of which are now in process of exploration. Preliminary results seem to indicate that, in some cases, it may actually be advantageous to approximate to hard constraints by fuzzy constraints and employ steepest ascent techniques or other methods to maximize the modified objective functions. There are many other cases, however, in which optimization under fuzzy constraints is ineffective or computationally infeasible as an alternative to conventional optimization methods for dealing with problems involving crisp constraints.

CONCLUDING REMARKS

In the foregoing sections, we have not attempted to do more than merely touch upon the concept of fuzziness and point to some of its implications in system theory. Whether the particular concepts defined in this paper will prove to be of value in system design or analysis remains to be seen. It is clear, though, that in one form or another, the notion of fuzziness will come to play an important role in pattern classification, control, system optimization and other fields, since fuzziness is a basic and all-pervasive part of life that cannot be avoided merely because it is difficult to deal with precisely.

REFERENCES

1. L. A. Zadeh, "Fuzzy Sets," *Information and Control*, 8, 338-353, (June, 1965).

2. L. A. Zadeh, "Shadows of Fuzzy Sets," to appear in *Problems of Information Transmission*, June, 1966.

3. J. W. Carlyle, "Equivalent Stochastic Sequential Machines," Tech. Report No. 415, ERL, Univ. of California, Berkeley, 1961.

4. L. A. Zadeh and C. A. Desoer, *Linear System Theory--The State Space Approach*, (New York: McGraw-Hill, 1963).

5. A. Tal, "Questionnaire Language and Abstract Synthesis of Minimal Sequential Machines," *Automatika i Telemechanika*, 25, 946-962 (June, 1964).

6. A. Tal, "Abstract Synthesis of Sequential Machines by Answers to Questions of First Type in Questionnaire Language," Automatika i Telemechanika, 26, 676-682 (April, 1965).

MONOTONE OPERATORS AND CERTAIN SYSTEMS OF NONLINEAR ORDINARY DIFFERENTIAL EQUATIONS*

George J. Minty
University of Michigan, Ann Arbor, Michigan

A nonlinear operator f in a Hilbert space H (with real scalars) is called *monotonic* provided, for any $x_1, x_2 \in H$, we have

$$\langle fx_1 - fx_2, x_1 - x_2 \rangle \geq 0.$$

A typical existence-theorem is as follows: if f is everywhere-defined and continuous, then $x + f(x) = u$ always has a solution. Variants on this theorem, due to F. E. Browder, E. H. Zarantonello, and Minty, will be discussed.

Applications will include existence of a steady-state solution of a nonlinear electrical network in which the current and voltage-drop are monotonically related in each branch; ordinary differential equations of heat or electrical flow in a circular wire, where the current is monotonically related to the potential-gradient, the equations being

$$\frac{du}{dx} = f(x, v)$$

$$\frac{dv}{dx} = g(x, u)$$

(it is assumed that the wire radiates or "leaks" in a way monotonically related to the potential); and the corresponding problem for a network of wires. The examples are not chosen so much for their "applied" interest as for their simplicity and value in illustrating the method.

The aim throughout is to replace the notion of "convexity" by a more powerful notion, in dealing with certain types of problems.

1. INTRODUCTION

The main topic of this discussion is a *method* rather than the problems we solve here by that method. We shall aim for "end-product" theorems that are easily understandable, rather than "most general possible." The problems that we attack by the "monotonicity" method are regarded mainly as vehicles to display the power of the method, although they *do* have obvious systems-analysis

*This paper was written while the author was a Visiting Member of the Courant Institute of Mathematical Sciences, New York University, under National Science Foundation Grant NSF-GP-3465. He is currently at Indiana University.

Presented at the Symposium on System Theory
Polytechnic Institute of Brooklyn, April 20, 21, 22, 1965

interest in themselves. The operators which we call "monotone" have also been called "isotone," "nonlinear accretive," and "nonlinear negative-dissipative" in the literature.

We shall study (the numbers refer to sections of this paper):

3) A nonlinear electrical-network problem, for a network whose "branches" involve a monotone nondecreasing relationship between current and voltage drop. There are no differential equations in this problem.

4) A flow problem (which could be electrical flow, heat flow, etc.) in a circular one-dimensional wire.

5) A flow problem in a straight-line wire of finite length, with various types of boundary conditions.

6) A flow problem in a network of wires.

In Sections 4, 5, and 6, there will be a nonlinear (but monotonic) conductivity law, which may vary from point to point along the wire(s), and nonlinear (monotonic) radiation, or "leakage" laws, also varying from point to point.

For concreteness, and to keep close to the physical problems of primary interest, we shall assume that all variables appearing are real numbers. *However*, in the development of the theory, all the "dependent" variables could be taken as *vectors*, substituting an appropriate new definition of "monotonicity," and the theory would still go through with little difficulty. All the problems discussed *could* be solved by a "variational" method (minimizing a convex function subject to linear constraints), but *not if the dependent variables are vectors.* The writer is, however, not prepared to present "physical" interpretations of the "vector results." The relationship is this: the variational method was the pioneer work out of which the (in the writer's opinion) much richer "monotonicity" method grew. The latter method is also usually simpler to apply.

We shall present only existence and uniqueness theorems; however, I feel that the solutions of the equations are quite "solid," and there should be little difficulty in getting "answers" by numerical methods.

It is hoped that the reader will see in Section 4 and Section 5 a parallel with modern theories of elliptic partial differential equations. "Weak solution" is defined, and a proof of regularity given, in Section 4, on a compact manifold; in Section 5, a boundary-value problem is considered, and regularity of the solution at the boundary is taken up. It is not necessary to invoke the complicated Sobolev spaces and Sobolev imbedding theorems in this simple one-dimensional context. See reference 7 for development of these topics in the linear case, and works of F. E. Browder cited in the References for development of the topic of nonlinear (monotonic) elliptic partial differential equations.

2. SOME TOOL-THEOREMS

Let H be a Hilbert space, and let E be a subset of $H \times H$. We shall say that E is a *monotone* set provided that for any pair (x_1, y_1), (x_2, y_2) of points of E, we have:

$$Re \left\langle x_1 - x_2, y_1 - y_2 \right\rangle \geq 0.$$

(The symbol Re can be dropped if the scalars are real.) Also, E will be called a *maximal* monotone set if it is not properly contained in another monotone set.

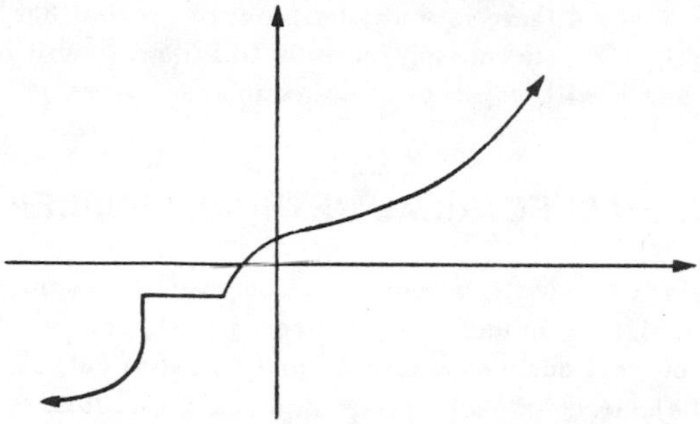

Figure 1.

If H is the real numbers, a typical maximal monotone set is simply "a curve going upward and to the right"—see Fig. 1.

Theorem 2.1. (See reference 10, Theorem 3.) If $E \subset H \times H$ is a maximal monotone set, then there exists a unique point $(x, y) \in E$ such that $x + y = \theta$ (the zero-vector.) In fact, the equation $x + y = u$ is always solvable for a unique pair $(x, y) \in E$, and both x and y depend continuously on u.

We shall call a function $\mathfrak{F}: H \longrightarrow H$ monotone if its *graph*:

$$\{(x, \mathfrak{F}_x): x \in H\}$$

is a monotone set; i.e., if for any $x_1, x_2 \in H$ we have $Re \left\langle x_1 - x_2, \mathfrak{F}x_1 - \mathfrak{F}x_2 \right\rangle \geq 0$.

Theorem 2.2. (See reference 10, Theorem 4.) Let $\mathfrak{F}: H \longrightarrow H$ be a continuous (with respect to the norm-topology) everywhere-defined (in H) monotone function. Then the graph of $\mathfrak{F}$ is a *maximal* monotone set.

Putting Theorems 2.1 and 2.2 together, we have

Theorem 2.3. For $\mathfrak{F}$ as in Theorem 2.3, the equation $x + \mathfrak{F}x = \theta$ has a solution, and this solution is unique.

Let us call $\mathfrak{F}: H \longrightarrow H$ *strongly* monotone if there is a positive constant c such that, for any two points x_1, x_2 in H, we have $Re \left\langle x_1 - x_2, \mathfrak{F}x_1 - \mathfrak{F}x_2 \right\rangle \geq c \| x_1 - x_2 \|^2$. Then a simple variant of Theorem 2.3 is:

Theorem 2.4. If $\mathfrak{F}$ is an everywhere-defined, continuous *strongly* monotone function, then the equation $\mathfrak{F}x = \theta$ has a solution, which is unique.

The brief proof of Theorem 2.4 is left to the reader, with the hint that the $\mathfrak{F}$ of Theorem 2.3 is not that of Theorem 2.4.

Our main tool-theorem will be the following one:

Theorem 2.5. Let $\mathfrak{F}$ be as in Theorem 2.4; let X be any closed linear subspace of H; and let Y be the orthogonal complement of X. Then there is a unique point (x, y) of $H \times H$ with $x \in X$, $y \in Y$, and $y = \mathfrak{F}x$; in other words, there is a unique point of X which is mapped by $\mathfrak{F}$ into a point of Y.

The proof of Theorem 2.5 is as follows: Let P be the operator of "projection on X"; consider the operator $P\mathfrak{F}: H \longrightarrow X$, and let $\mathfrak{R}: X \longrightarrow X$ be the restriction of $P\mathfrak{F}$ to X. It is easily verified that $\mathfrak{R}$ is strongly monotone, continuous, etc.; thus by Theorem 2.4 there is a unique point of X such that $\mathcal{R}x = \theta$; but then $P\mathcal{F}x = \theta$ and $\mathcal{F}x \in Y$. (In the applications to follow, $\mathcal{F}$ will be a rather simple object, but X and Y will be rather complex in some cases.)

3. AN ELECTRICAL-NETWORK PROBLEM

Let there be given an electrical network, composed of "branches" and "nodes" as usual; let the branches be numbered $i = 1, \ldots, n$. We seek a system $(u^1, \ldots, u^n)$ of (real numbers) currents and a system $(v^1, \ldots, v^n)$ of voltage drops such that the current in each branch is a monotonic function of the voltage drop: $u^i = f^i(v^i)$. Thus the problem is purely "steady-state." The functions f^i are "given" in the problem.

Let H be R^n, the n-tuples of real numbers. Let K_1 be the subspace of vectors satisfying Kirchhoff's current-conservation law, and K_2 the subspace of vectors satisfying his voltage-drop law. It is well known that K_1 and K_2 are orthogonal complements in R^n. (The orthogonality is sometimes called Tellegen's theorem, although its origin is apocryphal; the fact of complementarity follows by considering the dimensions.)

Assume that the f^i are everywhere-defined, continuous, real-valued functions of a real variable, and each is strongly monotone:

$$(v_1^i - v_2^i)\cdot[f^i(v_1^i) - f^i(v_2^i)] \geq c^i\,|\,v_1^i - v_2^i\,|^2.$$

Define $\mathcal{F}: R^n \longrightarrow R^n$ by $\mathcal{F}(v^1, \ldots, v^n) = (f^1(v^1), \ldots, f^n(v^n))$. Now $\mathcal{F}$ is everywhere-defined in $H = R^n$, and is continuous. Also

$$\left\langle \vec{v}_1 - \vec{v}_2, (\vec{v}_1) - (\vec{v}_2) \right\rangle = \sum_{i=1}^{n} (v_1^i - v_2^i)\cdot(f^i(v_1^i) - f^i(v_2^i))$$

$$\geq \sum_{i=1}^{n} c^i\,|\,v_1^i - v_2^i\,|^2$$

$$\geq (\min_i c^i) \sum_{i=1}^{n} |\,v_1^i - v_2^i\,|^2$$

$$= c\,\|\,\vec{v}_1 - \vec{v}_2\,\|^2, \quad \text{with} \quad c > 0.$$

Thus $\mathcal{F}$ is strongly monotone. Hence, by Theorem 2.5, it maps a unique point $\vec{v}$ of K_2 into a point $\vec{u}$ of K_1. This pair $(\vec{u}, \vec{v})$ are the desired currents and voltage drops.

The reader may be interested in going through the same argument with u's and v's *complex* numbers, and all the f^i *linear* functions. This corresponds to "each branch an ac generator and an impedance," and "strong monotonicity" means simply that each impedance has a little positive resistance.

(This problem, in the "nonlinear real" case, was treated by R. J. Duffin[5] by the "variational method"; an exhaustive treatment is given by the writer in references 8 and 9, by combinatorial methods; another treatment, by a monotonicity method, is given in reference 11, and goes somewhat further than the above discussion. See also reference 12.)

4. HEAT-FLOW IN A RING

A one-dimensional wire is bent into a circle, and its ends joined so that the joint is undetectable. Heat flows in the wire, with a nonlinear conductivity law: the rate of heat-transfer is monotonically related to the temperature-gradient *taken in the opposite direction.* The wire also radiates heat by a quasi-Newtonian cooling law: the rate of radiation is monotonically related to the temperature. We take this law in the following form: the *source-density* in the wire is monotonically related to the *negative* of the temperature.

Parameterizing the wire with the real variable t, with $0 \leq t < 1$, we translate into symbols as follows:

$$u(t) = \text{rate of flow (in direction of increasing } t).$$

$$du/dt = \text{source-density.}$$

$$v(t) = \textit{negative} \text{ of temperature.}$$

$$dv/dt = \text{negative of temperature-gradient.}$$

We propose to solve the differential equations

$$\left.\begin{aligned} du/dt &= f(t, v(t)) \\ dv/dt &= g(t, u(t)) \end{aligned}\right\} \tag{4.1}$$

subject to the boundary-conditions

$$u(0) = u(1), \quad v(0) = v(1). \tag{4.2}$$

The appearance of t in $f(t, v)$ and $g(t, u)$ is due to the physical properties (conductivity- and radiation-laws) of the wire changing from point to point.

(Enthusiasts of the Poincaré-Bendixson theorem for proof of existence of periodic solutions should note that this would be ill-advised because the solution is highly unstable if one regards t as a *time-variable*; i.e., by comparison with non-periodic solutions—which are meaningless if t is a space variable).

At this point, we are forced (by a weakness in our tool-theorem) to assume one of the equations "in solved form":

$$\left.\begin{aligned} du/dt &= f(t, v(t)) \\ u(t) &= h(t, dv/dt) \end{aligned}\right\} \tag{4.3}$$

and impose regularity conditions on f and h, as follows:

1) f and h are measurable in t for all values of second argument, and continuous in second argument for almost all t. For each t, they are defined for *all* real values of the second argument.

2) f and h are strongly monotone in second argument, with constants independent of t:

$$\left.\begin{aligned} \frac{f(t, v_1) - f(t, v_2)}{v_1 - v_2} &\geq c > 0 \\ \frac{h(t, q_1) - h(t, q_2)}{q_1 - q_2} &\geq c > 0 \end{aligned}\right\}. \tag{4.4}$$

3) There exists a function $b(t) \in L_2(0,1)$ and a constant $d > 0$ such that $|f(t,v)| \leq |b(t)| + d|v|$; and similarly for h.

Note that we *do not* require any Lipschitz-conditions, so that $f(t,v) = \sqrt[3]{v}$ would be admissible. Note also that (say) f need not be simultaneously continuous in its arguments; for example

$$f(t,v) = \begin{cases} 1 + v & \text{for} \quad 0 \leq t < 1/2 \\ -1 + v & \text{for} \quad 1/2 \leq t < 1 \end{cases} \tag{4.5}$$

is all right. Under these circumstances, it is clear that we cannot expect a continuous solution which is differentiable in the "usual sense," for we observe that a continuous $v(t)$ substituted into (4.5), which is in turn substituted into (4.3), yields a "jump-discontinuity" in du/dt; it is well known that an "ordinary" derivative cannot have a discontinuity "of the first kind."

As to the purposes of conditions (1), (2), and (3) above: consider the "Nemytskii operator" $\mathfrak{F}$, defined on $L_2(0,1)$ as follows:

$$(\mathfrak{F}x)(t) = f(t, x(t)).$$

Condition (1) (the so-called Carathéodory condition) insures that $\mathfrak{F}$ is defined for many $x(t)$ in $L_2(0,1)$; the additional hypothesis (3) prevents f from converting a "good," or L_2, singularity of $x(t)$ into a "bad" singularity, so that $\mathfrak{F}$ is actually defined for all $x(t) \in L_2$. Now, condition (2) makes $\mathfrak{F}$ strongly monotone:

$$\begin{aligned} \langle x_1 - x_2, \mathfrak{F}x_1 - \mathfrak{F}x_2 \rangle &= \int_0^1 [x_1(t) - x_2(t)] \cdot [f(t, x_1(t)) - f(t, x_2(t))]\, dt \\ &\geq \int_0^1 c\,|x_1(t) - x_2(t)|^2\, dt \\ &= c\,\| x_1 - x_2 \|^2. \end{aligned}$$

We do not have to prove that $\mathfrak{F}$ is continuous in the norm-topology, as this follows from the fact that it is everywhere defined in L_2; see reference 6, p. 27. All these remarks also apply to the operator $\mathfrak{H}$, defined analogously to $\mathfrak{F}$.

Now we set up the situation for application of Theorem 2.5. We need a Hilbert space and two orthogonal-complementary subspaces. Think for the moment of the problem as *electrical* flow rather than *heat* flow, and recall that the orthogonality in Section 3 came from a "total power = 0" idea. The corresponding fact here is:

$$\int_0^1 u(t)\, \frac{dv}{dt}\, dt + \int_0^1 \frac{du}{dt}\, v(t)\, dt = 0$$

(which follows, of course, from integration by parts for periodic $u(t)$ and $v(t)$; it is *inspired* but not *proved* by the physical energy principle.)

Let us define H as $L_2(0,1) \times L_2(0,1)$; also

$$\begin{aligned} X &= \{(dv/dt, v(t)) \colon v(t) \in C^\infty,\ v(0) = v(1)\} \\ Y &= \{(u(t, du/dt) \colon u(t) \in C^\infty,\ u(0) = u(1)\}. \end{aligned}$$

(The choice of C^∞ was rather arbitrary.) The integration-by-parts argument shows their orthogonality, but they are not orthogonal complements, since they are not *closed*. However, they are *almost* orthogonal complements, in the sense that

$$X + Y = \{x(t) + y(t) \colon x(t) \in X,\ y(t) \in Y\}$$

is dense in H. Let us prove this by showing $X + Y$ is $C^\infty \times C^\infty$. To do this, it suffices to show that there exists a C^∞ periodic solution to the system

$$\left.\begin{aligned} dv/dt + u(t) &= r(t) \\ u(t) + dv/dt &= s(t) \end{aligned}\right\} \tag{4.6}$$

for arbitrary $r(t)$ and $s(t)$ in C^∞. Now, every sophomore nowadays can write a *particular* solution $u^*(t)$, $v^*(t)$ as a convolution-integral, which is C^∞ because $r(t)$ and $s(t)$ are C^∞. Then the general solution can be written:

$$\left.\begin{aligned} u(t) &= \ \ Ce^t + De^{-t} + u^*(t) \\ v(t) &= -Ce^t + De^{-t} + v^*(t) \end{aligned}\right\}. \tag{4.7}$$

The constants C and D are determined from the boundary conditions; these lead to the equations

$$\left.\begin{aligned} C + D + u^*(0) &= \ \ Ce + De^{-1} + u^*(1) \\ -C + D + v^*(0) &= -Ce + De^{-1} + v^*(1) \end{aligned}\right\}. \tag{4.8}$$

We ask the reader's patience while we prove existence of a solution of (4.8) by an unnecessarily abstract argument. The steps are:

I) When one attempts to write a vector in a Hilbert space as a sum of two vectors in two *orthogonal* subspaces X and Y (which need not be orthogonal complements!), the "solution" is *unique* if it exists. It follows that the solution of (4.6) is unique if it exists. Consequently, the solution of (4.6) is uniquely the zero-solution when $r(t) = s(t) = 0$.

II) Thus when $u^*(0) = u^*(1) = v^*(0) = v^*(1) = 0$ in (4.8), the solution for C and D is unique.

III) Since in (4.8) *the number of equations matches the number of unknowns*, and the solution of the corresponding *homogeneous* equations is *unique*, therefore a solution to the *inhomogeneous* equations *exists*.

IV) Therefore, periodic solution of (4.6) exists.

(We shall use this argument again later, in much more complex situations.)

Our plan of attack is as follows: we consider the nonlinear operator in H

$$(p(t), q(t)) \longrightarrow ((\mathcal{H}p)(t)), (\mathcal{F}q)(t)).$$

This operator is everywhere defined, continuous, and strongly monotone. If we could find a vector in X which was mapped into a point of Y by this operator, we would have found $(dv/dt, v(t))$ carried into $(u(t), du/dt)$ by the operator; that is, $h(t, dv/dt) = u(t)$ and $f(t, v(t)) = du/dt$. But, as we remarked earlier, we cannot hope for so much under such weak hypotheses on f and h. Now, from the orthogonality of X and Y and the fact that $X + Y$ is dense in H, we conclude that $\bar{X}$ and $\bar{Y}$ (the closures of X and Y) are orthogonal complements (by well-known Hilbert space theory). So, by Theorem 2.5, there is a point of $\bar{X}$ mapped by the nonlinear operator into a point of $\bar{Y}$. We thus have a *weak solution* of the problem.

Now, what is the nature of this "weak solution?" I claim that

$$\bar{X} = \left\{ \left(V(t),\ C + \int_0^t V(t)\,dt \right) : V(t) \in L_2,\ \int_0^1 V(t)\,dt = 0,\ C \in R \right\}$$

$$\bar{Y} = \left\{ \left(D + \int_0^t U(t)\,dt,\ U(t) \right) : U(t) \in L_2,\ \int_0^1 U(t)\,dt = 0,\ D \in R \right\}$$

(It is easy to see that X and Y are dense in these spaces; the fact that they are closed follows easily from the continuity of the indefinite integral operator, which implies its closedness—i.e., its graph is closed.)

It would be easy to write down the problem we have "really" solved as a system of integral equations—but this would tend to obscure the method rather than illuminate it. Note now if we define

$$u(t) = D + \int_0^t U(t)\,dt$$

$$v(t) = C + \int_0^t V(t)\,dt$$

that $u(t)$ and $v(t)$ will be *continuous* and *periodic*; thus we have solved the system (4.1), (4.2), *but* with the stipulation that "$p(t)$ is the derivative of $q(t)$" shall mean "$q(t)$ is an indefinite integral of $p(t)$." One cannot find this weakening of the definition of "solution" particularly objectionable, especially in view of the fact that *if* f and g are simultaneously continuous in both arguments, *then* $u(t)$ and $v(t)$ *are* solutions in the usual C^1 sense. This follows from

$$U(t) = f\left(t,\ C + \int_0^t V(t)\,dt\right)$$

$$V(t) = g\left(t,\ D + \int_0^t U(t)\,dt\right)$$

(property of the weak solution), which shows that $U(t)$ and $V(t)$ are continuous, and hence by the Fundamental Theorem of Calculus,

$$U(t) = \frac{d}{dt}\left[D + \int_0^t U(t)\,dt\right] = du/dt$$

$$V(t) = \frac{d}{dt}\left[C + \int_0^t V(t)\,dt\right] = dv/dt.$$

It now follows in the usual way that if f and g are of class C^k, then $u(t)$ and $v(t)$ are of class C^{k+1}.

5. A BOUNDARY-VALUE PROBLEM

Now let us study the same heat-flow problem, but in a *straight* wire. We shall assume the temperature prescribed at one end of the wire (Dirichlet condition) and the rate of flow prescribed at the other end (Neumann condition). (Later we can discuss, say, two Dirichlet conditions).

The equations are:

$$\left.\begin{aligned} du/dt &= f(t, v(t)) \\ dv/dt &= g(t, u(t)) \\ u(0) &= u_0 \\ v(1) &= v_1 \end{aligned}\right\} \tag{5.1}$$

It seems a good idea to try first the easier problem $u_0 = 0$, $v_0 = 0$. We set up

$$H = R \times L_2(0,1) \times L_2(0,1) \times R$$

and the two linear subspaces

$$X = \{(v, dv/dt, v(t), v'): v' = v(1) = 0,\ v(t) \in C^\infty\}$$

$$Y = \{(u, u(t), du/dt, u'): u = u(0) = 0,\ u(t) \in C^\infty\}.$$

(Note the distinction between the numbers u and v and the functions $u(t)$ and $v(t)$; we shall keep things straight by always using the functional notation for the latter except in indicated derivatives, where no ambiguity is possible.)

As before, we first study the orthogonality. Consider, for a vector in X and a vector in Y, their inner product:

$$\begin{aligned} u \cdot v + \int_0^1 u(t)\, dv/dt\, dt + \int_0^1 du/dt\ v(t)\, dt + u'v' \\ = u \cdot v + u(t)\, v(t)\Big|_0^1 + u'v' \\ = u \cdot v + u(1)\, v(1) - u(0)\, v(0) + u'v' \\ = 0 \cdot v + u(1) \cdot 0 - 0 \cdot v(0) + u' \cdot 0 \\ = 0. \end{aligned}$$

We shall now show $X + Y$ is $R \times C^\infty \times C^\infty \times R$. It is sufficient to show that the system

$$\left.\begin{aligned} u + v &= p \\ u' + v' &= q \\ u(t) + dv/dt &= r(t) \\ du/dt + v(t) &= s(t) \\ u = u(0) &= 0 \\ v' = v(1) &= 0 \end{aligned}\right\} \tag{5.2}$$

is solvable, regardless of the "given" numbers p, q and the C^∞ functions $r(t)$, $s(t)$, and that the functions $u(t)$, $v(t)$ of the solution are C^∞ functions. Proceeding as in the previous section, we obtain six algebraic equations to be solved for the unknown numbers u, v, u', v', C, D. The steps (I), (II), (III), (IV) of the preceding section complete the argument for existence of a solution of (5.2).

Thus $\overline{X}$ and $\overline{Y}$ are orthogonal complements in H. Rewriting the nonlinear differential equations as in the preceding section, and placing the same regularity hypotheses on f and h, we construct the operator for the application of Theorem 2.5 as:

$$(p, r(t), s(t), q) \longrightarrow (\alpha(p), h(t, r(t)), f(t, s(t)), \beta(q))$$

(where α and β are completely arbitrary functions satisfying the hypotheses on the f^i in Section 3), and observe that it maps a point of $\overline{X}$ into a point of $\overline{Y}$. (Note: $r(t)$ and $s(t)$ are not those of eqs. (5.2).)

By arguments like those of the preceding section, we have

$$\overline{X} = \left\{\left(v,\ V(t),\ \int_t^1 V(t)\,dt,\ 0\right) : V(t) \in L_2,\ v \in R\right\}$$

$$\overline{Y} = \left\{\left(0,\ \int_0^t V(t)\,dt,\ V(t),\ u'\right) : U(t) \in L_2,\ u \in R\right\}.$$

So now we have a solution of the system

$$\left\{\begin{aligned} &\alpha(v) = 0 \\ &\int_0^t U(t)\,dt = h(t, V(t)) \\ &U(t) = f\left(t, \int_t^1 V(t)\,dt\right) \\ &\beta(0) = u \end{aligned}\right\} \qquad (5.3)$$

We discard the first and last of these relations and re-solve the second of them:

$$\left\{\begin{aligned} U(t) &= f\left(t, \int_t^1 V(t)\,dt\right) \\ V(t) &= g\left(t, \int_0^t U(t)\,dt\right) \end{aligned}\right\} \qquad (5.4)$$

Define $u(t)$ as $\int_0^t U(t)\,dt$, and correspondingly for $v(t)$. We now have the existence theorem for a weak solution, since clearly $u(0) = 0$ and $v(1) = 0$. We leave it to the reader to trace back through the argument and verify that the solution is unique. As before, if f and g are of class C^k, one shows $u(t)$ and $v(t)$ to be of class C^{k+1}. (It should be remarked that the proof that the boundary-conditions are satisfied is here quite trivial; in a corresponding discussion of *partial* differential equations, it would be formidable!)

Now, what shall we do when $u_0 \neq 0$, $v_1 \neq 0$? It is a standard trick of classical analysis to choose two C^∞ functions $\overline{u}(t)$, $\overline{v}(t)$ with $\overline{u}(0) = u_0$, $\overline{v}(1) = v_1$, then to substitute $u(t) = \overline{u}(t) + \Delta v(t)$ into (5.1). We obtain new equations to be solved for $\Delta u(t)$ and $\Delta v(t)$, with *homogeneous* boundary-conditions. The new equations will be of the "same type" as before, and the "new" f and h will have the same monotonicity, everywhere-definedness, and continuity as the "old" f and h. We might call this process "translation in the concrete." It would be convenient to have an abstract theorem in which this "translation" is already done, "in the abstract."

Theorem 5.1. Let X, Y be closed linear manifolds in H which are *translates* of a pair of orthogonal complementary subspaces X_0, Y_0; let $\mathfrak{F}: H \longrightarrow H$ be an everywhere-defined, continuous, strongly monotone function. Then there is a (unique) point $x \in X$ which is mapped by $\mathfrak{F}$ into a point $y \in Y$.

***Proof*:** There exist a, b in H such that

$$X_0 = X + a = \{x + a\colon x \in X\}$$

$$Y_0 = Y + b = \{y + b\colon y \in Y\}.$$

Define $\mathfrak{F}'(x)$ as $b + \mathfrak{F}(x - a)$. Then $\mathfrak{F}'$ is easily shown to have the same regularity properties as were hypothesized on $\mathfrak{F}$. Thus, there is an $x_0 \in X_0$ and a $y_0 \in Y_0$ with $y_0 = \mathfrak{F}'(x_0)$. Then $b + \mathfrak{F}(x_0 - a) = y_0$, or $\mathfrak{F}(x_0 - a) = y_0 - b$. Define x as $x_0 - a$, y as $y_0 - b$; note $x \in X$ and $y \in Y$, so we have the conclusion. Uniqueness is clear.

This is the correct form of the tool-theorem for treating *inhomogeneous* Dirichlet and Neumann conditions. We develop it here as a preview of a more powerful tool-theorem yet to come.

A final remark: to handle two Dirichlet conditions, both taken as homogeneous, let

$$X = \{(v,\ dv/dt,\ v(t),\ v')\colon v(t) \in C^\infty;\quad v = v' = v(0) = v(1) = 0\}$$

$$Y = \{(u,\ u(t),\ du/dt,\ u')\colon u(t) \in C^\infty;\quad u,\ u' \in R\}$$

and use their closures as the tool-subspaces.

6. HEAT-FLOW IN A NETWORK

Consider a network of wires, numbered $i = 1, \ldots, n$; each wire terminates in two "nodes," the nodes being numbered $j = 1, \ldots, m$. The physical properties of the wires (nonlinear conductivity- and radiation laws, variable from point to point of a wire) are essentially the same as in Section 4. Let each wire be parametrized by a real variable t, with $0 \leq t \leq 1$. Orientations are assumed arbitrarily, and $t = 0$ corresponds to the "tail of the arrow," and $t = 1$ to the "head."

Let $[\varepsilon_{ij}]$ be an $n \times m$ incidence matrix, defined as follows: $\varepsilon_{ij} = 1$ if wire i is incident on node j, *and directed into* the node; $\varepsilon_{ij} = 0$ otherwise. Define also $[\zeta_{ij}]$ similarly, but $\zeta_{ij} = 1$ if wire i is *directed out from* node j. (By poetic license, we might call $[\zeta_{ij}]$ the "*out*cidence matrix!") The difference of these two matrices is the "usual" incidence matrix of the directed graph. Note that *each row of each matrix has precisely one* 1.

The *nodes* of the network are also assumed to "have a physical property":

they radiate heat with the rate of radiation being monotonically related to the temperature.

We set:

u_j = rate of heat-flow *into* node j from the "outside world."

v_j = negative of temperature at node j.

$u_i(t)$ = rate of heat-flow (in direction of increasing t) in ith wire at the point parametrized by t.

$v_i(t)$ = negative of temperature at the point t of the ith wire.

The "abstract" problem can be formulated as follows: find numbers u_j, v_j, and functions $u_i(t)$, $v_i(t)$, satisfying the relations:

$$\alpha)\ \left.\begin{cases} \dfrac{du_i}{dt} = f_i(t, v_i(t)) \\ \dfrac{dv_i}{dt} = g_i(t, u_i(t)) \end{cases}\right\} i = 1, \ldots, n$$

$$\beta)\quad v_j = e_j(u_j) \qquad j = 1, \ldots, m$$

$$\gamma)\quad u_j + \sum_{i=1}^{n} \varepsilon_{ij}\, u_i(1) - \sum_{i=1}^{n} \zeta_{ij}\, u_i(0) = 0$$

$$\delta)\ \left.\begin{cases} \displaystyle\sum_{j=1}^{n} \zeta_{ij}\, v_j = v_i(0) \\ \displaystyle\sum_{j=1}^{n} \varepsilon_{ij}\, v_j = v_i(1) \end{cases}\right\} i = 1, \ldots, n.$$

Here, (α) are the nonlinear conductivity and radiation laws at interior points of the wires; (β) is the nonlinear radiation law at the nodes; (γ) is a "conservation of heat" law at the nodes; and (δ) is the requirement that, for each wire, the temperatures at the ends match the temperatnres of the corresponding nodes. (Note how ε_{ij} and ζ_{ij} behave like Kronecker deltas in (δ) in the sense of the "sifting property.")

We place the same assumptions on f_i and g_i (or rather, f_i and h_i) as in Section 4 and Section 5, and the same assumptions on e_j as we placed on the f^i in Section 3. We shall show existence and uniqueness of a solution to the system (α), (β), (γ), (δ). *Moreover, we shall do this for any arbitrary* $n \times m$ matrices $[\varepsilon_{ij}]$, $[\zeta_{ij}]$!!! (We shall not, from this point on, need to assume that they are incidence matrices!) Thus the discussion to follow really goes far beyond the physical problem we originally posed.

We choose the Hilbert space H as $R^m \times [L_2(0, 1)]^n \times [L_2(0, 1)]^n$. Define the linear subspaces X and Y using C^∞ functions v_i and u_i, as:

$$\left\{\left(v_1, \ldots, v_m; \ \frac{dv_1}{dt}, \ldots, \frac{dv_n}{dt}; \ v_1(t), \ldots, v_n(t)\right): \ \text{for each} \right.$$

$$\left. i = 1, \ldots, n, \ \sum_{j=1}^{m} \varepsilon_{ij} v_j = v_i(0) \ \text{ and } \ \sum_{j=1}^{m} \zeta_{ij} v_j = v_i(1) \right\}$$

and

$$\left\{\left(u_1, \ldots, u_m; \ u_1(t), \ldots, u_n(t); \ \frac{du_1}{dt}, \ldots, \frac{du_n}{dt}\right): \ \text{for each} \right.$$

$$\left. j = 1, \ldots, m, \ u_j + \sum_{i=1}^{n} \varepsilon_{ij} u_i(1) - \sum_{i=1}^{n} \zeta_{ij} u_i(0) = 0 \right\}.$$

If we can show that $\bar{X}$ and $\bar{Y}$ are orthogonal complements, then the rest of the argument will go through slickly; it is obvious how we should define the nonlinear monotone function, following the models of Section 3 and Section 4. Having obtained a point of $\bar{X}$ mapped by it into a point of $\bar{Y}$, we show the "interior regularity" of solution as in Section 3; once we know the "integral representations" of $u_i(t)$ and $v_i(t)$, it is relatively easy, as in Section 5, to verify the satisfaction of the constraints (γ) and (δ).

We show the orthogonality. For arbitrary elements of X and Y, we form the inner product in H:

$$\sum_{j=1}^{m} u_j v_j + \sum_{i=1}^{n} \int_0^1 u_i(t) \frac{dv_i}{dt} dt + \sum_{i=1}^{n} \int_0^t \frac{du_i}{dt} v_i(t)\, dt$$

$$= \sum_{j=1}^{m} u_j v_j + \sum_{i=1}^{n} u_i(t) v_i(t) \Big]_0^1$$

$$= \sum_{j=1}^{m} \left[\sum_{i=1}^{n} \zeta_{ij} u_i(0) - \sum_{i=1}^{n} \varepsilon_{ij} u_i(1) \right] v_i + \sum_{i=1}^{n} u_i(1) v_i(1) - \sum_{i=1}^{n} u_i(0) v_i(0)$$

$$= \sum_{i=1}^{n} \left[\sum_{j=1}^{m} \zeta_{ij} v_j - v_i(0) \right] u_i(0) - \sum_{i=1}^{n} \left[\sum_{j=1}^{m} \varepsilon_{ij} v_j - v_i(1) \right] u_i(1)$$

$$= 0.$$

(We used integration-by-parts, and conditions (γ) and (δ) as they appeared in the definitions of X and Y.)

Now we show that $X + Y = R^m + [C^\infty]^n + [C^\infty]^n$. Following the model of the preceding sections, we see it is sufficient to show that the system

$$\alpha') \left\{ \begin{array}{l} u_i(t) + \dfrac{dv_i}{dt} = r_i(t) \\ \\ \dfrac{du_i}{dt} + v_i(t) = s_i(t) \end{array} \right\} i = 1, \ldots, n$$

$$\beta') \quad u_j + v_j = p_j \qquad j = 1, \ldots, m$$

$$\gamma') \quad \text{(same as } \gamma)$$

$$\delta') \quad \text{(same as } \delta)$$

is solvable for the numbers u_j, v_j and the functions $u_i(t)$, $v_i(t)$, for *any given* numbers p_j and C^∞ functions $r_i(t)$, $s_i(t)$; *and* that the solutions $u_i(t)$, $v_i(t)$ are C^∞ functions. We remark here that $(\alpha')(\beta')(\gamma')(\delta')$ is precisely the *linear special case* of $(\alpha)(\beta)(\gamma)(\delta)$, with radiation and conductivity coefficients = 1, but with the signs of the v's reversed throughout. Also, as in previous sections, the orthogonality of X and Y proves *uniqueness* of any solution of $(\alpha')(\beta')(\gamma')(\delta')$.

As in earlier sections, we write the general solution of (α'):

$$u_i(t) = \ \ C_i e^t + D_i e^{-t} + u_i^*(t)$$

$$v_i(t) = -C_i e^t + D_i e^{-t} + v_i^*(t)$$

and substitute into (γ') and (δ'). Now, (β') and the substituted relations (γ') and (δ') are a system of $m + m + 2n$ linear algebraic equations in the unknowns u_j, v_j, C_i, D_i. The number of unknowns matches the number of equations. The rest of the existence argument follows the outline (I)(II)(III)(IV) of Section 4.

As remarked before, the rest of the discussion is easily filled in.

7. MORE POWERFUL TOOLS

Through the earlier sections of this paper, there have been two sources of constant annoyance, both to the writer and (I hope!) to the reader. One is the constant insistence on *strong* monotonicity; the other, which seems to me more serious, is the failure to treat the two spaces X and Y in the same way.

If one writes down Theorem 2.4 with "strong monotonicity" replaced merely by "monotonicity," one sees immediately that it is false, by considering obvious examples with H = the real numbers. However, with the additional hypothesis that $\mathfrak{F}(x)$ is negative as $x \longrightarrow -\infty$ and positive as $x \longrightarrow +\infty$, it is true (even without monotonicity!). In infinite dimensions, a condition of the type: "there exists $M > 0$ sufficiently large that for $\|x\| = M$, we have $Re\langle x, \mathfrak{F}x\rangle \geq 0$" provides the needed additional push to make the theorem true (see reference 4, p. 151). Note that while monotonicity is essentially a *local* condition as shown by Theorem 5 of reference 10), this new condition discusses only the behavior of $\mathfrak{F}$ for *large* $\|x\|$, that is, for x far away from the origin. Such a condition is called a *coerciveness* requirement—in some sense, it "prevents the solution from going off to infinity." The writer has experimented with coerciveness conditions of various types in reference 4 and in Theorem 1 of reference 11, Other experiments with such conditions have been carried out by F. E. Browder.[1,2,3]

The other source of annoyance—the lack of duality between X and Y—I believe to be caused by over-emphasis on the notions of (single-valued!) *function* and *equation*. In reference 8, the writer showed that it was possible to give a *better* mathematical model of the electrical-network problem of Section 3 *without ever writing down an equation* (except for Kirchhoff's laws!) and to give a complete mathematical treatment of the problem in this form, with "maximal monotone set'' substituted for ''graph of an everywhere-defined, continuous monotone function.''

We now give a theorem which is intended to slay both these dragons simultaneously:

Theorem 7.1: (Special case of theorem of reference 11) Let H be a Hilbert space. Let $E \subset H \times H$ be a maximal monotone set. Let the two coerciveness conditions be satisfied:

i) There exists $M > 0$ sufficiently large that for any x with $\| x \| = M$, there exists a y such that $(x, y) \epsilon E$ and $Re \langle x, y \rangle \geq 0$.

ii) (Dual to (i)). There exists $N > 0$ sufficiently large that for any y with $\| y \| = N$, etc. etc.

Then there is a point (x, y) (not necessarily unique) contained in E such that $x \epsilon X$ and $y \epsilon Y$.

The following is a hint for the application of this theorem to obtain generalizations of the theorems of the previous sections on solutions of differential equations:

Theorem 7.2: Let $H_1, \ldots, H_n$ be Hilbert spaces. Let $E_1, \ldots, E_n$ be maximal monotone sets in $H_1 \times H_1, \ldots, H_n \times H_n$ respectively. Then $E_1 \times \ldots \times E_n$ is a maximal monotone set in $H_1 \dot{+} \ldots \dot{+} H_n$. (By $H_1 \dot{+} \ldots \dot{+} H_n$, we mean $H_1 \times \ldots \times H_n$ endowed with the usual Hilbert space structure.)

Proof: For each $i = 1, \ldots, n$ let ϕ_i: $E_i \longrightarrow H_i$ be defined by $\phi_i(x, y) = x + y$. By Theorem 2.1, each ϕ_i maps E_i *onto* H_i. Thus, defining Φ: $E_1 \times \ldots \times E_n \longrightarrow H_i \dot{+} \ldots \dot{+} H_n$ by

$$\Phi(x_1, y_1; \ \ldots; \ x_n, y_n) = (x_1 + y_1, \ldots, x_n + y_n),$$

we see Φ is also an ''onto'' map. But if $E \supset E_1 \dot{+} \ldots \dot{+} E_n$ is monotone, then Φ: $E \longrightarrow H_i \dot{+} \ldots \dot{+} H_n$ is one-to-one (also by Theorem 2.1, using the ''uniqueness'' part of the theorem.) (*Note*: Φ is defined on E analogously.) Thus $E = E_1 \times \ldots \times E_n$, so $E_1 \times \ldots \times E_n$ is *maximal*.

To indicate use of these theorems: consider the problem of Section 4. Let H_1 and H_2 be $L_2(0, 1)$, and let $H = H_1 \dot{+} H_2$. The diagram

$$\begin{array}{c} H = H_1 + H_2 \\ \uparrow \mathcal{G} \quad \downarrow \mathcal{F} \\ H = H_1 + H_2 \end{array}$$

is almost self-explanatory: if the graphs of $\mathcal{F}$ and $\mathcal{G}$ are *both* maximal monotone sets, then the appropriate set E for application of Theorem 7.1 is the product of the two graphs, *but with the roles of domain and range interchanged* in one of them!

8. SUGGESTED PROBLEMS

The reader who is sufficiently interested may wish to try his hand at some extensions of the results given here. I suggest the following problems, which are incompletely stated in the sense that some of the hypotheses have yet to be filled in.

A) Try the electrical network problem of Section 3; instead of assuming functions f^i given, assume a maximal monotone set $E^i \subset R \times R$ given for each branch. Use Theorems 7.2 and 7.1. Compare the result with Theorem 7.1 of reference 11 or Theorem 8.1 of reference 8 to see how close it is to the "strongest possible" theorems.

B) Try the problem of Section 4 under the assumption that f and g are monotone, but not strongly monotone; use Theorem 7.1.

C) Try the problem of Section 5 with changes as in B.

D) Try the problem of Section 6 with any or all of the following complications:

1. Some of the node conditions are of Dirichlet and Neumann type.
2. Other node conditions replace the functions e_j with maximal monotone sets E_j in $R \times R$.
3. Some wires are "non-leaky," and are replaced by wires of the type discussed in Section 3.
4. Changes as in B above.

9. ACKNOWLEDGMENTS

This is an expository article, but not a "survey" of the applications of monotonicity methods to ordinary differential equations. The monotonicity method has enjoyed such rapid progress that most of the literature refers primarily to *partial* differential equations and does not emphasize the "special case $n = 1$." An adequate survey would prominently feature works of F. E. Browder, and would cite as contributors: E. H. Zarantonello, M. M. Vainberg, R. I. Kachurovskii, W. Strauss, T. Kato, J. L. Lions, J. Leray, C. B. Morrey, M. Shinbrot, I. I. Kolodner, E. H. Rothe, I. W. Sandberg. I apologize for any omissions from this list.

REFERENCES

1. F. E. Browder, "The Solvability of Non-Linear Functional Equations," *Duke Math. J.*, **30**, 557–566 (1963).
2. F. E. Browder, "Variational Boundary Value Problems for Quasi-Linear Elliptic Equations, III," *Proc. Nat. Acad. Sciences U.S.A.*, **50**, 794–798 (1963).
3. F. E. Browder, "Variational Method for Nonlinear Elliptic Eigenvalue Problems," *Bull. Amer. Math. Soc.*, **71**, 176–183 (1965).
4. C. L. Dolph and G. J. Minty, "On Nonlinear Integral Equations of the Hammerstein Type," in *Nonlinear Integral Equations*, P. Anselone, Ed. (Madison: University of Wisconsin Press, 1964).
5. R. J. Duffin, "Nonlinear Networks. II." *Bull. Amer. Math. Soc.*, **53**, 963–97 (1947).
6. M. A. Krasnosel'skii, *Topological Methods in the Theory of Nonlinear Integral Equations* (New York: Macmillan, 1964) [Original Russian edition 1956].
7. J. L. Lions, *Equations Differentielles Operationelles* (Berlin: Springer, 1961).
8. G. J. Minty, "Monotone Networks," *Proc. Roy. Soc. London*, **A257**, 194–212 (1960).
9. G. J. Minty, "Solving Steady-State Nonlinear Networks of 'Monotone' Elements," *IRE Trans. on Circuit Theory*, **CT-8**, 99–104 (1961).

10. G. J. Minty, "Monotone (Nonlinear) Operators in Hilbert Space," *Duke Math. J.*, **29**, 341–346 (1962).

11. G. J. Minty, "A Theorem on Maximal Monotonic Sets in Hilbert Space," to appear in *J. Math. Analy. and Appl.*

12. G. J. Minty, "On the Axiomatic Foundations of the Theories of Directed Linear Graphs, Electrical Networks and Network-Programming," to appear in *J. Math. and Mech.*

A CANONICAL FORM FOR NONLINEAR RLC NETWORKS*

R. K. Brayton

IBM Thomas J. Watson Research Center, Yorktown Heights, N. Y.

Electrical networks composed of two-terminal, nonlinear R, L, or C elements can be described by a system of first-order ordinary differential equations that have a special and useful form. Written in vector notation this form is

$$L(i)\frac{di}{dt} = \frac{\partial P}{\partial i}$$

$$C(v)\frac{dv}{dt} = -\frac{\partial P}{\partial v}$$

where the vector $i = (i_1, \ldots, i_k)$ is a set of linearly independent inductor currents and $v = (v_{k+1}, \ldots, v_{k+\ell})$ is a set of linearly independent capacitor voltages. L and C are matrices, and P is a scaler function of i, v called the mixed potential function for the network. The mixed potential function can be obtained directly from the network by following a simple recipe for constructing it. Some examples will be given and uses of the mixed potential function will be described, including the construction of Liapunov functions for deriving stability criteria. The extension of these ideas to distributed networks will also be discussed.

1. INTRODUCTION

In this paper it will be shown that the differential equations describing a class of nonlinear RLC electrical (and by analogy, mechanical) networks can be written in the special form

$$L(i)\frac{di}{dt} = \frac{\partial P}{\partial i}$$

$$C(v)\frac{dv}{dt} = -\frac{\partial P}{\partial v}$$

where i is a vector of independent currents through inductors and v is a vector of independent voltages across capacitors. $L(i)$ and $C(v)$ are positive definite symmetric matrices, and P is a scalar function of i, v. The class of networks admitted are those composed of two-terminal nonlinear RLC elements. Time-varying

*The results reported in this paper were obtained in the course of research jointly sponsored by the Air Force Office of Scientific Research (Contract AF 49(638)-1139) and IBM.

Presented at the Symposium on System Theory
Polytechnic Institute of Brooklyn, April 20, 21, 22, 1965

elements are also admitted. However, three-terminal devices such as transistors or vacuum tubes are not allowed.

The fact that the function $P(i, v)$ can be obtained directly from the network makes this form easily accessible and useful. Some applications will be mentioned, but for a more complete presentation we refer to reference 1. An extension of these ideas to distributed networks can be found in reference 2.

2. ADMISSIBLE ELEMENTS

The elements in the network will be classified as purely resistive, inductive, or capacitive. By a resistor we mean any continuous function $f(i, v)$ that relates the current in the element to the voltage across it by the relation

$$f(i, v) = 0.$$

This simply defines a continuous curve in the $i-v$ plane which is not necessarily a single-valued function of i or v. A battery and a constant current source are included in this definition of a resistor. Also, the restriction $f(0, 0)$ is not made.

An inductor is defined to be a positive function $L(i)$ which relates the time derivative of the current through the element to the voltage across it by the relation

$$L(i)\frac{di}{dt} = -v.$$

Clearly, not all inductive devices are inductors by this definition. However, if the flux linkages ϕ can be expressed as a monotone increasing function of the current; that is, $\phi = \phi(i)$, then

$$-v \equiv \frac{d\phi}{dt} = \frac{d\phi}{di}(i)\frac{di}{dt} \equiv L(i)\frac{di}{dt} \quad \text{and} \quad L(i) \geq 0.$$

Similarily, a capacitor is defined to be a positive function $C(v)$ relating the time derivative of the voltage across the element to the current through it by the relation

$$C(v)\frac{dv}{dt} = -i.$$

Again, if the charge q can be expressed as a monotone increasing function of v, that is, $q = q(v)$, then

$$-i \equiv \frac{dq}{dt} = \frac{dq}{dv}\frac{dv}{dt} \equiv C(v)\frac{dv}{dt} \quad \text{and} \quad C(v) \geq 0.$$

An admissible network in this discussion is any collection of the above elements tied together in an arbitrary fashion.

3. TOPOLOGICAL THEOREMS

The concept of an electrical network is logically divided into two parts, the topology and the electrical elements. Topologically, a network is simply a set of points called nodes and a set of connecting lines called branches. We label each branch by $\mu = 1, \ldots, b$ and associate with each branch two variables i_μ, v_μ. These variables are restricted by Kirchhoff's two laws; namely, the node law

$$\sum_{\text{node}} \pm i_\mu = 0,$$

and the loop law

$$\sum_{\text{loop}} \pm v_\mu = 0.$$

These conservation laws lead to a restriction on the b-dimensional vectors $i = (i_1, \ldots, i_b)$ and $v = (v_1, \ldots, v_b)$. This is stated geometrically in the following theorem due to Tellegen.[3]

Theorem 1: Let $\mathcal{J}$ be the set of all b-dimensional vectors for which Kirchhoff's node law holds and let $\mathcal{V}$ be the set of all b-dimensional vectors for which Kirchhoff's loop law holds. Then $\mathcal{J}$ and $\mathcal{V}$ are orthogonal subspaces, and $\mathcal{J} \oplus \mathcal{V} = \mathcal{E}_b$ (b-dimensional Euclidean space).

Thus, any vector $x \in \mathcal{E}_b$ can be decomposed into $x = i + v$ where

$$i \in \mathcal{J}, \quad v \in \mathcal{V} \quad \text{and} \quad \sum_{\mu=1}^{b} i_\mu v_\mu = 0.$$

The physical interpretation of this theorem is that for any admissible set of currents and voltages, power must be conserved in the network. We also note that any two of the three laws, the node law, the loop law, and the power law, imply the other.

A slight variation of this theorem is the following

Theorem 2: For any continuous curve $\Gamma(s) \in \mathcal{E}_b$.

$$\int_\Gamma \sum_{\mu=1}^{b} v_\mu \, di_\mu = \int_\Gamma \sum_{\mu=1}^{b} i_\mu \, dv_\mu = 0$$

where $\Gamma(s) = i(s) + v(s)$.

It is this form of Tellegen's theorem which leads directly to the canonical form of the differential equations.

4. THE FORM OF THE EQUATIONS

Each branch in the network can be classified according to whether it contains a resistor, an inductor, or a capacitor. Let the subscript ρ denote a resistive branch, λ an inductive branch, and γ a capacitive branch, and let $1 \leq \lambda \leq r$, $r + 1 \leq \gamma \leq r + s$, $r + s + 1 \leq \rho$. Also denote by $i^* = (i_1, \ldots, i_r)$ the vector of currents in the inductors, and by $v^* = (v_{r+1}, \ldots, v_{r+s})$ the vector of voltages across the capacitors. We assume for the moment that the i_λ are independent and that the v_γ are independent. Now suppose the network is such that given i^*, v^*, the voltages and currents in the branches can be expressed by algebraic relations; i.e., there exist functions f_μ, g_μ such that

$$v_\mu = f_\mu(i^*, v^*)$$
$$i_\mu = g_\mu(i^*, v^*)$$

for $\mu = 1, \ldots, b$. We note that these functions may be multivalued. However, if i^*, v^* are given, we can determine a parametrization $i^*(s), v^*(s)$ such that $i^*(0)$, $v^*(0)$ is an arbitrary constant; $i^*(1) = i^*$, $v^*(1) = v^*$; and $v_\mu(s)$, $i_\mu(s)$ are continuous functions of s given by

$$v_\mu(s) = f_\mu(i^*(s), v^*(s)),$$
$$i_\mu(s) = g_\mu(i^*(s), v^*(s)).$$

We denote this curve by $\Gamma^*(s)$.

From Theorem 2 we have

$$\int_{\Gamma^*} \sum_\rho v_\rho \, di_\rho + \sum_\lambda v_\lambda \, di_\lambda + \sum_\gamma v_\gamma \, di_\gamma = 0,$$

or integrating by parts,

$$\int_{\Gamma^*} \sum_\rho v_\rho \, di_\rho + \sum_\gamma v_\gamma \, i_\gamma \Big|_{\Gamma^*} = \int_{\Gamma^*} \sum_\gamma i_\gamma \, dv_\gamma - \sum_\lambda v_\lambda di_\lambda .$$

Now note the left-hand side is only a function of the end points of Γ^* and not the path of integration, since along Γ^*, $i_\rho(s)$, $v_\rho(s)$ must vary along this resistor's characteristic curve in the $i_\rho - v_\rho$ plane. We can then write

$$\int_{\Gamma^*} \sum_\rho v_\rho \, di_\rho + \sum_\gamma v_\gamma \, i_\gamma \Big|_{\Gamma^*} = \sum_\rho \int_{\Gamma^*} v_\rho \, di_\rho + \sum_\gamma v_\gamma \, i_\gamma \Big|_{\Gamma^*} \equiv P(i^*, v^*);$$

that is, this is a function of i^*, v^* only. Again we point out that $P(i^*, v^*)$ need not be a single-valued function. From the relation

$$P(i^*, v^*) = \int_{\Gamma^*} \sum_\gamma i_\gamma \, dv_\gamma - \sum_\lambda v_\lambda \, di_\lambda , \tag{1}$$

we have

$$\begin{aligned} \frac{\partial P}{\partial i_\lambda} &= -v_\lambda \equiv L_\lambda(i_\lambda) \frac{di_\lambda}{dt} \\ \frac{\partial P}{\partial v_\gamma} &= i_\gamma \equiv -C_\gamma(i_\gamma) \frac{dv_\gamma}{dt} \end{aligned} \tag{2}$$

which establishes the form of the differential equations in the case where the i_λ, v_γ are independent.

The dependent case where $i^* = \{\tilde{i}, \hat{i}\}$, $v^* = \{\tilde{v}, \hat{v}\}$ and $\tilde{v} = A\hat{v} + a$, $\tilde{i} = B\hat{i} + b$ can be easily obtained. Here A, B are constant matrices and a, b are constant vectors. For this purpose we use the notation

$$(x, y) = \sum_{k=1}^{n} x_k y_k$$

for the inner product of two n-vectors. Also, let $V = (v_1, \ldots, v_r) = \{\tilde{V}, \hat{V}\}$ and $I = (i_{r+1}, \ldots, i_{r+s}) = \{\tilde{I}, \hat{I}\}$. Since V is the vector of voltages across the inductors, we have

$$\begin{pmatrix} \tilde{L} & 0 \\ 0 & \hat{L} \end{pmatrix} \begin{pmatrix} \dfrac{d\tilde{i}}{dt} \\ \dfrac{d\hat{i}}{dt} \end{pmatrix} = - \begin{pmatrix} \tilde{V} \\ \hat{V} \end{pmatrix} = - V, \tag{3}$$

and similarly, since I is the vector of currents in the capacitors,

$$\begin{pmatrix} \tilde{C} & 0 \\ 0 & \hat{C} \end{pmatrix} \begin{pmatrix} \dfrac{d\tilde{v}}{dt} \\ \dfrac{d\hat{v}}{dt} \end{pmatrix} = - \begin{pmatrix} \tilde{I} \\ \hat{I} \end{pmatrix} = - I. \tag{4}$$

Here $\tilde{L}, \hat{L}, \tilde{C}, \hat{C}$ are diagonal positive definite matrices. From eq. (1),

$$P(i^*, v^*) = \int_{\Gamma^*} (I, dv^*) - (V, di^*),$$

or

$$\hat{P}(\hat{i}, \hat{v}) = \int_{\Gamma^*} (\tilde{I}, A\, d\hat{v}) + (\hat{I}, d\hat{v}) - (\tilde{V}, B\, d\hat{i}) - (\hat{V}, d\hat{i}).$$

Differentiating and using (3) and (4),

$$\frac{\partial \hat{P}}{\partial \hat{i}} = - \hat{V} - B^T \tilde{V} - \hat{L} \frac{d\hat{i}}{dt} + B^T \tilde{L} \frac{d\tilde{i}}{dt} = (\hat{L} + B^T \tilde{L} B) \frac{d\hat{i}}{dt}$$

$$\frac{\partial \hat{P}}{\partial \hat{v}} = \hat{I} + A^T \tilde{I} = - \hat{C} \frac{d\hat{v}}{dt} - A^T \tilde{C} \frac{d\tilde{v}}{dt} = - (\hat{C} + A^T \tilde{C} A) \frac{d\hat{v}}{dt},$$

which again establishes the form of the equations. Note that $\hat{L} + B^T \tilde{L} B$, $\hat{C} + A^T \tilde{C} A$ are positive definite symmetric matrices.

We have proved the following theorem:

Theorem 3: If an electrical network has the following properties:

a) each element is a two-terminal R, L, or C device of the type described in Section 2;

b) all currents and voltages in the branches of the network can be expressed as functions of i, v, where i is an independent set of currents in the inductors and v is an independent set of voltages in the capacitors;

then the differential equations describing this network can be written in the form

$$L(i)\frac{di}{dt} = \frac{\partial P}{\partial i},$$

$$C(v)\frac{dv}{dt} = -\frac{\partial P}{\partial v},$$

where L, C are positive definite symmetric matrices.

5. THE CONSTRUCTIVITY OF P

The function P can be constructed additively from different elements contained in the network. To see this we use the definition of P;

$$P(i^*, v^*) = \sum_\rho \int_{\Gamma^*} v_\rho di_\rho + \sum_\gamma i_\gamma v_\gamma \Big|_{\Gamma^*}$$

Now note that the line integral

$$\int_{\Gamma^*} v_\rho di_\rho = \int_{\Gamma^*_\rho} v_\rho di_\rho,$$

where Γ^*_ρ is a curve along the characteristic curve for the ρth resistor, given by $f_\rho(i_\rho, v_\rho) = 0$, from some fixed point to some variable end point given by i^*, v^*. Thus we write

$$P(i^*, v^*) = \sum_\rho \int_{\Gamma^*_\rho} v_\rho di_\rho + \sum_\gamma i_\gamma v_\gamma \Big|_{\Gamma^*}$$

This formula gives us the recipe for constructing P, namely:

1) determine $\int_{\Gamma^*_\rho} v_\rho di_\rho$ for each resistor,

2) determine $i_\gamma v_\gamma$ for each capacitor,

3) form the sum of these terms and express it in terms of i^*, v^*.

The integral $\int_{\Gamma^*_\rho} v_\rho di_\rho$ was originally defined by W. Millar,[4] who called it the content of the resistor.

As an example, consider the network shown in Fig. 1. The function $P(i, v)$ is constructed as follows:

$$P(i, v) = \int_0^i E\,di + \int_0^i (-Ri)di + \int_0^v v\,d(-f(v)) + v(f(v) - i)$$

$$= Ei - \frac{1}{2}Ri^2 + \int_0^v f(v)dv - iv.$$

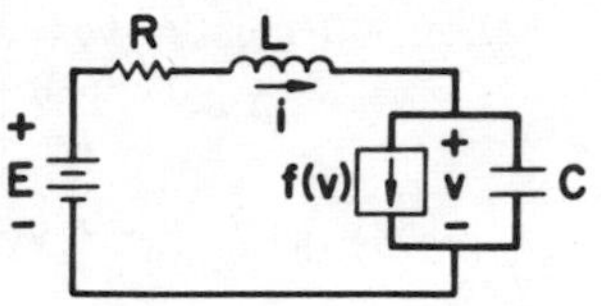

Fig. 1. Nonlinear network.

The differential equations are then

$$L \frac{di}{dt} = \frac{\partial P}{\partial i} = E - Ri - v,$$

$$C \frac{dv}{dt} = - \frac{\partial P}{\partial v} = i - f(v).$$

6. APPLICATIONS

Applications of this theory have been made to problems concerning the existence of periodic solutions, to the derivation of the equations in a symmetrical form which is useful for numerical purposes, to the derivation of known results for linear circuits, and especially to the question of the stability of a network. At the least, this theory gives a different approach to network theory which may furnish new insight into some problems. In this section we wish to discuss only the applications to stability.

The key idea behind this area of applications is that the P-function is not unique, and in the class of all P-functions there may exist one which is a Liapunov function. We will make this notion more precise. Let

$$x = \begin{pmatrix} i \\ v \end{pmatrix} \text{ and } J(x) = \begin{pmatrix} -L(i) & 0 \\ 0 & C(v) \end{pmatrix}.$$

Then the form of the equations is

$$-J(x) \frac{dx}{dt} = \frac{\partial P(x)}{\partial x}.$$

However, the flow described by this equation can be described also with other functions $\hat{J}(x)$, $\hat{P}(x)$; that is,

$$-\hat{J}(x) \frac{dx}{dt} = \frac{\partial \hat{P}(x)}{\partial x}. \tag{5}$$

In fact, if $\hat{J} = (\lambda I + P_{xx}M)J$, $\hat{P} = \lambda P + \frac{1}{2}(P_x, MP_x)$ where λ is a constant, M a constant symmetric matrix and $P_x = \partial P/\partial x$, $P_{xx} = \partial^2 P/\partial x^2$, then eq. (5) holds. We can then limit our search for a Liapunov function to a search for λ, M such that $\hat{J}(x)$ is positive definite and $\hat{P}(x) \longrightarrow \infty$ for $|x| \longrightarrow \infty$. Note that if $\hat{J}(x)$ is positive definite, then

$$\frac{dP}{dt} = \left(\frac{\partial P}{\partial x}, \frac{dx}{dt}\right) = - \left(\hat{J}(x) \frac{dx}{dt}, \frac{dx}{dt}\right) \leq 0.$$

An application of this idea is the following.

Theorem 4: If $P(i, v) = -\frac{1}{2}(i, Ai) + B(v) + (i, \gamma v - a)$, where A is a positive definite matrix, $B(v) + |\gamma v| \longrightarrow \infty$ as $|v| \longrightarrow \infty$, and $\|L^{1/2}(i) A^{-1} \gamma C^{-1/2}(v)\| \leq 1 - \delta < 1$,† then

$$\hat{P} = P + (Ai - \gamma v + a,\ A^{-1}(Ai - \gamma v + a))$$

is a Liapunov function.

The proof of this theorem simply consists of choosing

$$M = \begin{pmatrix} 2A^{-1} & 0 \\ 0 & 0 \end{pmatrix}, \quad \lambda = 1$$

and verifying that $\hat{P} \longrightarrow \infty$ with $|i| + |v| \longrightarrow \infty$ and that

$$\hat{J} = \begin{pmatrix} L & 0 \\ -2\gamma^T A^{-1} L & C \end{pmatrix}$$

is positive definite.

The application of Theorem 4 to the circuit shown in Fig. 1 leads to the conditions

$$\frac{L}{R^2 C} < 1 \quad \text{and} \quad \int_0^v f(v)\,dv \longrightarrow \infty, \quad |v| \longrightarrow \infty.$$

In other words, if these conditions hold, then all solutions eventually decay to equilibrium solutions.

In conclusion, we would like to suggest by example how these ideas for lumped-element networks can be extended to distributed-element networks. For a more complete discussion, see reference 2.

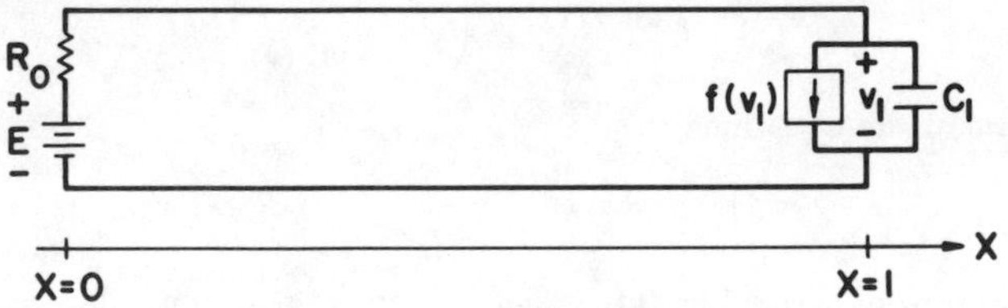

Fig. 2. Transmission line network.

Consider the network in Fig. 2 which consists of a transmission line terminated by two lumped-element networks. We assume that in the line the telegraph equations hold; that is,

$$L\frac{\partial i}{\partial t} = -\frac{\partial v}{\partial x} - Ri$$

$$0 \leq x \leq 1$$

$$-C\frac{\partial v}{\partial t} = \frac{\partial i}{\partial x} + Gv.$$

†The notation $\|K\|^2$ of a matrix K denotes $\max_{|x|=1} (Kx, Kx)$.

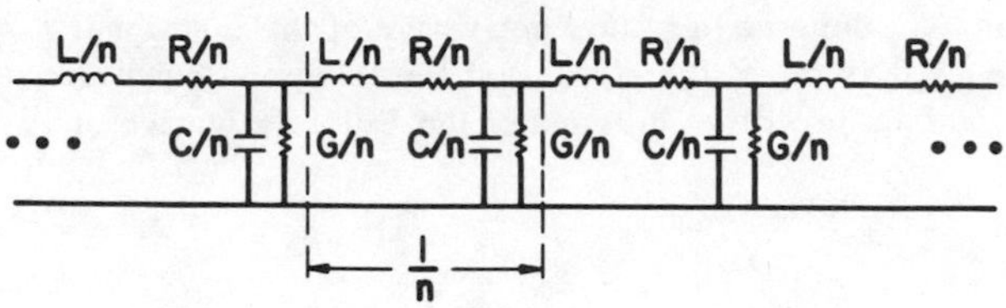

Fig. 3. Discrete form of transmission line network.

This can be viewed as the limit equations as $n \longrightarrow \infty$ of n-cascaded networks of the type shown in Fig. 3. The terminating networks lead to the following boundary conditions

$$0 = E - v_0 - R_0 i_0$$

$$-C_1 \frac{dv_1}{dt} = - i_1 + f(v_1)$$

where $v_0 = v(0, t)$, $v_1 = v(1, t)$, etc.

The P-function of the n-cascaded network is the following

$$P = -\frac{1}{2n} \sum_{k=1}^{n} \left[Ri_k^2 - Gv_k^2 + i_k \left(\frac{v_k - v_{k-1}}{n} \right) \right] - \frac{1}{2} R_0 i_0^2$$

$$+ (E - v_0) i_0 + \int_0^{v_n} f(v) dv.$$

In the limit as $n \longrightarrow \infty$, this becomes

$$\lim_{n\to\infty} P = \mathcal{P} = \int_0^1 \left(-\frac{1}{2} Ri^2 + \frac{1}{2} Gv^2 - i \frac{\partial v}{\partial x} \right) dx - \frac{1}{2} R_0 i_0^2$$

$$+ (E - v_0) i_0 + \int_0^{v_1} f(v) dv.$$

Now, if we require the functional $\mathcal{P}$ to be extremized, we obtain four conditions: an Euler equation by taking a variation in i, an Euler equation by taking a variation in v, a natural boundary condition at $x = 0$, and a natural boundary condition at $x = 1$. These equations are simply

$$\mathcal{P}_{[i]} = -\frac{\partial v}{\partial x} - Ri = 0$$

$$\mathcal{P}_{[v]} = \frac{\partial i}{\partial x} + Gv = 0$$

$$\mathcal{P}_{[i_0]} = E - v_0 - Ri_0 = 0$$

$$\mathcal{P}_{[v_1]} = - i_1 + f(v_1) = 0.$$

The notation $\mathcal{P}_{[u]}$ denotes the Euler derivative of the functional $\mathcal{P}$ with respect to the variable u. It is clear, therefore, that the telegraph equations with the boundary conditions can be written in terms of the Euler derivative of $\mathcal{P}$; that is,

$$L \frac{\partial i}{\partial t} = \mathcal{P}_{[i]}$$

$$-C \frac{\partial v}{\partial t} = \mathcal{P}_{[v]}$$

$$0 = \mathcal{P}_{[i_0]}$$

$$-C_1 \frac{\partial v_1}{\partial t} = \mathcal{P}_{[v_1]}$$

which is the analogous canonical form for distributed networks. Also by analogy with the method for constructing Liapunov functions from the function P, one can construct Liapunov functionals from the functional $\mathcal{P}$, and hence derive conditions under which distributed networks are stable.

ACKNOWLEDGMENT

This paper is based on a longer paper[1] on nonlinear networks co-authored with J. Moser of the Courant Institute, New York University. This research was jointly sponsored by the Air Force Office of Scientific Research (Contract AF 49(638)–1139) and IBM.

REFERENCES

1. R. K. Brayton and J. K. Moser, "A Theory of Nonlinear Networks," Part I, *Quart. Appl. Math.*, XXII, 1, 1-33 (April 1964); Part II, *Quart. Appl. Math.*, XXII, 2, 81–104 (July 1964).

2. R. K. Brayton and W. L. Miranker, "A Stability Theory for Nonlinear Mixed Initial Boundary Value Problems," *Arch. Ratl. Mech. and Anal.*, 17, 5, 358–376 (Dec. 1964).

3. B. D. H. Tellegen, "A General Network Theorem with Applications," *Phillips Res. Reports*, 7, 259–269 (1952).

4. W. Millar, "Some General Theorems for Nonlinear Systems Possessing Resistance," *The Philosophical Mag.* 42, 1150–1160 (1951).

DISCUSSION ON

A CANONICAL FORM FOR NONLINEAR RLC NETWORKS

by

R. K. BRAYTON

A. K. Newman, Moore School of Electrical Engineering, University of Pennsylvania Philadelphia, Pa.

It appears that if the stability condition $L/R^2C < 1$ is applied to a linear constant coefficient network, some stable networks are not shown as stable. Does your stability theory show all linear constant stable networks as stable?

Brayton:

The stability condition $L/R^2C < 1$ and, in general, the condition $\|L^{1/2}(i) A^{-1} \gamma C^{-1/2}(v)\| < 1$ are only sufficient conditions for stability and not necessary. This theory does not show that all stable linear constant coefficient networks are stable. The only necessary and sufficient condition I know is that all the eigenvalues of the coefficient matrix have real part negative. In general, any condition such as in Theorem 4 depending on the norm of a nonnormal matrix is weaker than a specific statement about the eigenvalues, but it is easier to verify.

LINEAR SYSTEMS WITH INFINITE DIMENSIONAL STATE SPACES*

A. V. Balakrishnan
Department of Engineering, University of California, Los Angeles, Calif.

The state space theory of linear dynamical systems has proved to be a fruitful one in recent years. So far, it is essential in this theory, however, that the state space be finite dimensional. On the other hand, any nonrational transfer function leads to a system for which the state space cannot be finite-dimensional. This paper develops a theory of linear systems whose state is not restricted to finite dimensions. Specifically, the state space, the input space, and the output space are all allowed to be Banach spaces. The theory of semigroups of linear operators plays a central role in this extension, which now embraces distributed parameter systems as well as stochastic systems.

1. INTRODUCTION

It is generally agreed that we do not as yet possess any general framework for dealing with what may be described as systems optimization problems. Among the many difficulties in evolving such a framework is the distinct dichotomy in language, depending on whether one is describing a finite-state system or a continuous state system (lumped or distributed parameter system in the usual terminology). The recent work of Zadeh,[1] Kalman,[2] and others may be viewed as efforts to erase this dichotomy and provide a unified theory. For much of the background and exposition of this so-called state space approach to systems the reader is referred to reference 1. It is natural that in this theme one should place the emphasis, at least initially, on linear systems, since they provide a nonempty intermediate stage between the highly restrictive finite state systems and the unproductively large generality of nonlinear systems. So far, however, the state space theory of linear systems has been restricted to state spaces of finite dimension. On the other hand, it is evident that the state space of a nondynamic system—a linear time-invariant system whose weight function has a nonrational transform—cannot be finite dimensional. Indeed, one of the main results of Zadeh[1] is that the system is characterized by ordinary differential equations if, and only if, the state space is finite dimensional.

In this paper we study the state space description of linear time-invariant systems without restricting the state space to be finite dimensional. In this extension, we first consider the case where the state space is a Hilbert space as

*The research reported in this paper was supported in part by the Air Force Office of Scientific Research, Applied Mathematics Division, U.S. Air Force, under Grant No. AFOSR 700-65.

Presented at the Symposium on System Theory
Polytechnic Institute of Brooklyn, April 20, 21, 22, 1965

being perhaps the most natural infinite dimensional generalization. We also allow the input and output to be Hilbert-space valued. The main tool is the analytical theory of semigroups of linear operators as developed by Hille-Phillips[3] and Yosida.[6] The main result here is that, under suitable conditions, the state-input relation has the form:

$$x(t) = T(t)x(0) + \int_0^t T(t-s)Lu(s)ds \tag{1.1}$$

where $T(t)$ is a one-parameter semigroup of linear bounded transformations on the state space H, and L is a linear bounded transformation mapping the input Hilbert space into the domain of the infinitesimal generator of the semigroup. Under a few additional conditions we have the dynamical representation:

$$\dot{x}(t) = Ax(t) + Lu(t), \quad 0 < t; \tag{1.2}$$

where A is the generator. This generalization includes stochastic systems and systems governed by partial differential equations, see references 4 and 7. The above relations are too strong to include nondynamic systems; for these we obtain a representation in locally convex spaces and show that (1.1) and (1.2) can be generalized to such spaces.

We begin in Section 2 with a review of the basic notation and definitions, following Zadeh[1] but without restricting dimensionality. In Section 3 we give a different proof of the Zadeh result by specializing known theorems in semigroup theory. The generalization to Hilbert spaces is given in Sections 4 and 5. In Section 6 we show how to obtain the state space representation for a linear system described in terms of a weighting function. Here we show that either the (reduced) state space is finite-dimensional and the transfer function is rational, or we have to extend the state space to be a locally convex space. We can still derive "dynamic" equations for the state, but these are "weak" versions of (1.2).

2. BASIC DEFINITIONS

We begin by defining some of the basic concepts of linear system theory following Zadeh,[1] but making appropriate modifications to take care of the non-finite dimensionality, among other things. Thus a system will be characterized by three functions of time, the input $u(t)$, the output $y(t)$ and the state $x(t)$. The input and output will be scalars* (complex numbers) while the state will range over a separable Hilbert space H. The functions of time will, in general, be assumed to be "piecewise" continuous, although only the necessary minimal assumptions required will be used, and these stated. In any half-open interval $a < t \leq b$, the output $y(t)$ is determined by the state at $t = a$ and the input by the functional relationship:

$$y(t) = A(t, a; x(a); u(s), a < s \leq t) \; a < t \leq b \tag{2.1}$$

*Extension to the case where these take values in a unitary space requires but minor modifications. The case where $u(t)$ is also Hilbert-space valued is taken up in Section 5.

and by definition of "state," (see reference 1 for more elaboration):

$$y(t) = A(t, \tau; x(\tau); u(s), \tau < s \leq t), \quad \tau < t \leq b \tag{2.2}$$

for any τ, $a < \tau \leq b$. Relation (2.1) can, of course, also be described in terms of a mapping on appropriate product spaces.

For a linear system, we have by definition that (2.1) becomes:

$$y(t) = A(t, a; x(a); 0) + A(t, a; 0; u(s), a < s \leq t), \tag{2.3}$$

where, moreover, the first term (the "zero-input" response) for fixed t and a is a linear functional on H, while the second term (the "zero-state" response) is for each t, a linear functional on the class of piecewise continuous functions in $[a, b]$. The second term can be handled as in reference 1, leading to a generalized function or Schwartz distribution $h(t, s)$ such that the zero-state response can be expressed:

$$\int_a^t h(t, s)u(s)\,ds, \quad a < t \leq b. \tag{2.4}$$

Since H is possibly infinite dimensional, we shall assume that the zero-input response is a continuous (or bounded) linear functional on H. Thus we have, using the Riesz theorem: that there is a two-parameter family of elements in H, $x^*(t, s)$ such that the zero-input response is given by

$$y(t) - [x^*(t, s), x(s)], \quad s < t, \tag{2.5}$$

where $[\,,\,]$ denotes the inner-product in H.

In what follows we shall assume that the system is time-invariant. We have then that for any x in H and any Δ,

$$y(t) = [x^*(t, s), x] = [x^*(t + \Delta, s + \Delta), x], \quad s < t,$$

from which it follows that

$$y(t) = [x^*(t - s, 0), x], \quad s < t.$$

Next let us note that the set of all x in H such that

$$0 = y(t) = [x^*(t, 0), x], \quad 0 < t$$

is a linear sub-space, in fact a closed linear subspace. Let H_0 be this subspace. Let H_1 be its orthogonal complement. Let P be the projection operator projecting H into H_1. Then

$$y(t) = [x^*(t, 0), x] = [x^*(t, 0), Px] = [Px^*(t, 0), Px], \quad 0 < t,$$

so that we may, without loss of generality, limit consideration to H_1, making the state space "reduced" as well. Letting

$$Px^*(t, 0) = \alpha(t)$$

we have then that the zero-input response is given by:

$$y(t) = [\alpha(t - s), x(s)], \quad t > s, \tag{2.6}$$

where $\alpha(t)$ and x are now elements in the reduced state space H_1. Moreover, for any x in H_1, we have for $t > 0$,

$$y(t) = [\alpha(t), x]$$

and if we assume that $y(t)$ is always continuous from the right, it follows that $\alpha(t)$ converges weakly as $t \longrightarrow 0$, and we define this limit to be $\alpha(0)$. We also note that the closed linear subspace generated by $\{\alpha(t), t > 0\}$ is all of H_1. Suppose this is not true. Then we can find a non-zero element x in H_1 such that

$$[\alpha(t), x] = 0$$

or, the zero-input response is zero identically, which is impossible.

3. LINEAR TIME-INVARIANT SYSTEMS WITH FINITE DIMENSIONAL STATE SPACES

Before embarking on the main problem for non-finite dimensional state spaces, we shall find it convenient to consider the case where the state space is finite-dimensional. The proof will be different from that of Zadeh[1] and will be along the lines of the more general proof to follow, except for taking advantage of the finite dimensionality. It will thus focus on the essential features of the problem.

We follow the notation and development in Section 2, and, in addition, assume that the state space H is of dimension n. As we have seen, we may take the state to be reduced without loss in generality. Let us first consider the zero-input response. Let us denote the state at time zero by $x(0)$. Then

$$y(t) = [\alpha(t), x(0)] = [\alpha(t-s), x(s)], \quad 0 < s < t.$$

Hence we have

$$[\alpha(t), x(0)] = [\alpha(t-s), x(s)], \quad 0 < s < t. \tag{3.1}$$

We may use (3.1) to define a transformation on H for each $s > 0$, by defining

$$x(s) = T(s)\, x(0). \tag{3.2}$$

For, first of all, by the basic definition of state (2.2), we know that there is an $x(s)$ satisfying (3.1). Secondly, there is only one such element. For if there were more than one, say, x_1 and x_2, then from (3.1) we should have:

$$[\alpha(t-s), x_1 - x_2] = 0, \quad t < s$$

from which, since the state is reduced, it follows that

$$x_1 = x_2.$$

Again $T(s)$ for each s is a linear transformation on H. It is a *bounded* linear since H is finite dimensional. Moreover, $T(s)$ forms a semigroup in s. For

$$\begin{aligned}[\alpha(t), x(0)] &= [\alpha(t - s_1 - s_2), T(s_1 + s_2)\, x(0)] \\ &= [\alpha(t - s_1), x(s_2)]\end{aligned}$$

Or,

$$T(s_1)\, x(s_2) = T(s_1)\, T(s_2)\, x(0) = T(s_1 + s_2)\, x(0).$$

We define

$$T(0) = I\,(\text{Identity})$$

We next note that for any x in H, and fixed $\Delta > 0$,

$$[\alpha(\Delta),\ T(t)\,x] = [\alpha(t + \Delta),\ x] = [\alpha(t),\ T(\Delta)\,x], \quad 0 < t, \tag{3.2}$$

and since the extreme right member being a zero-input response is (Lebesgue) measurable in t, it follows that so is the left member. Since $\alpha(\Delta)$, $\Delta > 0$, span H, it follows that for any y in H,

$$[y,\ T(t)\,x]$$

is measurable, or, since H is finite-dimensional, the semigroup of transformations $T(t)$ is strongly measurable. We can now use the well-known result due to Phillips-Miyadera[3] that measurability implies (strong) continuity of $T(t)\,x$ for $t > 0$. To examine what happens at the origin, we again use that for any $t > 0$,

$$[\alpha(t),\ T(\Delta)\,x - x] = [\alpha(t/2), T(t/2 + \Delta)\,x - T(t/2)\,x]$$

and hence goes to zero with Δ. Since $\alpha(t)$, $t > 0$, span H (and H is finite dimensional), this implies that $T(t)$ is weakly continuous at the origin, and hence strongly continuous. Again, since H is finite-dimensional, this implies that $T(t)$ is uniformly continuous, so that from the general theory we know[3] that

$$T(t) = \exp At \tag{3.3}$$

where

$$A = \lim_{\Delta \to 0}\, [T(\Delta) - I]\,\Delta^{-1}. \tag{3.4}$$

Finally, we note that because H is finite dimensional, $\alpha(t)$ which was shown to converge *weakly* to $\alpha(0)$ as t goes to zero, now actually converges *strongly*. It follows that

$$y(t) = [\alpha(t),\ x(0)] = [\alpha(0),\ T(t)\,x(0)] = [\alpha(0),\ x(t)] \tag{3.5}$$

where from (3.3),

$$x(t) = A\,x(t). \tag{3.6}$$

Moreover, we may note that

$$\alpha(t) = (\exp A^* t)\,\alpha(0). \tag{3.7}$$

Again in (3.5), because of (3.3), $y(t)$ is actually infinitely differentiable for $t > 0$.

Let us next consider the total response. For a time-invariant system, it is easy to see that in (2.4) we can set

$$h(t, s) = h(t - s,\ 0) = w(t - s), \quad s \le t,$$

where $w(t)$ is now defined for $t \ge 0$. If we take the special case where the state at time zero is zero and the input $u(t)$ is a δ-function:

$$u(t) = \delta(t),$$

we obtain from (2.3) that

$$y(t) = w(t), \quad t > 0, \tag{3.8}$$

and from (2.2) and (3.7)

$$w(t) = [\alpha(t-s),\ x(s)] = [\alpha(t),\ e^{-As}\ x(s)], \quad 0 < s < t. \tag{3.9}$$

Letting s go to zero in this, we note that $x(s)$ converges weakly, and, since the space is finite dimensional, strongly, to an element B in H. Hence

$$\begin{aligned} w(t) &= [\alpha(t),\ B] \\ &= [\alpha(0),\ e^{At}\ B], \end{aligned} \tag{3.10}$$

so that $w(t)$ is actually infinitely differentiable for $t > 0$. We may proceed as in reference 1 and classify the systems further depending on the behavior of $w(t)$ at the origin. Here let us simply consider the case where the system is a "proper" system, so that $w(t)$ has a delta function of order zero at the origin. We note from (3.10) that $w(t)$ approaches a limit as $t \longrightarrow 0+$. Removing the delta function, and defining the limit to be $w(0)$, we have finally

$$y(t) = \left[\alpha(0),\ T(t)\,x(0) + \int_0^t T(t-s)\,B\,u(s)\,ds\right] + a\,u(t). \tag{3.11}$$

Defining

$$x(t) = T(t)\,x(0) + \int_0^t T(t-s)\,B\,u(s)\,ds, \tag{3.12}$$

we have

$$\dot{x}(t) = A\,x(t) + B\,u(t) \tag{3.13}$$

and

$$y(t) = [\alpha(0),\ x(t)] + a\,u(t), \tag{3.14}$$

as the final representation for a time-invariant proper linear system. Finally, let

$$f(z) = \sum_0^m a_k z^k, \quad m \le n,$$

be the minimal polynomial of A. Then it readily follows from (3.13) and (3.14) that

$$\sum_0^m a_k\, y^{(k)}(t) = \sum_0^m b_k\, u^{(k)}(t) \tag{3.15}$$

provided, of course, that $u(t)$ has all derivatives up to the mth order. The derivatives may be taken in the distribution sense, the equality in (3.15) being again taken in the distribution sense.

4. LINEAR TIME INVARIANT SYSTEMS WITH STATE SPACES OF NON-FINITE DIMENSION

We come to the main problem of linear time invariant systems with infinite-dimensional state spaces. We drop the assumption, in other words, that the state space H which is a Hilbert space has finite dimension. We follow the notation and definitions as in Section 2. We may, as we have seen, assume that the state space is reduced, so that the closed linear subspace generated by $\alpha(t)$, $t > 0$ is all of H. We define the transformation $T(s)$ for each s by

$$[\alpha(t), x] = [\alpha(t-s), T(s)x], \quad t > s. \tag{4.1}$$

It is easy to see that $T(s)$ is linear, and defined on all of H. We next show that $T(s)$ is actually "bounded" or "continuous." For this, let x_n be a sequence converging to x. Then for fixed s and any $t > 0$, we have

$$[\alpha(t+s), x_n] = [\alpha(t), T(s)x_n]. \tag{4.2}$$

Assume that the sequence $T(s)x_n$ converges and that the limit is y. It follows from (4.2), upon taking limits, that

$$[\alpha(t+s), x] = [\alpha(t), T(s)x] = [\alpha(t), y], \quad 0 < t,$$

so that

$$T(s)x = y.$$

This shows that $T(s)$ is a closed linear transformation. Since it is defined on all of H, it follows (reference 3, p. 47) that $T(s)$ is actually bounded. As in Section 3, we can now show that $T(s)$ for $0 < s < \infty$ is a semigroup in s.

Next, for any $s > 0$, and any x in H, as in (3.2),

$$[\alpha(s), T(t)x] = [\alpha(t), T(s)x]$$

and the right side, being an admissible zero state response, is Lebesgue measurable. Since $\{\alpha(s), s > 0\}$, span H, it follows that the semigroup $T(t)$ is weakly measurable. Since we have assumed H to be separable, $T(t)$ is thus strongly measurable, and hence by the Phillips-Miyadera theorem (reference 3, p. 305), it is strongly continuous. Since H is reflexive, $T^*(t)$ is also strongly continuous for $t > 0$. If we now let s approach t in (4.1), since $\alpha(t-s)$ converges weakly to $\alpha(0)$, and $T(s)x$ converges strongly to $T(t)x$, it follows that

$$[\alpha(t), x] = [\alpha(0), T(t)x] = [T^*(t)\alpha(0), x]. \tag{4.3}$$

To examine the situation regarding continuity at the origin, we note that

$$[\alpha(t), T(s)x - x] = [\alpha(0), T(s+t)x - T(t)x] \tag{4.4}$$

and hence goes to zero with s for every $t > 0$. However, this is not quite enough to yield strong continuity at the origin. Hence we invoke the assumption that the state function is piecewise continuous. Hence, for each x, $T(t)x$ converges to a limit as t goes to zero. From (4.4) it follows that this limit must be x. But $T(t)x$ is not necessarily differentiable, unless x is in the domain D of the infinitesimal generator A which is now defined as:

$$Ax = \lim\,(T(t)x - x)t^{-1}, \quad x \in D.$$

The domain D is dense in H; in fact the domain of x such that $T(t)x$ infinitely differentiable $D(A^\infty)$ is dense in H. We note in particular that (3.3) is not true unless $x \in D$.

Let us next consider the zero state response. Let the input be the delta function $\delta(t)$, leading as before in Section 3, to:

$$y(t) = w(t) = [\alpha(t-s), x(s)], \quad 0 < s \leq t.$$

Again, since $x(t)$ the state function being (assumed) continuous on the right,* it follows from (4.3) that

$$w(t) = [\alpha(0),\ T(t)x(0+)] \tag{4.5}$$

and denoting $x(0+)$ by B, we obtain as before, for the total response:

$$y(t) = [\alpha(0),\ x(t)]$$

where

$$x(t) = T(t)x(0) + \int_0^t T(t-s)Bu(s)\,ds. \tag{4.6}$$

To obtain the dynamical equation (3.13) we have to make additional assumptions. Also, $w(t)$ is not necessarily differentiable without additional assumptions. One such assumption is that the state corresponding to the zero input response is differentiable, except at a finite number of points in each finite interval. This implies that $T(t)x$, for each x has the same property, the semigroup property then implying that the range of $T(t)$ is contained in D for every $t > 0$. An equivalent way of characterizing such semigroups is to say that the semigroup is uniformly continuous for $t > 0$. We note that $T(t)x$ is then necessarily infinitely differentiable for $t > 0$ (reference 3, p. 310). The last assumption would also then imply that $w(t)$ is infinitely differentiable for $t > 0$. To see what is involved in obtaining (3.13) for infinite-dimensional H, let us note that from (4.6):

$$\frac{x(t+\Delta) - x(t)}{\Delta} = \left(\frac{T(t+\Delta) - T(t)}{\Delta}\right)x(0) + \frac{1}{\Delta}\int_t^{t+\Delta} T(t+\Delta-s)Bu(s)\,ds$$
$$+ \int_0^t \left(\frac{T(t+-s) - T(t-s)}{\Delta}\right)Bu(s)\,ds.\ldots \tag{4.7}$$

Now

$$\left(\frac{T(t+\Delta) - T(t)}{\Delta}\right)x(0) = (T(\Delta) - I)\,T(t)\,x(0),$$

and hence goes to $A\,T(t)\,x(0)$, if $T(t)\,x(0) \in D$. Similarly, the second term on the right in (4.7) converges to $B\,u(t)$, provided t is a point of continuity of $u(s)$ (or, almost everywhere in t, in general). Now, in the term in (4.7), the integrand can be written

$$\left(\frac{T(\Delta) - I}{\Delta}\right) T(t-s)Bu(s).$$

For convergence, it is enough if B is in the domain $D(A)$, for in this case, the integrand is in norm

$$\le \|T(t-s)\| \left\|\left(\frac{T(\Delta) - I}{\Delta}\right)B\right\| |u(s)|$$

$$\le \text{Constant}\ \|AB\|\ |u(s)| \quad 0 \le s \le t$$

and the limit, since A is closed, is

$$= A\int_0^t T(t-s)Bu(s)\,ds$$

*See Section 6 for an example where this assumption is violated.

so that we obtain

$$\dot{x}(t) = A\,x(t) + B\,u(t), \quad 0 < t \text{ (almost everywhere, in general).} \tag{4.8}$$

Finally, it need hardly be pointed out that there is no version of (3.15) in general, any more, even if A is bounded linear (in the latter case, $T(t) = \exp.\ tA$, and just about everything goes through as in Section 3).

5. TIME-INVARIANT LINEAR SYSTEMS WITH INFINITE DIMENSIONAL INPUT SPACES

In the previous sections, the input function $u(t)$ was taken to be scalar valued. We shall now go on to consider the case where $u(t)$ for each t is an element of a (not necessarily separable) Hilbert space, denoted H', and possibly different from the Hilbert space H of states. The minimal assumption on $u(t)$ is that it is strongly Lebesgue measurable and squared-norm-integrable on each finite interval.

The zero input response can be handled exactly as in Section 4 since it does not involve $u(t)$. We shall continue to use the same notation, $T(t)$ denoting the semigroup and A its infinitesimal generator.

Let us next consider the zero state response. Let a be the initial time at which the initial state is zero. For fixed $t > a$, the response has to be a linear functional on the class of measurable functions $u(\cdot)$ such that

$$\int_a^t \| u(s) \|^2 \, ds < \infty.$$

But this class is a Hilbert space, and let us denote it by $L_2[H't]$. The inner product between two elements $u(\cdot)$, $v(\cdot)$ in this space is given by:

$$[u, v] = \int_a^t [u(s), \; v(s)] \, ds.$$

We shall now assume that the linear functional is continuous on $L_2[H', t]$, and hence by the Riesz theorem as applied to this space (reference 3, p. 89) we can find $h(t, \cdot)$ in this space, so that the zero state response is given by

$$y(t) = \int_a^t [h(t, s), \; u(s)] \, ds. \tag{5.1}$$

Proceeding as in the scalar input case, and using the time invariance, we obtain a function $w(t)$, $0 < t$, whose range is in H', is strongly measurable and squared-norm-integrable on each finite interval, and such that the zero-state response (5.1) has the form:

$$y(t) = \int_0^t [w(t - s), \; u(s)] \, ds. \tag{5.2}$$

To relate the zero-state response to the state, we again use (2.2). Thus for any $\tau < t$, eq. (5.2) can be written, denoting the state function by $x(\cdot)$:

$$y(t) = [\alpha(t-\tau), x(\tau)] + \int_\tau^t [w(t-s), u(s)]\,ds.$$

As τ tends to t, the second term in this goes to zero and we get, as in Section 4, since $\alpha(t-\tau)$ converges weakly to $\alpha(0)$ and $x(\tau)$ converges strongly to $x(t-)$ (by assumption):

$$y(t) = [\alpha(0), x(t-)]. \tag{5.3}$$

Next let u be any element of H' and let

$$u_n(t) = nu, \quad 0 \le t \le 1/n,$$
$$= \text{zero otherwise}.$$

Let $x_n(t)$ be the corresponding state functions, $x_n(0)$ being zero. For each t, n, $x_n(t)$ is a linear function of u. If we let

$$x_n(t) = L(n, t)\,u, \tag{5.4}$$

then $L(n, t)$ is a linear operator on H' with range in H; it is clearly closed linear, and being defined on all of H' is actually bounded linear. Let us denote the corresponding zero state responses by $y_n(t)$. Then, we have:

$$y_n(t) = [\alpha(0), T(t-1/n)\,x_n(1/n)] \quad \text{for} \quad t \ge 1/n. \tag{5.5}$$

Now $w(t)$ is Bochner integrable over finite intervals, since

$$\left(\int_a^t \|w(t)\|\,dt\right)^2 \le \int_a^b \|w(t)\|^2\,dt\,(b-a).$$

Hence we can write:

$$y_n(t) = \left[n\int_0^{1/n} w(t-s)\,ds,\ u\right], \quad t \ge 1/n$$
$$= [L(n,t)^*\alpha(0), u], \quad t \ge 1/n$$

where $L(n, t)^*$ is the adjoint of $L(n, t)$ and maps H into H'. Hence we have:

$$L(n,t)^*\alpha(0) = n\int_0^{1/n} w(t-s)\,ds, \quad 1/n \le t. \tag{5.6}$$

Now the right side converges almost everywhere with respect to t to $w(t)$. However we shall need a sharper statement. We note that the sequence $u_n(t)$ is a "delta convergent sequence"[5] converging to a delta function with support at the origin. We now assume that the state functions $x_n(t)$ converge (strongly) for each t to the state function $x(t)$, which (as an admissible state function) is piecewise continuous, or, minimally, that it has right limits for $t \ge 0$, the points of discontinuity being finite in any finite interval.† This means first that $L(n, t)u$ con-

†See Section 6 for an example where this condition is violated.

verges for every u to a limit, and hence must be given by $L(t)u$. $L(t)$ being linear bounded for each t. Moreover $L(t)u$ converges for each u as t goes to zero. The limit again can be expressed Lu, where L is a linear bounded operator also. Now from (5.6) it follows that

$$[\alpha(0), L(t)u] = [w(t), u] \text{ almost everywhere in } t. \tag{5.7}$$

Again from (5.5) we have:

$$T(t-s)L(n,s)u = L(n,t)u, \quad 1/n \leq s \leq t.$$

Hence, by taking limits, we have

$$T(t-s)L(s)u = L(t)u,$$

and hence, letting s go to zero,

$$L(t)u = T(t)Lu \tag{5.8}$$

and

$$w(t) = L^*(t)\alpha(0) = L^*T(t)^*\alpha(0) = L^*\alpha(t). \tag{5.8a}$$

Hence, finally in (5.2) and (5.3), using (5.7) and (5.8):

$$\begin{aligned} y(t) &= [\alpha(0), x(t)] \\ &= \left[\alpha(0), \int_0^t T(t-s)Lu(s)\,ds\right]. \end{aligned}$$

The total response thus can again be expressed:

$$y(t) = [\alpha(0), x(t)]; \quad x(t) = T(t)x(0) + \int_0^t T(t-s)Lu(s)\,ds \tag{5.9}$$

To obtain the dynamical equation (4.8), let us recall the observations regarding the semigroup itself. Here we assume that $T(t)x(0) \in D$ for every $t > 0$ (or, alternately that the semigroup is say, analytic), and that the range of L is contained in D. Then proceeding as in (4.7), we need only discuss the third term on the right in (4.7). We have now in the integrand therein:

$$\left(\frac{T(t+\Delta-s) - T(t-s)}{\Delta}\right) Lu(s) = T(t-s)\left(\frac{T(\Delta)-I}{\Delta}\right) Lu(t).$$

Now for every u in H',

$$\lim \left(\frac{T(\Delta)-I}{\Delta}\right) Lu = ALu$$

so that the integrand is in norm, since AL is linear bounded,

$$\text{const.}\ \|AL\|\ \|u(s)\|.$$

Since A is closed, it follows that the integral converges to

$$A\int_0^t T(t-s)Lu(s)\,ds$$

and (4.8) now reads:

$$\dot{x}(t) = A\,x(t) + L\,u(t) \text{ almost everywhere in } t. \tag{5.10}$$

It may be noted conversely that (5.10) under the same assumptions on the semigroup leads to the right side of (5.9), and from (5.8a):

$$w(t) = L^*T(t)^*y$$

where y is some fixed element of H, satisfies the condition of the limiting zero state response for a delta function input. The conditions are thus necessary and sufficient.

6. AN EXAMPLE

By way of illustrating and amplifying on some of the concepts and results, it may be of interest to examine a simple example which is to some extent canonical. Thus let us consider a physically realizable linear time invariant system, the input $u(t)$ and the output $y(t)$ characterized by

$$y(t) = \int_{-\infty}^{t} w(t-s)\,u(s)\,ds \tag{6.1}$$

where we shall take $w(\cdot)$ to be in $L_2[0, \infty]$. Let us examine the state space description. Since

$$y(t) = \int_{-\infty}^{0} w(t-s)\,u(s)\,ds + \int_{0}^{t} w(t-s)\,u(s)\,ds,$$

the history up to time zero, or, $u(s)$, $-\infty < s < 0$, would qualify for the state variable at time zero. Let us take the space $L_2[-\infty, 0]$ as the state space. Let us now introduce the shift semigroup $S(t)$ on this space defined by:

$$S(t)f = g; \quad g(s) = f(s-t), \quad s \leq 0.$$

Then, clearly $S(t)$ is a strongly continuous semigroup over the space, and further so is also the adjoint semigroup $S(t)^*$ which is also defined on the same space being a Hilbert space. We can then write, defining

$$w_-(s) = w(-s),$$

so that $w_-(\cdot)$ is now in $L_2[-\infty, 0]$, the zero input response as

$$\int_{-\infty}^{0} w(t-s)\,u(s)\,ds = [S(t)w_-, u] \tag{6.2}$$

where $[\,,\,]$ denotes the inner product in the space, $L_2[-\infty, 0]$.

The first point to be noted is that the state space may not be reduced, and hence the first step is to reduce it. Thus let H_0 be the linear subspace of states $u(\cdot)$ in $L_2[-\infty, 0]$ such that

$$[S(t)w_-, u] = 0, \quad \text{for every } t \geq 0. \tag{6.3}$$

This is a closed subspace. Let H_1 be its orthogonal complement. Let P denote the projection operator projecting $L_2[-\infty, 0]$ into H_1. Then, we note that if we define for every u in $L_2[-\infty, 0]$

$$T(t) P u = P S(t)^* P u, \tag{6.4}$$

then $T(t)$ is readily seen to be a semigroup of linear bounded transformations over H_1 and is strongly continuous at the origin. For, let $x \in H_1$, and let u be any element of $L_2[-\infty, 0]$ such that

$$x = P u.$$

Now for any z in H_0, $S(t)^* z$ is also in it, since

$$[S(\Delta) w_-, S(t)^* z] = [S(t + \Delta) w_-, z] = 0, \quad \Delta \geq 0.$$

Hence

$$P S(t)^* z = 0 \tag{6.5}$$

and

$$P S(t)^*(u - P u) = 0$$

so that

$$T(t) x = P S(t)^* u = P S(t)^* P u = P S(t)^* x \tag{6.6}$$

and

$$\begin{aligned} T(t_1 + t_2) x &= P S(t_1)^* S(t_2)^* x \\ &= P S(t_1)^* P S(t_2)^* x \text{ (from 6.5)} \\ &= T(t_1) T(t_2) x. \end{aligned}$$

Also

$$\| T(t) x \| = \| P S(t)^* x \| \leq \| P \| \, \| x \| = \| x \|$$

since

$$\| S(t)^* \| = 1.$$

The zero input response (6.2) can now be written as:

$$\begin{aligned} [S(t) w_-, u] &= [w_-, S(t)^* P u] \\ &= [w_-, P S(t)^* P u] \end{aligned}$$

where we have used the fact that for any z in H_0

$$[w_-, z] = 0,$$

so that finally

$$[S(t) w_-, u] = [w_-, T(t) x]. \tag{6.7}$$

It is clear that w_- itself belongs to H_1, since from (6.3)

$$[w_-, w_- - P w_-] = 0 = \| w_- - P w_- \|^2.$$

We are now at the point where the dimensionality of H_1 begins to play a role. As in Section 3, let us first assume that H_1 is finite dimensional, say of dimension n. Then, the semigroup $T(t)$ is uniformly continuous for $t \geq 0$, and hence has the form:

$$T(t) = \exp At \tag{6.8}$$

where A is a linear bounded operator on H_1. Let λ_1 be an eigenvalue of A, and e_1 the (one) corresponding eigenvector in H_1. Then

$$T(t)e_1 = (\exp \lambda_1 t)e_1.$$

Also

$$[e_1, T(t)e_1] = [S(t)e_1, e_1] \tag{6.9}$$

so that

$$\int_{-\infty}^{0} e_1(s-t)e_1(s)\,ds = \| e_1 \|^2 \exp \lambda_1 t, \quad t \geq 0$$

from which it follows that

$$e_1(s) = e_1(0) \exp - \lambda_1 s, \quad s \leq 0.$$

Also, since (6.9) goes to zero as t goes to infinity, $Re\,\lambda_i$ is actually negative. Considering, for simplicity, the case where the eigenvalues are distinct (the extension to the general case being obvious) we have in particular that

$$w_-(s) = \sum_{1}^{n} a_k \exp - \lambda_k s. \tag{6.10}$$

Next let us consider the zero state response. We want to show that we can find an element B in H_1 such that

$$w(t) = [w_-, T(t)B] \tag{6.11}$$

or,

$$= [S(t)w_-, B]$$

$$= \sum_{1}^{n} a_k \exp \lambda_k t\,[e_k, B]$$

and comparing with (6.10) we need then that

$$[e_k, B] = 1 \tag{6.12}$$

and this is obviously possible since there are only a finite number of basic functions $\{e_k\}$. Hence we have that in (6.1) the system can be described in terms of a state space:

$$y(t) = [w_-, x(t)], \quad x(t) \quad H_1$$

where

$$x(t) = T(t)x(0) + \int_0^t T(t-s)B\,u(s)\,ds$$

and the dynamical equation can be derived as in Section 3. Conversely, if we had assumed that (6.1) can be described in terms of a finite dimensional state space, we could proceed as in Section 3 and wind up with (6.13), or strictly speaking, an equivalent system.

Let us next examine the case where H_1 is infinite dimensional. Here, unfortunately, it is no longer possible to find an element in H_1 satisfying (6.11), for the corresponding equation

$$\int_{-\infty}^{0} w(t-s)\,b(s)\,ds = w(t), \quad t \geq 0, \quad b(\cdot) \in L_2(-\infty, 0)$$

does not have a solution for $b(\cdot)$ in $L_2(-\infty, 0)$, unless the Laplace transform of $w(\cdot)$ is rational. A proof of this result is given in the Appendix. If the Laplace transform of $w(\cdot)$ is rational, then obviously H_1 is finite dimensional. We note then that either H_1 is finite dimensional, or all of H. In the latter case, the zero-state response due to a delta function input cannot be described in terms of a state function in H. For examples of systems with state spaces which are Hilbert spaces, one has thus to turn to distributed parameter systems governed by partial differential equations, or stochastic systems.[4]

Continuing now the study of the case $H_1 = H$, for the system described by (6.1), we note that the projection operator P in (6.4) is now the identity and

$$T(t) = S(t)^*$$

where the semigroup $T(t)$ is described by:

$$T(t)u = v; \quad v(s) = u(s+t), \quad -\infty < s < -t, \quad = 0 \text{ otherwise.} \tag{6.13}$$

Since there is no element in H satisfying (6.11), the next step is to enlarge the state space to include such an element. We have to make such an enlargement at the expense of a norm, of course. The state space can be still chosen to be a locally convex linear topological space, as we shall now show.

In order not to complicate matters unduly, we shall now assume that $w(t)$ is continuous on finite intervals of $[0, \infty)$, although not necessarily in $L_2(0, \infty)$. Let us first consider the class of Lebesgue measurable functions $u(\cdot)$ on $(-\infty, 0]$, such that

$$\int_{-\infty}^{0} |w(t-s)|\,|u(s)|\,ds < \infty, \quad t \geq 0.$$

Let us denote this class by $L(w)$. Then $L(w)$ is clearly a linear vector space, and is non-empty since it contains functions which are square integrable on finite intervals of $(-\infty, 0]$. Moreover,

$$1(t; u) = \int_{-\infty}^{0} w(t-s)\,u(s)\,ds$$

yields a linear functional on $L(w)$ for each $t \geq 0$. Let $L_0(w)$ denote the linear subspace of $L(w)$ of elements such that

$$1(t; u) = 0, \quad t \geq 0,$$

and $L_1(w)$ denote the factor (quotient) space modulo $L_0(w)$. Let us denote by Γ the linear subspace generated by the functionals $\{1(t; \cdot),\ t \geq 0\}$. Then Γ is a total set for $L_1(w)$. We now define the Γ-topology on $L_1(w)$ to be the topology induced by the functionals in Γ. As is known, $L_1(w)$ is then a locally convex linear topological space, with the functionals in Γ being precisely the continuous linear functionals. It is readily verified that for each t, (6.13) again defines a linear transformation on $L(w)$, and that

$$T(t)L_0(w) < L_0(w)$$

and also that

$$1(t; u) = 1(t-s; T(s)u), \quad 0 \leq s \leq t.$$

Let us now complete the space $L_1(w)$ in the Γ-topology, and denote the completed space by X.

Let P denote the (projection) operator mapping $L(w)$ onto the factor space $L_1(w)$. For any element v in $L_1(w)$, define the transformation $T'(t)$ by

$$T'(t)\,v = P\,T(t)\,u, \tag{6.14}$$

where u is any element in $L(w)$ such that

$$Pu = v.$$

Then $T'(t)$ can be extended to be a continuous linear transformation on X, and such that for any u in X

$$1(t; u) = 1(t - s;\ T'(s)u), \quad 0 \le s \le t.$$

The completed space X contains delta functions. For, let $u_n(\cdot)$ be again a "delta convergent sequence,"

$$\begin{aligned} u_n(t) &= n, \quad -1/n \le t \le 0, \\ &= 0 \text{ otherwise.} \end{aligned}$$

Then

$$1(s; u_n) = n \int_{-1/n}^{0} w(t - s)\,ds$$

so that u_n is a directed Cauchy sequence in X, since $w(t)$ is continuous. Let us denote the limit in X by B. Then

$$\begin{aligned} 1(s; B) &= w(s) \\ &= 1(0;\ T'(s)B), \end{aligned} \tag{6.15}$$

which is what we have been after. If $L_1(w)$ is finite dimensional, then, of course, it would be homeomorphic and isomorphic to a finite dimensional Euclidean space, and we have already seen how the theory simplifies, implying in particular that the Laplace transform of $w(t)$ is rational. On the other hand, if $L_1(w)$ is normable, $T'(s)$ would be a semigroup strongly continuous for $s > 0$, and (6.15) will then imply that the Laplace transform of $w(t)$ is rational, and hence that $L_1(w)$ is finite dimensional. A proof of this is given in the Appendix. It follows that either $L_1(w)$ is finite dimensional or all of $L(w)$. Continuing with the latter case, we need not any longer distinguish between $T(t)$ and $T'(t)$. We note that $T(t)B$ is continuous in t (in the Γ-topology) since

$$1(s;\ T(t)B) = w(t + s).$$

It follows that, for any continuous function $u(\cdot)$,

$$\int_0^t T(t - s)\,B\,u(s)\,ds$$

can be defined as a Riemann integral. For any measurable function square integrable on finite intervals we can define the integral as the limit of the Cauchy sequence:

$$\int_0^t T(t - s)\,B\,u_n(s)\,ds,$$

where $u_n(\cdot)$ is a sequence of continuous functions approximating $u(\cdot)$ in $L_2(0, t)$. We have, moreover, that

$$1\left(s; \int_0^t T(t-s)\,B\,u(s)\,ds\right) = 1(s; v)$$

where v is the element in X defined by:

$$\begin{aligned} v(s) &= u(t+s), \quad -t \leq s \leq 0 \\ &= 0 \text{ otherwise.} \end{aligned}$$

We have thus that the zero state response due to a delta function input at time zero can be expressed:

$$Z_s(t; \delta) = 1(0; T(t)B)$$

where $T(t)B$ is now continuous in the I'-topology. Finally, corresponding to (6.1), we have:

$$y(t) = 1(0; x(t)), \quad t > 0,$$

where

$$x(t) = T(t)\,x(0) + \int_0^t T(t-s)\,B\,u(s)\,ds, \tag{6.16}$$

yielding the state space representation. For the corresponding dynamical equations, we have to place additional restrictions on $x(0)$ and $u(\cdot)$. Thus we require first that $x(0)$ be in the domain of the infinitesimal generator of the semigroup. Here the infinitesimal generator may be defined as follows: its domain consists of all elements x such that

$$\lim_{t\to 0} 1\left(s; \frac{T(t)x - x}{t}\right) = 1(s; y), \; y \in X,$$

and we define

$$Ax = y,$$

where A denotes the infinitesimal generator. Let

$$y(t) = \int_0^t T(t-s)\,B\,u(s)\,ds,$$

where $u(\cdot)$ is absolutely continuous and the derivative is square integrable on finite intervals, and in addition $u(0)$ is zero. Then it can be readily verified that $y(t)$ belongs to the domain of A and that

$$1(s; A\,y(t)) = 1(s; \dot{y}(t)) - 1(s; B\,u(t))$$

so that under these conditions on $x(0)$ and $u(\cdot)$, we have the following dynamical equation corresponding to (6.16):

$$\dot{x}(t) = A\,x(t) + B\,u(t) \tag{6.17}$$

It is natural that we delineate (6.16) and (6.17) as weak representations to distinguish them from the "strong" representations (4.6) and (4.8).

APPENDIX

The purpose of this appendix is to collect together the kind of results needed in Section 6 concerning the solutions of the equation:

$$\int_{-\infty}^{0} w(t-s)\, b(s)\, ds = w(t), \quad t \geq 0. \tag{A.1}$$

Since these results do not appear to be generally known, we shall state and prove them here. We begin with the L_2 version.

Theorem A.1: Let A.1 have a solution in $L_2(0, \infty)$, for given $b(\cdot)$ in $L_2(-\infty, 0)$. Then $w(\cdot)$ is necessarily of the form:

$$w(t) = \sum_{\nu=1}^{n} \sum_{p=1}^{n} C_{\nu,p}\, t^{p-1} \exp - k_\nu t \tag{A.2}$$

or, the Laplace transform of $w(\cdot)$ is rational.

Proof: In the usual fashion (see reference 8), let

$$K(\sigma + it) = \lim \int_{-\infty}^{0} b(s) \exp 2\pi(\sigma + it) s\, ds, \quad \sigma \geq 0,$$

$$F(\sigma + it) = \lim \int_{0}^{\infty} w(s) \exp 2\pi(\sigma + it) s\, ds, \quad \sigma \leq 0.$$

Then, $K(\sigma + it)$ is analytic in $\sigma > 0$, and $F(\sigma + it)$ is analytic in $\sigma < 0$, the assumed "bouhdary values" on the imaginary axis being the Fourier transforms. Also the convolution

$$\int_{-\infty}^{0} w(t-s)\, b(s)\, ds, \quad -\infty < t < \infty,$$

defines a function in $L_2(-\infty, +\infty)$, whose Fourier transform is

$$F(it) \cdot K(it).$$

Hence

$$F(it)(1 - K(it))$$

is the Fourier transform of a function in $L_2(-\infty, +\infty)$. But from (A.1), we note that this function vanishes on the positive real axis, so that it is actually in $L_2(-\infty, 0)$. Hence, there is a function analytic in $\sigma > 0$, such that

$$\lim L(\sigma + it) = F(it)(1 - K(it)).$$

But, from the definition, $(1 - K(it))$ is the limit of a function analytic in the right half plane, and hence it follows that $F(it)$ is the boundary value of a function analytic in the right half plane except for poles at the zeros of $(1 - K(\sigma + it))$. Since $F(\sigma + it)$ is analytic in $\sigma < 0$, it follows that $F(z)$ must be a rational function of z, proving (A.2).

Next we want to prove the result stated in Section 6 that if $L_1(w)$ is normable, it is finite dimensional. Let us assume then that $L_1(w)$ is a normed linear space in the Γ-topology. We note that the class C of summable (with respect to Lebesgue measure) functions that vanish outside compact intervals is dense in $L(w)$ and its completion. In other words, given any element b in the completion of $L(w)$, we can find a sequence of elements $\{u_n\}$ in C such that for each s,

$$1(s; u_n) \longrightarrow 1(s; b).$$

Hence it follows that, given any element v in X (which is now a Banach space), we can find a sequence u_n in C such that

$$\| P u_n - v \| \longrightarrow 0$$

where $\| \ \|$ denotes the norm in X. Now for each n,

$$1(s; T'(t) P u_n) = 1(s; T(t) u_n) = \int_{-L_n}^{0} w(t + s - \sigma) u_n(\sigma) d\sigma, \quad L_n < \infty,$$

and since $w(\cdot)$ is continuous on finite intervals, this is continuous in t, for each s, and hence

$$T'(t) P u_n$$

is strongly continuous in t for $t > 0$. It follows that the limit

$$T'(t) v$$

is strongly measurable, or that the semigroup $T'(t)$ is strongly measurable for $t > 0$, and hence by the Phillips-Miyadera result,[3] it is strongly continuous for $t > 0$. In particular, it follows that $\| T'(t) \|$ is measurable and hence

$$\| T'(t) \| = 0 [\exp \omega_0 t]$$

for some

$$\omega_0 \geq 0, \quad \text{as } t \longrightarrow \infty.$$

But from (6.15) we have then that

$$| w(t) | = 0 (\exp \omega_0 t) \quad \text{as } t \longrightarrow \infty.$$

Hence we can find λ such that

$$\int_{-\infty}^{0} | w(t_1 - s) | \, | w(t_2 - s) | \exp \lambda s \, ds < \infty, \quad \text{for } t_1, t_2 \geq 0. \tag{A.3}$$

Next, we invoke the Kolmogorov theorem[6] that a locally convex space is normable if and only if there is a convex symmetric bounded neighborhood of the origin. The norm is then given by the Minkowski functional of this neighborhood. An implication of this in the present context is that we can find a finite set of functionals in Γ, such that, if for each functional $f(\cdot)$ in this set

$$f(v) = 0, \quad v \in X,$$

then the norm of v is zero, In turn, this implies that we can find a finite set of indices t_k such that if for every t_k in this set

$$1(t_k; v) = 0,$$

then

$$1(t; v) = 0, \quad t \geq 0. \tag{A.4}$$

It follows from this that if we denote the delta function by δ, then we can find a function $u(\cdot)$ of the form:

$$u(s) = \sum_{1}^{m} a_k\, w(t_k - s) \exp \lambda s$$

such that

$$\int_{-\infty}^{0} w(t_k - s)\, u(s)\, ds = w(t_k) = 1(t_k; \delta).$$

Since $u(\cdot)$ is in $L(w)$ by virtue of (A.3), it follows that

$$1(s;\, u - \delta) = 0, \quad s \geq 0,$$

or,

$$\int_{-\infty}^{0} w(t - s)\, u(s)\, ds = w(t), \quad t \geq 0.$$

Writing

$$w'(t) = w(t) \exp a\, t,$$

it is clear that, by suitable choice of a, we can write:

$$\int_{-\infty}^{0} w'(t - s)\, v(s)\, ds = w'(t), \quad t \geq 0.$$

$v(\cdot)$ is in $L_2(-\infty, 0)$ and $w'(\cdot)$ is in $L_2(0, \infty)$. By Theorem A.1, it follows that $w'(\cdot)$ must be of the form (A.2), and it readily follows from this that the Laplace transform of $w(\cdot)$ must be rational, and hence $L_1(w)$ must, as before, be finite dimensional.

REFERENCES

1. L. Zadeh and C. Desoer, *Linear System Theory* (New York: McGraw-Hill, 1964).
2. R. E. Kalman, "Mathematical Description of Linear Dynamical Systems," *J. SIAM Control* (1963).
3. E. Hille and R. S. Phillips, *Functional Analysis and Semigroups* (AMS Colloquium Publications, 1957).
4. A. V. Balakrishnan, "Optimal Control Problems in Banach Spaces," *SIAM Journal*, Series A on Control, 3, 1 (1965).
5. I. M. Gelfand and G. E. Shilov, *Generalized Functions*, Vol. 1 (New York: Academic Press, 1964).
6. K. Yosida, *Functional Analysis* (New York: Academic Press, 1965).
7. A. V. Balakrishnan, "Semigroup Theory and Control Theory," *Proceedings of the IFIP* (1965), Vol. 1 (Washington, D.C.: Spartan Books, 1965).
8. R. Paley and N. Wiener, *Fourier Transforms in the Complex Domain*, Vol. 19 (AMS Colloquium Publications, 1934).

PARTITIONING AND TEARING LARGE SYSTEMS OF EQUATIONS*

Donald V. Steward

Social Systems Research Institute, and U.S. Army Mathematics Research Center, University of Wisconsin, Madison, Wisc.

Kron has developed a technique for tearing large, sparse linear systems of equations into smaller systems, then putting the solutions of these smaller systems together to form the solution of the original problem. This can result in a great saving over solving the whole system in one piece. The trick is to find where to tear, so that on the one hand the remaining pieces are small and easily solvable, but on the other hand not so much violence is done to the equations that the task of putting their solutions back together becomes too difficult. Kron has formal procedures for solving the pieces and putting their solutions together. The widespread use of Kron's technique has perhaps been limited severely for lack of practitioners skilled in this art of determining effective ways of tearing specific problems. It is the purpose of this paper to refer to formal procedures which can be performed on a computer for obtaining partitions and tears by analyzing the structures of the systems of equations themselves.

Partitions and tears are defined here for nonlinear as well as linear systems. In linear or nonlinear systems, tears may reveal a good iterative procedure, or may be used with extensions of dynamic programming to optimize engineering systems.

Large systems of algebraic equations can often be solved more easily if they can first be torn into smaller systems. How difficult it is to reconstruct the solution of the whole system from the solutions of the pieces depends upon how much violence was done to the equations in the tearing process. Clues on how to do the tearing have, in the past, been gained primarily through insight into the meaning of the problem which the equations represent. Kron has been very successful in applying these techniques, using analogous electrical networks to see where to tear and how to reconstruct the solution. Our concern in this paper is with systematic methods for extracting information from the structure of the equations themselves to augment our insight into how to tear systems of equations.

We will illustrate what we mean by partitioning and tearing with an example. Let the structural matrix given in Fig. 1 represent a system of equations. The X's indicate what variables appear in the equations. The equations may be nonlinear.

Partitioning is determining blocks, i.e., subsets of the set of equations, which must be solved simultaneously such that the blocks can be solved sequentially.

---

*An expanded treatment by the author of this subject will appear in the *SIAM Journal: Series B, Numerical Analysis.*

Presented at the Symposium on System Theory
Polytechnic Institute of Brooklyn, April 20, 21, 22, 1965

Variables

Equations	a	b	c	d	e	f	g	h	i	j	k	l	m	n	o	p	q	r	s	t	u	v	w	y
1					x														x	x				
2											x	x												x
3										x					x	x			x			x		
4	x										x							x						
5								x						x	x									
6						x											x				x		x	
7			x						x															
8					x																		x	
9			x										x				x							
10															x	x								
11	x	x																						
12				x															x	x				
13										x														x
14									x								x							
15							x															x		
16						x							x										x	
17											x										x			
18										x				x										x
19	x							x				x				x								
20		x					x				x											x		
21				x												x				x				
22	x										x													
23									x				x				x							
24		x					x											x			x			

Figure 1.

Partitioning the set of equations in Fig. 1, we use the blocks to permute row and columns and rewrite the structural matrix in block triangular form in Fig. 2.

Thus we see that the largest system of equations which must be solved simultaneously has been reduced from 24 to 10.

Now we may ask how we might remove elements from a block so that a block could be partitioned further. Removing such elements is called here tearing.

By identifying some key tear elements we can partition the blocks in our example further, as indicated in Fig. 3.

From the structural matrix we can develop the precedence diagram of Fig. 4.

There are a number of ways which may be employed to take advantage of tearing in solving systems of equations, depending upon the form of the equations themselves. Given a linear system represented by a matrix, its inverse may be expressed as the inverse of the matrix with the coefficient represented by a torn element removed, plus a simple correction matrix. In a nonlinear system, the tearing may suggest an iteration scheme. For example, if we were to iterate on variable c in equation 7 to solve that block of equations, in each iteration, equations 7, 14, 23 and 9 may be solved sequentially.

A tearing is not unique. Choice of the best tearing depends not only on the structural matrix, but also on how the variables appear in the equations. Gen-

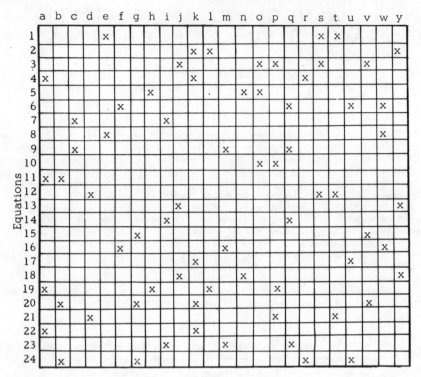

Variables

Equations	i	c	q	m	a	b	v	u	g	k	r	f	w	e	s	l	o	n	p	t	j	y	h	d
7	x	x																						
9		x	x	x																				
14	x		x																					
23	x		x	x																				
4					x					x	x													
11					x	x																		
15							x		x															
17								x		x														
20						x	x		x	x														
22					x					x														
24						x		x	x		x													
6			x					x				x	x											
16				x								x	x											
8													x	x										
1														x	x					x				
2										x						x						x		
3							x								x		x		x		x			
5																	x	x					x	
10																	x		x					
12															x					x				x
13																					x	x		
18																		x			x	x		
19					x											x			x				x	
21																			x	x				x

Figure 2.

erally, however, we will be interested in exploring first the properties of those tearings which leave the smallest blocks remaining.

Let us consider the following example (Fig. 5) to motivate the concepts which are used to develop the algorithms.

Wc assign one X in each row and circle it such that only one X is circled in each column. The circled X's we will call outputs. They may be considered to be the dependent variable in each equation, as shown in Fig. 6. A vertical line eminating from an output indicates the substitution of that output variable into another equation. A horizontal line into the output variable represents the use of an independent variable in solving for that output variable. When these paths form a cycle, as in equations 3, 4, and 5, it indicates that the equations involved in the cycle must be solved simultaneously. Thus, in the example (Fig. 5) we can solve equation 1 for X_a, then substitute X_a into equation 2 to solve it for X_b. Substituting X_b into equation 3 we are left with equations 3, 4, and 5 which must be solved simultaneously.

Partitioning consists of grouping into blocks those equations which occur in the same cycle. When the cycles are confined to within blocks, then the blocks themselves must have a precedence ordering.

Although, in general, there may be many possible assignments of the outputs,

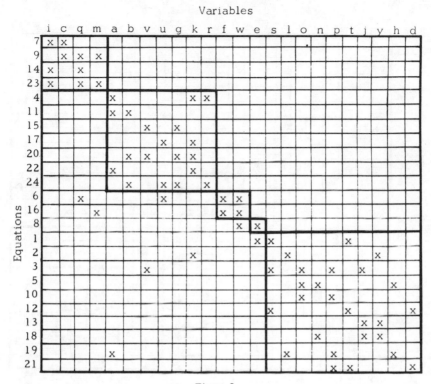

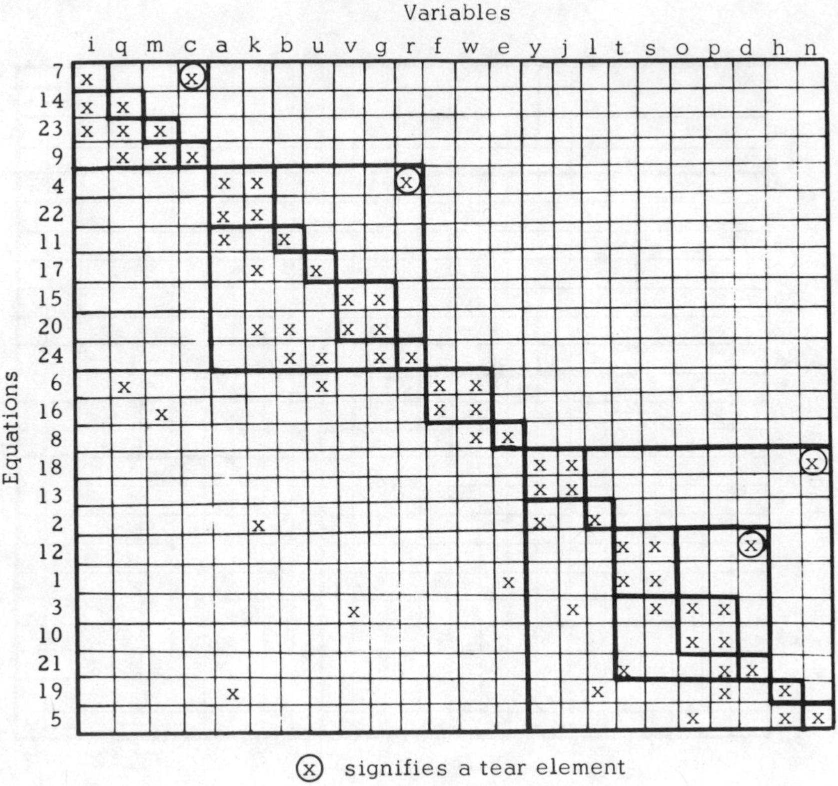

Figure 3.

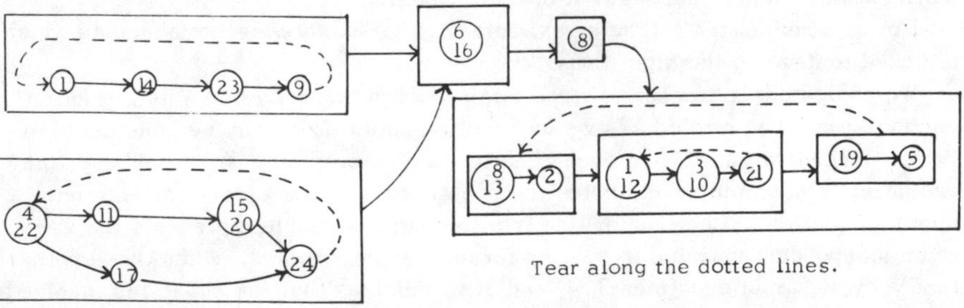

Figure 4.

any allowable assignment of outputs may be obtained from any other by moving the output labels around cycles. For example, see Fig. 7. By this property we can show that the partition we find is unique and can be obtained using any of the possible choices of output assignment.

The problem of tearing concerns how to identify elements in the structural matrix whose removal will so break the cycles that smaller blocks remain.

$$F_1(X_a) = 0$$
$$F_2(X_a, X_b) = 0$$
$$F_3(X_b, X_c, X_e) = 0$$
$$F_4(X_c, X_d) = 0$$
$$F_5(X_d, X_e) = 0$$

	a	b	c	d	e
1	X				
2	X	X			
3		X	X		X
4			X	X	
5				X	X

Structural Matrix

Figure 5.

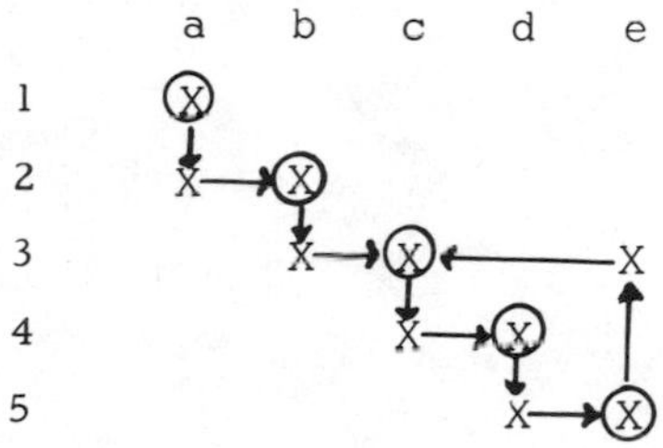

Figure 6.

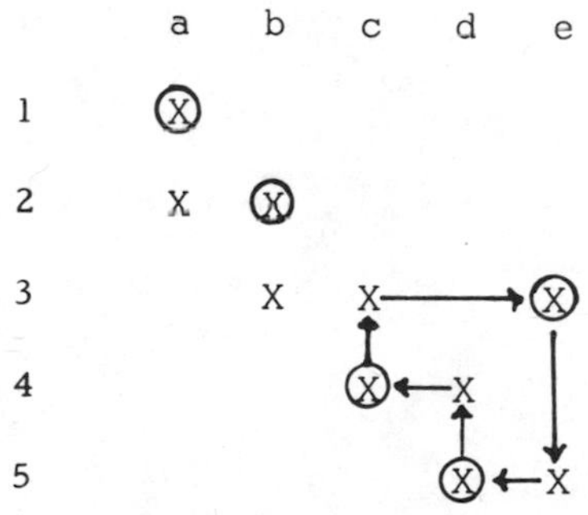

Figure 7.

Algorithms are given in the reference cited for partitioning and tearing and examples are worked out. The algorithm for partitioning is very fast, and the computing time does not rise very rapidly with the size of the problem. The computing time required for the tearing algorithm, however, does increase very rapidly with the size of the block to be analyzed. Further work will be required to develope a practical algorithm for tearing very large problems.

DISCUSSION ON

PARTITIONING AND TEARING LARGE SYSTEMS OF EQUATIONS

by

DONALD V. STEWARD

F. J. Davison, University of Toronto, Toronto, Ontario, Canada.

Numerical procedures for obtaining the inverse of large systems of sparse matrices are very valuable. Am I correct in assuming that Steward's technique would not necessarily work for large sparse matrices with regular structure? I am thinking primarily of tridiagonal matrices.

Steward:

I assume that this question has in mind the solution of such systems as arise in the numerical solution of partial differential equations. These systems are usually solved iteratively, choosing some part of the system to be assumed known from the previous iteration and the rest of the system to be solved in the present iteration. The notion of tearing is certainly applicable here. Kron has given quite a bit of consideration to such problems. I have used the notion of tearing, although not the formal tool discussed in this paper, to develop a scheme for solving elliptic partial differential equations in three dimensions, which would appear to have some computational advantages, but have not been able to find the time to explore the convergence properties. However, the structures of these systems are usually quite simple, not of great variety, and of sufficiently obvious and general application that they have already received a great deal of specific attention. My technique is primarily a tool for acquiring a feeling for more structurally complex and unique systems.

L. M. Naphtali, Polytechnic Institute of Brooklyn, Brooklyn, N. Y.

When a nonlinear system is torn, the parts have to be solved, usually by an iterative procedure, before they can be joined again, by an overall iterative process. Would it not be better to restrict tearing to linear systems and only iterate the overall problem (by linearization)? This eliminates the iterations within iterations.

Steward:

Nonlinear systems of equations are typically solved iteratively by linearizing around the present estimates for the unknowns, then solving the linear system to obtain new estimates, etc. It seems the question here is whether for a large nonlinear system one should: 1) tear first, solve each of the pieces by iterative linearization, then join the parts together by another probably iterative process; or 2) solve the whole system by iterative linearization, using tearing to simplify the task of solving the full linearized system.

The second method joins the parts in the form of linear subsystems where the linearity makes the joining easier. Thus I would be inclined to agree with Professor Naphtali that this is usually the better technique. However, for systems that have linear parts, or where the sensitivities of the torn elements are not significant, the first method may be superior.

Of course, if the system can be partitioned without tearing, then there is no problem in partitioning first and then solving the parts in sequence.

CONCEPTS AND PROBLEMS OF MODERN DYNAMICS

L. A. MacColl

Department of Mathematics, Polytechnic Institute of Brooklyn, Brooklyn, N. Y.

The concept of the phase space of a dynamical system and the representation of the motions of the system by means of moving points in the phase space are familiar tools in classical dynamics. In recent years, these ideas have led to the development of an abstract and generalized dynamics. Roughly stated, a dynamical system in this modern sense is any space (conventionally called a phase space), together with a continuous family of transformations (called a flow) of the space into itself. The possible applications of this dynamics include most of the specifically physical applications of classical dynamics, as well as applications to many other situations in both pure and applied mathematics. Among the more important results of the theory may be mentioned classifications of the possible "motions" of dynamical systems, important information concerning the relations between the different "motions," and the possibility of dealing with a large variety of particular problems by means of a small number of general concepts and laws. In this paper some of the more important parts of the generalized dynamics are described as precisely as is possible without entering into lengthy technical mathematical details. Some of the chief problems with which the theory has been concerned are discussed, and some of the actual or potential applications, particularly applications which are of interest in system theory, are indicated.

INTRODUCTION

In recent years the usage of the terms "dynamics" and "dynamical system" has changed considerably, in the direction of greater abstractness and generality. Formerly a dynamical system was always a physical system of some kind— usually a mechanical system. Now, however, the term "dynamical system" is applied to differential equations considered in the abstract, to certain groups of transformations, and perhaps to still other purely mathematical objects. It is the purpose of this paper to describe the origin and nature of this new view of dynamics, and to indicate some of the questions that are studied in the modern theory.

The origin of the new view can be described easily. The concept of the phase space (or state space) of a dynamical system and the representation of the motions of the system by means of moving points in the phase space are familiar tools in ordinary dynamics. The motions of the points in the phase space constitute a flow of the space into itself, and any study of the dynamical system amounts mathematically to a study of properties of the flow. Now, to state the matter roughly, we proceed to the modern view of dynamics by ignoring the spe-

Presented at the Symposium on System Theory
Polytechnic Institute of Brooklyn, April 20, 21, 22, 1965

cifically physical features of the foregoing, by retaining the essential notions of the phase space and the flow, and by simply defining a dynamical system to be a space (still conventionally called a phase space) together with a continuous family of transformations (called a flow) of the space into itself.

It is clear that these vague ideas must be made considerably more precise, before they can lead to anything in the way of a significant theory. Specifically, we must introduce definite assumptions concerning the properties of the phase space and of the flow. The sets of assumptions that have been employed by different authors are all more or less similar, but they differ in detail in various ways. Consequently, the modern dynamics that is under discussion here is not a single unified theory, but is rather a group of closely related theories, differing among themselves in generality, in methods, and perhaps in other respects also. We cannot undertake a review of all the possible varieties of modern dynamics, and shall confine our attention to two particular varieties, which we can associate loosely with the names of G. D. Birkhoff and V. V. Nemyckii, respectively.

At this point, it will be well to say something about the kind of information sought by modern dynamics, as contrasted with the kind of information sought by the older theory.

A large part of a typical treatise on the older dynamics is devoted to the basic physical principles of the subject, and to the various forms into which the fundamental equations can be put. The remaining parts are usually devoted to the study of particular motions, or of small classes of particular motions, of the systems under consideration. Only in a few places, notably in the theory of small vibrations, is there much discussion of broad classes of motions. Furthermore, much of the attention is directed toward the quantitative aspects of motions, and it is rather a rarity for the phase space of a system to be considered in its entirety.

Modern dynamics, on the other hand, takes all possible motions of a system into account, seeking to describe qualitatively the various types of motions, and studying the relations between the various motions.* It is to be emphasized that the phase spaces of all systems are considered in their entireties, and this frequently necessitates the consideration of spaces having rather unfamiliar topological structures.

Finally, it should be said that the modern dynamics contains little or nothing in the way of novel algorithms, and that consequently its results tend to give information as to what may happen under various broad conditions, rather than to give information as to what does happen in particular cases.

DYNAMICS IN THE SENSE OF NEMYCKII

As far as abstractness and generality are concerned, the theory of Nemyckii stands near the top of the list of dynamical theories. In the following statement of the basic assumptions, we omit, for the sake of simplicity, certain assumptions

*In Birkhoff's words: "The final aim of the theory of the motions of a dynamical system must be directed toward the qualitative determination of all possible types of motions and of the interrelations of these motions."

which are contained in Nemyckii's own statement. Consequently, the theory that will be described is somewhat more general than is the theory given by Nemyckii himself. However, the differences between the two theories are not important for the present purposes.

It will be observed that throughout this paper we are confining attention to *autonomous* systems. This is because these systems are easier to deal with, as well as being, in a certain sense, more fundamental than are nonautonomous systems.

Let X be an arbitrary topological space, and let T be the set of real numbers with its usual topology (i.e., the real line). Let $F(x, t)$ be a single-valued function which is defined on the product of X and T, which has points of X as values, and which satisfies the following further conditions:

I. $F(x, t)$ is continuous on the product of X and T.

II. For any given $t \in T$, and any given $x' \in X$, there exists a point $x \in X$ such that $F(x, t) = x'$.

III. The relation $F(F(x, t_1), t_2) = F(x, t_1 + t_2)$ holds for any point $x \in X$ and for any pair of numbers t_1, t_2 (distinct or not).

Under these circumstances, the pair $(X, F(x, t))$ constitutes a dynamical system in what we are calling the sense of Nemyckii. The space X is the phase space of the system; and the function $F(x, t)$ defines the flow of X into itself, in the sense that the moving point which is at x at the instant 0 is at the point $F(x, t)$ at the instant t.

It is easily seen that this abstract theory comprises much of the older physical dynamics. However, the theory also has applications to many situations of a nonphysical nature. This is illustrated by the following example, which is a simplification of an example due to M. V. Bebutov.

Let X be the set of all bounded and uniformly continuous functions $x(u)$ defined on the infinite interval $-\infty < u < \infty$. We make X into a metric space (and hence also a topological space) by defining the distance between the typical functions $x_1(u)$, $x_2(u)$ by the formula

$$\rho(x_1, x_2) = \sup_u |x_1(u) - x_2(u)|.$$

Then if we define the function $F(x, t)$ by the formula

$$F(x(u), t) = x(u + t),$$

it is clear that the pair $(X, F(x, t))$ constitutes a dynamical system in the sense of Nemyckii.

Among the objects of major interest in ordinary dynamics are fixed points in the phase space (i.e., states of equilibrium) and closed orbits in the phase space (representing periodic motions). It is interesting and instructive to observe that these objects appear in novel forms in the above example. In fact, a little consideration suffices to show that a fixed point is merely a constant function $x(u)$, and that a closed orbit in the phase space is constituted by the functions $x(u + t)$, $0 \leqq t < p$, where $x(u)$ is a (bounded and uniformly continuous) periodic function with the fundamental period p.

DYNAMICS IN THE SENSE OF BIRKHOFF

This variety of modern dynamics stands much closer to ordinary dynamics than does the Nemyckii theory. Its foundations are relatively complicated, and are not easy to describe in a completely precise and satisfactory way. Hence we shall not attempt anything more than a sketchy description of the theory.

The phase space X is now an n-dimensional analytic manifold.* As such, X is covered by a system of open "coordinate neighborhoods," the points in the typical neighborhood U being represented by means of a system of local coordinates $q^1, q^2, \ldots, q^n$. If two of the coordinate neighborhoods have a non-empty intersection, the two associated systems of local coordinates are related in the intersection by a nonsingular analytic transformation.

Let $\mathcal{V}$ be a continuous contravariant vector field defined over X. In the typical coordinate neighborhood U, the components of the field vector are functions of the local coordinates $q^1, q^2, \ldots, q^n$. We denote these functions by the symbols

$$v^\lambda(q^1, q^2, \ldots, q^n), \qquad (\lambda = 1, 2, \ldots, n).$$

If the symbols $\bar{v}^\lambda(\bar{q}^1, \bar{q}^2, \ldots, \bar{q}^n)$ denote the components of the field vector in an overlapping coordinate neighborhood $\bar{U}$ with the local coordinates $\bar{q}^1, \bar{q}^2, \ldots, \bar{q}^n$, the functions $v^1, v^2, \ldots, v^n$ and the functions $\bar{v}^1, \bar{v}^2, \ldots, \bar{v}^n$ are related in the intersection of the neighborhoods by the familiar formulae for the transformation of the components of a contravariant vector.

We now let t be an unrestricted real independent variable, and we set up the tensor "differential equations of motion"

$$\frac{dq^\lambda}{dt} = v^\lambda(q^1, q^2, \ldots, q^n), \quad (\lambda = 1, 2, \ldots, n).$$

The existence of local solutions of this system of equations is assured by the assumed continuity of the right-hand members. We assume that the v^λ's satisfy conditions (e.g., Lipschitz conditions) that suffice to assure the uniqueness of the local solution satisfying an arbitrary set of initial conditions of the form

$$x^\lambda(t_0) = x_0^\lambda, \quad (\lambda = 1, 2, \ldots, n).$$

The local solution of the differential equations and initial conditions is continued beyond its original domain of definition by the familiar process; and we assume that the continuation ultimately results in a solution defined over the infinite interval $-\infty < t < \infty$. In the course of the continuation, the moving phase point may pass from one coordinate neighborhood to another. The continuation of the solution from one neighborhood to another is dealt with in the obvious way, the tensor character of the differential equations of motion playing an essential part.

Under these circumstances, the space X and the flow generated by the differential equations of motion (i.e., effectively by the vector field $\mathcal{V}$) constitute a dynamical system in the sense of Birkhoff. It is clear that this theory is a sub-

*We assume analyticity for the sake of convenience: some weaker assumption would suffice for most of our purposes.

variety of the Nemyckii theory. On the other hand, the Birkhoff theory comprises a large part of ordinary physical dynamics, and much besides. However, there are systems considered in ordinary dynamics such that certain motions are defined only over finite or semi-infinite time intervals. Such systems, sometimes termed "singular," are not within the purview of the Birkhoff theory as formulated here.

ORBITS AND THEIR ELEMENTARY PROPERTIES

As has been said, modern dynamics seeks qualitative information concerning the various types of motions of a system, and concerning the relations existing between the different motions. We shall now consider some of the first steps in this program. It is to be understood that we are thinking primarily in terms of a Nemyckii-type theory.

Let A and B be subsets of the phase space X and the real line T, respectively. We use the symbol $F(A, B)$ to denote the set of all points $F(x, t)$, where x belongs to A and t belongs to B.

We are particularly interested in sets of the form $F(x_0, T)$, where x_0 is a particular point of X. Such a set is called an orbit, and in particular the orbit determined by x_0.

We are also interested in sets of the forms $F(x_0, T^+)$ and $F(x_0, T^-)$, where x_0 is as before, and the symbols T^+ and T^- denote the sets of non-negative and non-positive real numbers, respectively. $F(x_0, T^+)$ and $F(x_0, T^-)$ are called the positive semi-orbit determined by x_0 and the negative semi-orbit determined by x_0, respectively.

It is easily seen that the orbits are disjoint subsets of X, and hence that an orbit is determined by any one of its points. Also, each point of X is contained in an orbit.

The following theorem, the easy proof of which will be omitted, gives the first information concerning the properties of the orbits.

Theorem. *An orbit is either a single point, a one-to-one continuous image of a circumference, or a one-to-one continuous image (but not necessarily a topological image) of the real line T.*

Further information concerning the qualitative properties of orbits is obtained by means of the concepts of the α- and ω-limit sets of an orbit. These concepts are defined as follows.

Let $t_1, t_2, t_3, \ldots$ be an infinite sequence of values of t such that

$$t_1 < t_2 < t_3 < \ldots, \quad t_n \longrightarrow +\infty,$$

or such that

$$t_1 > t_2 > t_3 > \ldots, \quad t_n \longrightarrow -\infty.$$

Now if $\bar{x}$ is a limit point of the sequence

$$F(x_0, t_1),\ F(x_0, t_2),\ F(x_0, t_3), \ldots,$$

$\bar{x}$ is called an α-limit point of the orbit $F(x_0, T)$ in the case of the decreasing sequence of values of t, and is called an ω-limit point of the orbit in the case of the increasing sequence of values of t. The set of all ω-limit points of the orbit is called the ω-limit set of the orbit, and is denoted by Ω_{x_0}. Similarly, the set of all α-limit points of the orbit is called the α-limit set of the orbit, and is denoted by A_{x_0}. The following examples illustrate these notions, and indicate something of the variety of situations that can arise.

Example 1. Let X be the real line with its usual topology, and let $F(x, t) = xe^t$. In this case we have $A_0 = \Omega_0 = 0$. If $x_0 \neq 0$, $A_{x_0} = 0$, and Ω_{x_0} is the empty set.

Example 2. Let X be the square $0 \leqq x \leqq 1$, $0 \leqq y \leqq 1$ in the xy-plane, with the following identifications of boundary points

$$(0, y) \equiv (1, y), \quad (x, 0) \equiv (x, 1).$$

(Thus X is a two-dimensional topological torus.) Let the flow be defined by the system of differential equations

$$\frac{dx}{dt} = 1, \quad \frac{dy}{dt} = \eta,$$

where η is an irrational number. It can be shown that in this case the α- and ω-limit sets of any orbit are both identical with X.

These examples serve also to illustrate the following important theorem.

Theorem. *Any α-limit set or ω-limit set is a union (possibly the empty union) of orbits.*

To prove the part of the theorem relating to ω-limit sets, suppose Ω_{x_0} is not empty, and let y_0 be one of its points. Then y_0 is a limit point of a sequence $F(x_0, t_1)$, $F(x_0, t_2)$, $F(x_0, t_3)$, . . . , where the t's form an increasing sequence which diverges to $+\infty$. Let τ be any real number. Then the point $F(y_0, \tau)$ is a limit point of the sequence $F(x_0, t_1 + \tau)$, $F(x_0, t_2 + \tau)$, $F(x_0, t_3 + \tau)$, ... For, if U is any open neighborhood of $F(y_0, \tau)$, $F(U, -\tau)$ is an open neighborhood of y_0. Hence $F(U, -\tau)$ contains an infinite number of terms of the sequence $F(x_0, t_1)$, $F(x_0, t_2)$, . . . ; and therefore U contains an infinite number of terms of the sequence $F(x_0, t_1 + \tau)$, $F(x_0, t_2 + \tau)$, ... Hence every point of the orbit $F(y_0, T)$ belongs to Ω_{x_0}. Since y_0 is an arbitrary point of Ω_{x_0}, the conclusion of the part of the theorem relating to ω-limit sets is proved. The other part is proved similarly.

It is a consequence of this theorem that any α- or ω-limit set is invariant under the flow of the dynamical system.

The notions of the limiting sets leads to the following classification of orbits with respect to their behaviors for large values of t.

(1) If Ω_{x_0} or A_{x_0} is the empty set ϕ, the orbit $F(x_0, T)$ is said to be positively or negatively divergent, as the case may be. If $A_{x_0} = \Omega_{x_0} = \phi$, the orbit is said to be divergent.

(2) If $\Omega_{x_0} \neq \phi$, but $F(x_0, T^+) \cap \Omega_{x_0}$ (the intersection of $F(x_0, T^+)$ and Ω_{x_0}) is empty, the orbit $F(x_0, T)$ is said to be positively asymptotic. Similarly, if $A_{x_0} \neq \phi$ and $F(x_0, T^-) \cap A_{x_0} = \phi$, the orbit is said to be negatively asymptotic. If an orbit is both positively and negatively asymptotic, it is simply said to be asymptotic.

(3) If $F(x_0, T^+) \cap \Omega_{x_0} \neq \phi$, the orbit $F(x_0, T)$ is said to be stable according to Poisson in the positive direction. The terms "stable according to Poisson in the negative direction" and "stable according to Poisson" are now defined in an obvious way.

Stability according to Poisson has another aspect, which should be mentioned briefly. Suppose that the orbit $F(x_0, T)$ is stable according to Poisson in the positive direction. Then the orbit has a point in common with the limit set Ω_{x_0}; and hence, as we have seen in the course of the proof of the preceding theorem, every point of the orbit belongs to Ω_{x_0}. That is, given a point y_0 of $F(x_0, T)$ and a neighborhood U of y_0, the point $F(x_0, t)$ lies in U for infinitely many values of t, forming an increasing sequence which diverges to $+\infty$. On the basis of this, we say that the orbit is recurrent in the positive direction. Recurrence in the negative direction, and recurrence without qualification, are defined in the obvious ways.

We conclude at this point, because carrying the discussion further would soon involve us with complications that are unsuitable for a paper of this character.

REFERENCES

The references to the works of Birkhoff and Nemyckii are based on the following:

1. G. D. Birkhoff, *Dynamical systems,* American Mathematical Society Colloquim Publications, Vol. IX (1927).

2. V. V. Nemyckii, *Topological Problems in the Theory of Dynamical Systems,* American Mathematical Society Translation, Number 103 (1954). [Original in Russian: Uspehi Matematiceskih Nauk (N. S.), 4, No. 6(34), 91-153 (1949)]. This paper contains an extensive discussion of the example due to Bebutov.

3. For a very abstract and general formulation of dynamics, see W. H. Gottschalk and G. A. Hedlund, *Topological Dynamics,* American Mathematical Society Colloquium Publications, Vol. XXXVI (1955). This book contains an extensive bibliography, presumably nearly complete up to about 1952.

DYNAMICAL SYSTEMS WITH INPUTS*

Emilio Roxin
Brown University, Providence, R. I., and University of Buenos Aires, Buenos Aires, Argentina

Systems with inputs or control systems are defined by axioms characterizing the properties of the "attainability function" $F(x_0, t_0, t)$; this is the set of points in phase-space which are attainable at time, t, starting at x_0 at time t_0. Motions and trajectories are defined a posteriori, without specific reference to control functions. All basic properties expected for control systems can be derived.

This approach seems especially suitable for developing the stability properties of control systems. Strong and weak stability are defined according to the fact that *all* or *some* motions satisfy the required stability behavior. Similar to asymptotic stability, the *finite stability* is defined by the requirement that the motions actually reach the origin (or the point of rest) in finite time. Liapunov's second method is applicable to this kind of problem, provided the definitions are generalized to allow the Liapunov functions to be discontinuous, and upper and lower generalized derivatives are defined properly.

This theory seems important as a framework in which concepts are defined and their behavior studied in the greatest generality so that the basic features appear clearly and the ideas are not obscured by circumstantial details.

1. INTRODUCTION

One of the major tasks of a general theory of systems with inputs or, as we shall call them, control systems, is to give a description of their possible behaviour, characterize important properties and related concepts, and constitute the framework in which special methods can be developed for solving specific problems. That description should be as general as possible, in the sense of being applicable to many specific cases and also of being independent of special analytical (or functional) representations which are not inherent to the problem. Taking, for example, the common differential equation of a control system

$$\dot{x} = f(x, t, u) \tag{1.1}$$

where x is an n-vector, t the (scalar) independent variable called time, and u a variable control function, restricted to belong to a certain family of admissible controls

$$u(t) = u \in \Omega. \tag{1.2}$$

The function $f(x, t, u)$ is not inherent to the mathematical problem, in the sense

*This research was supported in part by the National Aeronautics and Space Administration under Grant No. NGR-40-002-015 and in part by the United States Air Force through the Air Force Office of Scientific Research under Grant No. AF-AFOSR-693-64.

Presented at the Symposium on System Theory
Polytechnic Institute of Brooklyn, April 20, 21, 22, 1965

that if, for example, u is a scalar, it can be replaced by log v, or if $|u| \leqq 1$, it can be replaced by sin w, changing of course the function $f(x, t, u)$ and the set Ω.

If the requirement (1.2) means that the values of $u(t)$ must belong, for any t, to the set Ω, a representation of eq. (1.1), independent of the special form of $f(x, t, u)$, is obtained considering the set

$$C(x, t) = \{f(x, t, u) | u \in \Omega\} \tag{1.3}$$

and the equation

$$\dot{x} \in C(x, t), \tag{1.4}$$

which is called a "contingent equation": $x(t)$ is called a solution of (1.4) if, for every t, all possible limit values of $\Delta x/\Delta t$ belong to the corresponding set $C(x(t), t)$. Contingent equations were studied in 1934 and 1935 by Marchaud[1,2] and Zaremba;[3] its relation with control systems was examined in reference 8.

In the classical theory of ordinary differential equations, it is also interesting to start directly from the solution curves $x = F(x_0, t_0, t)$, interpreted as a group of transformations. This gives the general theory of topological dynamics which includes systems that do not satisfy, in principle, differentiability conditions. Similarly, in our case, one should consider a control system given by the set

$$F(x_0, t_0, t) \tag{1.5}$$

of all points x which is possible to reach at time t, starting at x_0 at time t_0. This will be called the "attainable set" and considered as a function of its three arguments. On it we will base the whole development of the theory.

2. NOTATION

Consider the systems describable, at each moment, by a state-vector of the real n-space $X = R^n$. Points of X (vectors) will be designated by small letters, subsets of X by capitals, numbers (scalars) by Latin or Greek small letters. Furthermore

$$\rho(x, y) = \text{distance between the points } x, y \in X. \tag{2.1}$$

$$\rho(A, x) = \rho(x, A) = \inf \{\rho(a, x) | a \in A\}. \tag{2.2}$$

$$\beta(A, B) = \sup \{\rho(a, B) | a \in A\}. \tag{2.3}$$

$$\alpha(A, B) = \max \{\beta(A, B), \beta(B, A)\}. \tag{2.4}$$

$$S_\delta(A) = \{x \in X | \rho(x, A) < \delta\}. \tag{2.5}$$

3. BASIC AXIOMS

We will consider that to give a control system means to assume given an attainability function $F(x_0, t_0, t)$ with the following properties:

I. $F(x_0, t_0, t)$ is a closed non-empty subset of X, defined for every $x \in X$; t_0, $t \in R^+ = [0, +\infty]$.

II. $F(x_0, t_0, t_0) = \{x_0\}$ for every $x_0 \in X$; $t_0 \in R^+$ (initial condition).

III. For any $t_0 \leqq t_1 \leqq t_2$, $x_0 \in X$,

$$F(x_0, t_0, t_2) = \bigcup_{x_1 \in F(x_0, t_0, t_1)} F(x_1, t_1, t_2) \text{ (semigroup property).}$$

IV. $x_1 \in F(x_0, t_0, t_1) <=> x_0 \in F(x_1, t_1, t_0)$.

V. $F(x_0, t_0, t)$ is continuous in t: given x_0, t_0, t_1 and $\varepsilon > 0$, there is $\delta > 0$ such that

$$\alpha(F(x_0, t_0, t), F(x_0, t_0, t_1)) < \varepsilon, \text{ for all } t \text{ such that } |t - t_1| < \delta.$$

VI. $F(x_0, t_0, t)$ is upper-semicontinuous in the triple (x_0, t_0, t): given x_0, t_0, t and $\varepsilon > 0$, there is $\delta > 0$ such that

$$\rho(x, x_0) < \delta, \; |\tau_0 - t_0| < \delta, \; |\tau - t| < \delta$$

imply

$$\beta(F(x, \tau_0, \tau), F(x_0, t_0, t)) < \varepsilon.$$

These axioms are slightly less general than those adopted in reference 7. Indeed, in that paper the function $F(x_0, t_0, t)$ was supposed to be defined only for $t_0 \leqq t$, and the backward extension, denoted there by $G(x_0, t_0, t)$, was introduced later. As a consequence, this extension turned out to have almost all the properties of the original function, but it may fail to be continuous in t. Therefore, although for $t_0 \leqq t_1$, $F(x_0, t_0, t_1)$ is always compact, this is not necessarily true for the extension $G(x_0, t_1, t_0)$. For simplicity, and being sufficient for most applications, the axioms adopted here are symmetric with respect to $\pm t$. Therefore, all properties proved in reference 7 apply here in both time-directions.

4. MOTIONS

Consider a mapping $u: [t_0, t_1] \longrightarrow X$, not necessarily continuous, such that $\tau_0, \tau_1 \in [t_0, t_1]$ implies

$$u(\tau_1) \in F(u(\tau_0), \tau_0, \tau_1).$$

Then, continuity of $u(t)$ follows; such a mapping is called a *motion* of the control system, the image of $[t_0, t_1]$, a *trajectory*.

A motion $u_1(t)$ defined in $[a, b]$ is a prolongation of the motion $u_2(t)$ defined in $[c, d]$, if $[a, b] \supset [c, d]$ and in $[c, d]$, $u_1(t) = u_2(t)$.

The following property makes the abstractly defined control systems intuitively meaningful:

If $x_1 \in F(x_0, t_0, t_1)$, then there exists a motion $u(t)$ defined in $[t_0, t_1]$ such that $u(t_0) = x_0$, $u(t_1) = x_1$. One can say briefly that $u(t)$ joins (x_0, t_0) and (x_1, t_1). This was proved first by Barbashin,[4] who also proved that:

Given, for a certain control system, a sequence of motions $u_i(t)$ $(i = 1, 2, 3, \ldots)$ defined in some interval $[a, b]$, if $t_0 \in [a, b]$ and $u_i(t_0) \longrightarrow x_0$ for $i \longrightarrow \infty$, then there is some subsequence $u_{ij}(t)$ $(j = 1, 2, 3, \ldots)$ which converges uniformly in $[a, b]$ to some motion $u_0(t)$.

This last property is a very powerful tool for proving theorems, especially in the field of stability.

5. STABILITY

A point $x_0 \in X$ is called a *strong point of rest,* if for any $0 \leqq t_0 \leqq t$, $F(x_0, t_0, t) = \{x_0\}$.

A point $x_0 \in X$ is called a *weak point of rest,* if $u(t) \equiv x_0$ is a motion of the system for $0 \leqq t < +\infty$.

In a physical interpretation, these definitions mean:

i) Starting at a strong point of rest, one cannot get away from it.

ii) Starting at a weak point of rest, one can, with a suitable control action, stay there.

These two general possibilities—what one is forced to do, and what one can accomplish—also hint how to apply the stability properties to control systems in a strong and a weak form. So, the common Liapunov stability gives the two following definitions:

Assume that x_0 is a strong point of rest. It will be called *strongly stable,* if for any $t_0 \geqq 0$, $\varepsilon > 0$, there is $\delta > 0$ such that $\rho(x, x_0) < \delta$ implies

$$F(x, t_0, t) \subset S_{\varepsilon}(x_0)$$

for all $t \geqq t_0$. In other words: *all* motions starting at (x_0, t_0) remain in the ε-neighborhood of x_0.

Assume x_0 is a weak point of rest. It will be called *weakly stable,* if for any $t_0 \geqq 0$, $\varepsilon > 0$ there is $\delta > 0$ such that $\rho(x, x_0) < \delta$ implies the existence of a motion $u(t)$ such that $u(t_0) = x$ and $\rho(u(t), x_0) < \varepsilon$ for all $t \geqq t_0$. In other words: there is *some* motion starting at (x, t_0) and remaining in the ε-neighborhood of x_0.

These stabilities should be called *uniform* if $\delta(\varepsilon, t_0)$ can be taken independently of $t_0 \geqq 0$.

The definitions of the different kinds of asymptotic (uniform, equi-asymptotic, etc.) stability can be phrased in a strong and a weak form for control systems. Here only the most common case will be considered.

The strong point of rest x_0 will be called *asymptotically strongly stable,* if it is strongly stable and if for every $t_0 \geqq 0$ there is some $\eta(t_0) > 0$ such that if $\rho(x, x_0) < \eta$, for every motion $u(t)$ starting at $u(t_0) = x$, $\lim u(t) = x_0$ for $t \longrightarrow +\infty$.

The weak point of rest x_0 will be called *asymptotically weakly stable,* if for every $t_0 \geqq 0$ there is $\eta(t_0) > 0$ such that $\rho(x, x_0) < \eta$ implies the existence of a motion $u(t)$, which will now be denoted by $u(x, t_0, t)$, so that $u(x, t_0, t_0) = x$, $u(x, t_0, t) \longrightarrow x_0$ for $t \longrightarrow +\infty$, and $u(x, t_0, t) \longrightarrow x_0$ for $x \longrightarrow x_0$, t_0 fixed, uniformly in $t \geqq t_0$. This last condition implies weak Liapunov stability.

The following kind of stability, called *finite stability,* appears naturally in many applications of practical importance, in spite of which nobody seems to have treated it systematically.

The strong point of rest x_0 will be called *finitely strongly stable*, if it is strongly stable and if for every $t_0 \geqq 0$ there is $\eta > 0$ such that every motion $u(t)$ for which $\rho(u(t_0), x_0) < \eta$, reaches the point x_0 in finite time, i.e., there is t_f $(t_0 < t_f < +\infty)$ such that $u(t_f) = x_0$.

The weak point of rest x_0 will be called *finitely weakly stable*, if for every $t_0 \geqq 0$ there is $\eta(t_0) > 0$ such that $\rho(x, x_0) < \eta$ implies the existence of a motion $u(t)$, which will now be denoted by $u(x, t_0, t)$, so that $u(x, t_0, t_0) = x$, for some value $t_f = t_f(x, t_0)$ this motion reaches x_0 $(u(x, t_0, t_f) = x_0)$, where $t_0 \leqq t_f < +\infty$, and $u(x, t_0, t) \longrightarrow x_0$ for $x \longrightarrow x_0$, t_0 fixed, uniformly in $t \geqq t_0$. This last condition implies weak Liapunov stability.

In a physical interpretation, in the strong case one is forcibly driven into x_0 in finite time, while in the weak case one is able to reach x_0 in finite time.

The finite stability can, of course, be defined for ordinary differential equations, but it was never considered systematically, probably because it is impossible to hold when there is a unique solution through each point. In the practical world, however, all asymptotic motions die out after a finite time and correspond, therefore, to the finite stability. Also, the well-known concept of controllability of control systems is nothing but a weak finite stability. It seems that the most important finitely weakly stable systems have the additional property that, with the notation of the above definition, $t_f \longrightarrow t_0$ for $x \longrightarrow x_0$. These systems probably play an important role in applications.

6. APPLICATION OF LIAPUNOV'S DIRECT METHOD

This powerful method can be successfully applied to the above defined stabilities in control systems. The Liapunov functions to be considered need not be continuous. The upper and lower, left and right generalized derivatives of a scalar function with respect to the control system, are defined by:

$$D^+ v(x, t) = \overline{\lim_{\tau \to t^+}} \sup \left\{ \frac{v(y, \tau) - v(x, t)}{\tau - t} \,\middle|\, y \in F(x, t, \tau) \right\}$$

$$D_+ v(x, t) = \underline{\lim_{\tau \to t^+}} \inf \left\{ \frac{v(y, \tau) - v(x, t)}{\tau - t} \,\middle|\, y \in F(x, t, \tau) \right\}$$

Similarly D^- and D_- (for $\tau \longrightarrow t^-$) and, finally,

$$D^{\pm} = \max [D^+, D^-],$$

$$D_{\pm} = \min [D_+, D_-].$$

Then it is possible to prove the following results:

A necessary and sufficient condition for x_0 to be strongly stable, is the existence of a function $v(x, t)$ defined in $S_\eta(x_0) \times R^+$ for some $\eta > 0$ with the properties:

i) $v(x_0, t) = 0$ for all $t \geqq 0$;

ii) given $t_0 \geqq 0$, $\varepsilon > 0$, there is $\delta > 0$ such that $\rho(x, x_0) < \delta$ implies $v(x, t_0) < \varepsilon$;

iii) there is a strictly increasing and continuous function $v_1(r)$ of the real variable $r \geqq 0$, such that $v_1(0) = 0$, and $x \neq x_0$ implies $v(x, t) > v_1(\rho(x, x_0))$;

iv) $D^{\pm} v(x, t) \leqq 0$ in $S_\eta(x_0) \times R^+$.

A necessary and sufficient condition for x_0 to be weakly stable, is the existence of a function $v(x, t)$ defined in $S_\eta(x_0) \times R^+$ for some $\eta > 0$, with the properties:

(i) , (ii) , (iii) as before;

(iv) $v(x, t)$ is lower semicontinuous;

(v) $D_+ v(x, t) \leqq 0$ in $S_\eta(x_0) \times R^+$.

To the uniform (strong and weak) stabilities correspond the same necessary and sufficient conditions plus the requirement that the function $v(x, t)$ has an "infinitesimal upper bound" (i.e., $v(x, t) \longrightarrow 0$ for $x \longrightarrow x_0$ uniformly in $t \geqq 0$).

For the uniform asymptotic and finite (strong and weak) stabilities, similar theorems can be proved, with the restriction that the necessity of existence of the Liapunov function is proved only for periodic (or autonomous) systems.

For these latest results, the reader is referred to references 11, 12 and 13, which will be published soon.

REFERENCES

Very early papers related to these questions are:

1. M. A. Marchaud, "Sur les champs des demi-droites et les equations differentielles du premier ordre," *Bull. Soc. Math. France*, **63**, 1–38 (1934).
2. M. A. Marchaud, "Sur les champs continus des demicones convexes et leur integrales," *Compositio Math.*, **3**, 89–127 (1936).
3. M. S. C. Zaremba, "Sur les equations au paratingent," *Bull. Sci. Math.*, I, 60, 139–160 (1936).

The definition of control systems in the sense of this paper, was given by:

4. E. A. Barbashin, "On the theory of generalized dynamical systems," *Uch. Zap. M. G. U.*, **135**, 110–133 (1949).

A slightly different definition of control systems and a broad development of the theory, including definition of strong and weak stability, was given in:

5. E. Roxin, "Axiomatic Theory of Control Systems," RIAS Tech. Rep. 62.16 (1962).
6. E. Roxin, "Axiomatic Foundation of the Theory of Control Systems," Second Internat. Conf. of the I.F.A.C., Basel, 1963.
7. E. Roxin, "Stability in General Control Systems," *J. Diff. Eq.*, **1**, 2, (1965). [N. Y.: Acad. Press].

The relation with contingent equations was discussed in:

8. E. Roxin, "On Generalized Dynamical Systems Defined by Contingent Equations," *J. Diff. Eq.*, 1, 2 (1965) [N. Y.: Acad. Press].

Further development of the theory of stability is found in:

9. E. Roxin, "Stabilität in allgemeinen Regelungssystemem," Third Conference on Non-Linear Oscillations, Berlin, 1964.
10. E. Roxin, "Local Definition of Generalized Control Systems," to be published in *Michigan J. Math.*
11. E. Roxin, "On Stability in Control Systems," to be published in the *S.I.A.M. J. on Control.*
12. E. Roxin, "On asymptotic stability in control systems," to be published in *Rendiconti del Circolo Matem. di Palermo.*
13. E. Roxin, "On finite stability in control systems," to be published in *Rendiconti del Circolo Matem. di Palermo.*

DISCUSSION ON

DYNAMICAL SYSTEMS WITH INPUTS

by

EMILIO ROXIN

E. Kreindler, Research Dept., Grumman Aircraft Engineering Corp., Bethpage, L. I., N. Y.

Would Professor Roxin please comment on the following questions:

1) In many cases a differential equation modeling a physical system is given explicitly and thus the results of the theory of differential equations can be directly applied to concrete problems. On the other hand, the attainability function $F(x_0, t_0, t)$ is (at least at the present time) given only abstractly and thus the results of the general theory cannot be directly applied; i.e., one has to either determine $F(x_0, t_0, t)$ from the differential equation or translate the results of the theory back in terms of differential equations.

2) If differential equations remain a basic description of physical systems, then the requirement in Axiom I that $F(x_0, t_0, t)$ be closed, places (as your theorem on the existence of optimal controls shows) severe restrictions on the corresponding class of differential equations.

Roxin:

1) This axiomatic general theory cannot claim to be directly applicable as, for example, explicit differential equations. On the other hand, as said in the paper, a general theory should give a picture of the possible behaviour and general properties, and this, I claim, the present theory is able to do. The applications to stability theory show that quite sharp results can be obtained, in spite of all generality.

In short, our knowledge of the physical world is obtained by finite observations, and differential relations appear as mathematical abstractions. From a philosophical point of view, therefore, this axiomatic theory is a more natural description of the physical world than differential equations.

2) Because of the approximate character of physical measurements, the attainable set $F(x_0, t_0, t)$ can always be considered closed, with sufficient approximation. When the mathematical model does not show this behaviour, additional difficulties arise. In such cases one tries to avoid this mathematical "misbehaviour" with the aid of theories "ad hoc," like the "generalized curves," "generalized solutions," "quasi-trajectories," etc. (Young, Warga, Filipov, Gamkrelidze, Wazewski). This shows that our assumption of closedness of $F(x_0, t_0, t)$ is reasonable.

SOME NOTIONS OF STABILITY AND RECURRENCE IN DYNAMICAL SYSTEMS*

Joseph Auslander
Department of Mathematics, Yale University, New Haven, Conn.

We consider an approach to the problem of classification of dynamical systems which places recurrence in the foreground. All notions of recurrence which have been studied express the idea of a point "returning to itself" for arbitrarily large time. This may be made precise by introducing the prolongation and the prolongational limit set of a point, which are generalizations, respectively, of the positive semi-orbit closure and the omega (positive) limit set of a point. By an iterative procedure it is possible to define a (possibly transfinite) succession of prolongations and prolongational limit sets. A point is called a (generalized) recurrent point if it is contained in at least one of its own prolongational limit sets. This generalizes the classical notions of Poisson stable and non-wandering points.

From this point of view, the simplest dynamical systems are those which contain no recurrent points. These systems can also be characterized by the existence of a continuous real-valued function which is strictly decreasing along every orbit. Even for this extremely restricted class of dynamical systems, many interesting questions remain.

An important subclass of these are the *dispersive* or *parallelizable* dynamical systems. These are the ones for which all prolongational limit sets are empty, or equivalently, for which all prolongations are as small as possible—that is, coincide with the positive semi-orbits. In general, the more complicated a dynamical system is, the larger are its prolongations and prolongational limit sets.

If these considerations are suitably localized, they may be used to study the stability properties of compact invariant sets. Notions of stability are defined in terms of invariance under prolongations. Liapunov stability may be formulated in this manner, and a notion of "absolute stability," which is invariance under all prolongations, also may be studied. In this connection it can be shown that a compact invariant set is asymptotically stable if and only if it is absolutely stable and possesses a neighborhood which is free of recurrent points.

We consider a dynamical system on a locally compact separable metric space X. This is, if T denotes the real numbers, there is a continuous map from $X \times T$ into X, written as $(x, t) \longrightarrow xt$, which satisfies $x0 = x$, and $(xt_1)t_2 = x(t_1 + t_2)$, $(x \epsilon X,\ t_1,\ t_2 \epsilon T)$.

We shall denote the dynamical system by the pair (X, T). The term "flow" is used synonymously with "dynamical system." As a general reference, see reference 6.

In this paper, we study two families of sets, the prolongations and the prolongational limit sets of a point. These sets have proved to be useful in the study of stability and recurrence, and it is hoped they will aid in the classifica-

*Research supported by SAR/DA-31-124-ARO(D)165.

Presented at the Symposium on System Theory
Polytechnic Institute of Brooklyn, April 20, 21, 22, 1965

tion of dynamical systems. They are obtained by means of certain point-to-set maps, and, before continuing the discussion of dynamical systems, we shall collect some information about such maps.

As is customary, let 2^X denote the class of subsets of X, and let $P: X \longrightarrow 2^X$ (so, if $x \in X$, $P(x)$ is a subset of X). If $A \subset X$, then $P(A) = \cup \{P(x) | x \in A\}$, and if m is a positive integer $P^m: X \longrightarrow 2^X$ is defined inductively by $P^1 = P$ and $P^m = P(P^{m-1})$. If $\{P_i\}$ is a family of maps from X to 2^X, then by $\cup P_i$ we mean the map $P: X \longrightarrow 2^X$ given by $P(x) = \cup P_i(x)$.

We also define two operators, $\mathfrak{D}$ and $\mathfrak{S}$ on the class of maps from X to 2^X. (That is, if P is such a map, then so are $\mathfrak{D}P$ and $\mathfrak{S}P$.) If $x \in X$, $(\mathfrak{D}P)(x) = \bigcap_{U \in n(x)} \overline{P(U)}$ (where $n(x)$ denotes the neighborhood system of x and $(\mathfrak{S}P)(x) = \bigcup_{n=1,2,\ldots} P^n(x)$. We can give simple criteria for a point y to be a member of $\mathfrak{D}P(x)$ and $\mathfrak{S}P(x)$, namely: $y \in \mathfrak{D}P(x)$ if and only if there are sequences $\{x_n\}$ and $\{y_n\}$ with $y_n \in P(x_n)$ such that $x_n \longrightarrow x$ and $y_n \longrightarrow y$; $y \in \mathfrak{S}P(x)$ if and only if there are points $x_0 = x, x_1, \ldots, x_n = y$ in X such that $x_i \in P(x_{i-1})$ $(i = 1, 2, \ldots, n)$.

Now returning to dynamical systems, let $x \in X$, and let $\gamma^+(x)$ denote the positive semiorbit of X; that is, the set $\{xt | t \geq 0\}$. Starting with $D_0(x) = \overline{\gamma^+(x)}$ (the positive semiorbit closure of x) we define, by alternate application of the operators $\mathfrak{D}$ and $\mathfrak{S}$, a family of maps $D_\alpha: X \longrightarrow 2^X$.

The map D_1 is defined to be $\mathfrak{D}\mathfrak{S}D_0 = \mathfrak{D}D_0$ (since $\mathfrak{S}D_0 = D_0$ already). If α is an ordinal number, and D_β is defined for every $\beta < \alpha$, then we define, inductively, $D_\alpha = \mathfrak{D}\left(\bigcup_{\beta<\alpha} \mathfrak{S}D_\beta\right)$. (Hence, if α is a successor ordinal, $D_\alpha = \mathfrak{D}\mathfrak{S}D_{\alpha-1}$; in particular, $D_2 = \mathfrak{D}\mathfrak{S}D_1$, and, for any positive integer n, $D_n = \mathfrak{D}\mathfrak{S}D_{n-1}$.)

Note that $y \in D_1(x)$ if and only if there are sequences $\{x_n\}$ in X and $\{t_n\}$ in T, with $t_n \geq 0$ such that $x_n \longrightarrow x$ and $x_n t_n \longrightarrow y$. It is natural to single out the subset of $D_1(x)$ consisting of those y for which there exist $x_n \longrightarrow x$ and $t_n \longrightarrow \infty$ such that $x_n t_n \dashrightarrow y$. This set we denote by $\Lambda_1(x)$. Just as above, we define $\Lambda_2 = \mathfrak{D}\mathfrak{S}\Lambda_1$, and, inductively, $\Lambda_\alpha = \mathfrak{D}\left(\bigcup_{\beta<\alpha} \mathfrak{S}\Lambda_\beta\right)$, for any ordinal number α.

The set $D_\alpha(x)$ is called the αth *prolongation* of x and $\Lambda_\alpha(x)$ is called the αth *prolongational limit set* of x. It is clear that, for each ordinal number α, $\Lambda_\alpha(x) \subset D_\alpha(x)$; indeed, it can be shown that $D_\alpha(x) = \gamma^+(x) \cup \Lambda_\alpha(x)$ (reference 1, lemma 4). If $\beta < \alpha$, then $D_\beta(x) \subset D_\alpha(x)$, $\Lambda_\beta(x) \subset \Lambda_\alpha(x)$, and for a sufficiently large ordinal α, $D_\lambda = D_\alpha$ and $\Lambda_\lambda = \Lambda_\alpha$ whenever $\lambda \geq \alpha$ (reference 2, theorem 3).

As we shall presently indicate, the prolongations D_α are related to stability and the prolongational limit sets Λ_α to recurrence. Therefore, at this point, we recall some of the stability and recurrence notions which have occurred in the study of dynamical systems.[6]

Let M denote a compact invariant subset of X. (By invariant we mean that if $x \in M$, then $xt \in M$, for all $t \in T$.)

M is said to be *Liapunov stable*, if, for every neighborhood W of M, there is a neighborhood U of M such that $\gamma^+(U) \subset W$.

M is said to be an attractor if there is a neighborhood W of M such that if $x \in W$, $d(xt, M) \longrightarrow 0$ as $t \longrightarrow \infty$.

(If we define the *positive* or *omega limit set of* x as the set $\Lambda_0(x)$ of all y in X such that $xt_n \longrightarrow y$, for some sequence $t_n \longrightarrow \infty$, then it is easy to see that M is an attractor if and only if $\Lambda_0(x)$ is a non-empty subset of M, for each $x \in W$.)

If M is both an attractor and Liapunov stable, we say that M is *asymptotically stable.*

Let $x \in X$. Then x is said to be *recurrent* (or *Poisson stable*) if $x \in \Lambda_0(x)$ (that is, there is a sequence $t_n \longrightarrow \infty$ such that $xt_n \longrightarrow x$). We say that x is *nonwandering* if for every neighborhood U of x there is a sequence $t_n \longrightarrow \infty$ such that $Ut_n \cap U \neq \phi$.

Now, it is immediate that x is nonwandering if and only if $x \in \Lambda_1(x)$, and it is not difficult to show that the compact set M is Liapunov stable if and only if $D_1(M) = M$. Motivated by these remarks, we define the compact invariant set M to be *stable of order* α (or simply α *stable*) if $D_\alpha(M) = M$, and the point $x \in X$ to be *recurrent of order* α if $x \in \Lambda_\alpha(x)$.

Thus, Liapunov stability and nonwandering take their places in this scheme as, respectively, stability and recurrence of order 1. Indeed, invariance may be regarded as stability of order 0, and Poisson stability as recurrence of order 0. However, it is not in general the case that $\Lambda_1 = \mathfrak{D}\mathfrak{S}\Lambda_0$.

The compact invariant set $\mathfrak{M}$ is said to be *absolutely stable* if it is stable of every order α, and the point x is called a *generalized recurrent point* if it is α recurrent for some ordinal number α. The set of generalized recurrent points will be denoted by $\mathfrak{R}$.

Generalized recurrence is closely connected with the continuous real valued functions defined on the space X. It can be shown that there is an $f \in C(X)$ such that, whenever $x \in \mathfrak{R}$ and $t \in T$, then $f(xt) = f(x)$, and if $x \notin \mathfrak{R}$ and $t > 0$, then $f(xt) < f(x)$ (reference 1, theorem 2).

These notions of stability and recurrence are discussed at length in reference 2, pages 244–248, and in reference 1. In these references examples are constructed which show that different ordinal numbers give rise to essentially different concepts of stability and recurrence. (For example, Liapunov stability does not imply stability of order 2, and stability of order n for every positive integer n does not imply absolute stability.)

Consider, now, the following conditions on a compact invariant set M:

a) M is Liapunov stable,

b) M is an attractor,

c) There is a neighborhood U of M such that $U-M$ contains no generalized recurrent points.

First, observe that these conditions are independent. A center in the plane satisfies (a) but not (b) or (c); an interesting example in reference 5 satisfies (b) but not (a) or (c); and a saddle point in the plane satisfies (c), but not (a) or (b).

However, when we combine any two of these conditions, the situation changes.

Conditions (a) and (b) imply (c): By theorem 4 of reference 3, there is a neighborhood U of M such that $\Lambda_1(U) \subset M$. It follows by an easy induction that $\Lambda_\alpha(U) \subset M$ for all ordinals α. Thus if $x \in U-M$, it is impossible for $x \in \Lambda_\alpha(x)$.

Conditions (a) and (c) imply (b): Let W be a compact invariant neighborhood of M which is contained in U, and let $x \in W-M$. Then $\Lambda_0(x)$ is a non-empty subset of W. Since an omega limit point is always nonwandering, and therefore in $\mathfrak{R}$, it follows from (c) that $\Lambda_0(x) \subset M$. This is a generalization of theorem 5 in reference 1.

It is not in general true that (b) and (c) imply (a). Consider, for example a dynamical system on the non-negative real numbers with singular points at 0 and 1. There are two other orbits, one linking the singular points and tending to 0 as $t \longrightarrow \infty$, and the other consisting of all $x > 1$, tending to 1 as $t \longrightarrow \infty$. Let $M = \{0, 1\}$. Then M is an attractor, and $\mathcal{R} = M$, but M is obviously not stable.

However, if we suppose, in addition to (b) and (c), that for every $x \in M$ there is an ordinal number α such that $D_\alpha(x) \supset M$, then (a) holds. For, let $f \in C(X)$ such that $f(xt) < f(x)$ for $x \notin \mathcal{R}$ and $t > 0$ and $f(xt) = f(x)$ for $x \in \mathcal{R}$, $t \in T$. If $x, x' \in M$, then $x \in D_\alpha(x')$, $x' \in D_\beta(x)$, and, by lemma 6 of reference 1, $f(x) = f(x')$. That is, f is constant on M. We may suppose $f = 0$ on M. Since M is an attractor, if $y \in U\text{–}M$, $f(y) > 0$. Now, let $x \in M$ and $y \in D_1(x)$. It follows easily that $f(y) \leq f(x) = 0$, so $y \in M$. That is, M is Liapunov stable.

Note that if M is a singular point, a periodic orbit, or, more generally, a minimal set, then the discussion just concluded tells us that (b) and (c) imply (a).

Until now, our considerations have been primarily local, that is, we have studied the dynamical system in the neighborhood of a singular point or a compact invariant set. An interesting assumption of a global nature is that the recurrent set $\mathcal{R}$ is empty. As we have seen, this is equivalent to the existence of a continuous real valued function f on X such that $f(xt) < f(x)$, for all $x \in X$ and $t > 0$.

Although this is obviously a very restrictive condition, dynamical systems of this type are at present not classified. However, an important subclass of these systems may be characterized in several equivalent ways.

Theorem. The following conditions on a dynamical system (X, T) are equivalent:

(1) It is *parallelizable*; that is, there is a closed set S in X and a homeomorphism h of X onto $S \times T$ such that, if $x \in S$ $t \in T$, then $h(xt) = (x, t)$.

(2) It is *dispersive*; that is, $\Lambda_1(x) = \phi$, for all $x \in X$.

(3) The generalized recurrent set $\mathcal{R} = \phi$, and for some $f \in C(X)$ with $f(xt) < f(x)$, $(x \in X,\ t > 0)$ there is a real number c such that $f^{-1}(c)$ meets every orbit.

(4) There are no singular points or periodic orbits, and $D_1(x) = \gamma^+(x)$, for all $x \in X$.

Proof. The equivalence of (1) and (2) is the main theorem in reference 4. It is trivial that (1) implies (3). If (3) holds, let $S = f^{-1}(c)$, and it follows easily that S satisfies the conditions of (1). The implication (2) $\Longrightarrow$ (4) follows from the representation $D_1(x) = \gamma^+(x) \cup \Lambda_1(x)$, and the fact that singular and periodic points are recurrent. Finally, suppose (4) holds. We prove (2). If, for some $x \in X$, $\Lambda_1(x) \neq \phi$, then $\Lambda_1(x) \subset D_1(x) = \gamma^+(x)$, and $\gamma^+(x)$ contains a non-empty invariant set (see reference 1, lemma 2). But then $\gamma^+(x)$ must be singular or periodic, and this contradicts (4).*

A few comments on this theorem are in order. The flows discussed here are evidently the simplest dynamical systems; (1) says that for such systems the space X is of the form $S \times T$, and T acts on X by translation on the second coordinate. Now, (2) and (4) tell us that these systems are also the simplest from

*The proof of this implication was communicated to me by Darrel Desbrow.

the point of view of the prolongations and the prolongational limit sets; these sets are as small as possible. (An easy induction shows that $D_\alpha(x) = \gamma^+(x)$ and $\Lambda_\alpha(x) = \phi$, for every ordinal number α.) This lends support to the feeling that the study of prolongations and prolongational limit sets is appropriate for the classification of dynamical systems.

We call dynamical systems for which $\mathcal{R} = \phi$ *almost dispersive*. Condition (3) in the preceding theorem shows that dispersive flows are almost dispersive. The converse is not true; a counter-example is provided by an improper saddle point (see reference 1, p. 72).

The next lemma applies to any dynamical system.

Lemma. Let $x \in X$ such that $\Lambda_1(x)$ is non-empty and compact. Then $\Lambda_0(x)$ is non-empty.

Proof. Let K be a compact set containing x and $\Lambda_1(x)$ in its interior. Let $x_n \longrightarrow x$, $t_n \longrightarrow \infty$, such that $x_n t_n \longrightarrow y \in \Lambda_1(x)$. We may suppose that x_n and $x_n t_n$ are in the interior of K. If $\gamma^+(x_n) \subset K$ for infinitely many n, then $\gamma^+(x) \subset K$ and $\Lambda_0(x) \neq \phi$. If, for some subsequence of $\{x_n\}$ (which we still denote by $\{x_n\}$) there are $s_n \longrightarrow \infty$ such that $x_n s_n \in \partial K$ (the boundary of K), then (a subsequence of) $x_n s_n \longrightarrow z \in \partial K$ and this contradicts $\Lambda_1(x) \subset$ interior K. The only remaining possibility is: there is a $T > 0$ and $0 < s_n < T$ such that $x_n s_n \in \partial K$, and $x_n t \in K$ for $t > s_n$. It follows that $xt \in K$ for $t \geq T$, and $\Lambda_0(x) \neq \phi$.

Now let (X, T) be an almost dispersive flow, and let $f \in C(X)$ such that f is strictly decreasing along every orbit. Let $f^*(x) = \lim_{t \to \infty} f(xt)$. Then f^* is an invariant function but is not, in general, continuous. However, since f^* is a pointwise limit of a sequence of continuous functions, it is continuous outside of a first category set. The next lemma relates the continuity of f^* with the first prolongational limit set.

Lemma. If f^* is continuous at x, then $\Lambda_1(x) = \phi$.

Proof. If $y \in \Lambda_1(x)$, it is easy to see that $f(y) \leq f(x)$. Now, if $t, \tau \in T$ then $y\tau \in \Lambda_1(xt)$ (see reference, 1 lemma 3); so, if $\tau > 0$, then $f(y) < f(y(-\tau)) \leq f(xt)$. Letting $t \longrightarrow \infty$, we obtain $f(y) < f^*(x)$. Now, there are sequences $x_n \longrightarrow x$, $t_n \longrightarrow \infty$ such that $x_n t_n \longrightarrow y$. Then $f^*(x_n) < f(x_n t_n)$, and, by continuity of f and and f^*, $f^*(x) \leq f(y)$, which contradicts $f(y) < f^*(x)$.

Our final result tells us that in almost dispersive dynamical systems "most" prolongational limit sets are empty, and those which are not are "long and thin."

Theorem. Let (X, T) be almost dispersive. Then:

(1) If $x \in X$, interior $\Lambda_1(x) = \phi$.

(2) $\Lambda_1(x) = \phi$ except for x in a first category set.

(3) If $\Lambda_1(x) \neq \phi$, it is not compact.

Proof. Suppose y is an interior point of $\Lambda_1(x)$. Let $x_n \longrightarrow x$, $t_n \longrightarrow \infty$ such that $x_n t_n \longrightarrow y$. For n sufficiently large, $x_n t_n \in \Lambda_1(x)$, and, since $\Lambda_1(x)$ is invariant, $x_n \in \Lambda_1(x)$. But $\Lambda_1(x)$ is closed, so $x \in \Lambda_1(x)$. That is, $x \in \mathcal{R}$. This is a contradiction, and (1) is proved. The other assertions follow easily from the last two lemmas.

REFERENCES

1. J. Auslander, "Generalized Recurrence in Dynamical Systems," *Contributions to Differential Equations*, III, 1, 65–74 (1964).

2. J. Auslander and P. Seibert, "Prolongations and Stability in Dynamical Systems," *Ann. Inst. Fourier*, XIV, 237–268 (1964).

3. J. Auslander, N. P. Bhatia, and P. Seibert, "Attractors in Dynamical Systems," *Bol. Soc. Mat. Mexicana*, to appear.

4. J. Dugundji and H. A. Antosiewicz, "Parallelizable Flows and Liapunov's Second Method," *Ann. Math*, **73**, 543–55 (1961).

5. P. Mendelson, "On unstable attractors," *Bol. Soc. Mat. Mexicana*, **5**, 270–76 (1960).

6. V. V. Nemytskiĭ and V. V. Stepanov, *Qualitative Theory of Differential Equations* (Princeton, N. J: Princeton University Press, 1960).

DIRECTION AND INSTRUCTION-CONTROLLED MACHINES

Calvin C. Elgot
IBM Thomas J. Watson Research Center
Yorktown Heights, N. Y.

A gross classification of deterministic discrete machines will be introduced and discussed. Special attention will be given to machines which may be said to be instruction controlled. Both idealized digital computers and Turing machines exemplify the discussion.

INTRODUCTION

Informal discussions concerning machines have an intuitive appeal which often vanishes when the notions are formalized. This unfortunate state of affairs may in part be intrinsic to formalization. But we believe it is also partly due to choosing, as a formal notion of machine, any of various ad hoc objects which can serve as descriptions of machines. Besides being unpleasant, this circumstance tends to blur distinctions between the essential and inessential.

Since this symposium is concerned in the main with continuous, as opposed to discrete, phenomena it does not seem inappropriate to restrict our remarks to exploring certain notions in an attempt to augment the palatability and the coherence of certain aspects of the theory of discrete machines. Many of the notions we use are borrowed from reference 1.

1. DETERMINISTIC DISCRETE MACHINES

By a deterministic discrete machine shall be meant an object M which has associated with it a set Σ of objects called *states*. At any instant t of time the machine M is in a particular state $\sigma \epsilon \Sigma$ and under the influence of an *environment* which at any instant t is in a certain state $e \epsilon E$. The future behavior of the machine, i.e., the state of the machine for all $t' \geqslant t$, is determined by its state at time t and the future history of states of the environment. The machine M also has associated with it a function ν_M, called the *direct transition function*, from $\Sigma \times E$ into Σ. If at time t machine M is in state σ and the environment is in state e, then, by definition, at time $t + 1$ the state of the machine is $\nu_M(\sigma, e)$. In any physical realization of the machines under discussion, however, it may well be the case that the interval of physical time between successive states σ and $\nu_M(\sigma, e)$ is variable. Indeed, in the physical situation, one is tempted to regard a

Presented at the Symposium on System Theory
Polytechnic Institute of Brooklyn, April 20, 21, 22, 1965

machine as being in a certain state at every instant of time t, where t is a real number. There are, however, only certain distinguished instants of time at which the states are "relevant." The mathematical notions we discuss take cognizance only of these distinguished instants of time which are then "renumbered": 0, 1, 2, 3, ...

2. THE STABLE STATE FUNCTION OF AN AUTONOMOUS MACHINE

At this level of analysis, then, a machine M is specified by sets Σ, E finite or infinite, and a function ν_M of $\Sigma \times E$ into Σ. The *transition function* is a function from $\Sigma \times F(E)$ into Σ, where $F(E)$ is the set of all finite sequences of elements of E including the null sequence Λ, defined inductively from ν_M as follows:

$$\nu_M^*(\sigma, \Lambda) = \sigma, \quad \nu_M^*(\sigma, ue) = \nu_M(\nu_M^*(\sigma, u), e).$$

Here ue is the finite sequence $(e_0, e_1, \ldots, e_{n-1}, e)$ if u is the finite sequence $(e_0, e_1, \ldots, e_{n-1})$. Then $\nu_M^*(\sigma, u) = \sigma'$ may be interpreted as saying: if machine M is in state σ at time t_0, and at time t, if $t_0 \leq t < t_0 + n$, the state of the environment is e_i, then at time $t_0 + n$ the state of M is σ'.

If $E = \{e\}$, that is, the state of the environment is fixed, we call the machine *autonomous*. In this case, we may (and we do) regard the direct transition function as a function from Σ into Σ and the transition function, a function from $\Sigma \times N$ into Σ, where N is the set of non-negative integers. The defining equations for ν_M^* then become:

$$\nu_M^*(\sigma, 0) = \sigma, \quad \nu_M^*(\sigma, n+1) = \nu_M(\nu_M^*(\sigma, n)).$$

In the case of an autonomous machine M, we call the infinite sequence $\nu_M^*(\sigma, 0)$, $\nu_M^*(\sigma, 1)$, $\nu_M^*(\sigma, 2)$, ... a computation of M; it is the computation of M determined by σ. A state σ of M is *stable* with respect to M if $\nu_M(\sigma) = \sigma$, and the computation of M determined by σ is *successful* if there exists an n such that $\nu_M^*(\sigma, n)$ is stable. It is immediately verifiable that a computation of M has at most one stable state. If $\nu_M^*(\sigma, n)$ is stable, we define $M^\dagger(\sigma) = \nu_M^*(\sigma, n)$; this is well-defined by the preceding remark; $M^\dagger$ is a function from Σ into Σ which is defined on σ if and only if the computation of M determined by σ is successful. We call $M^\dagger$ the *stable state function* of M.

3. FINITE AUTOMATA

The theory of *finite automata* concerns itself with the case that the set Σ and (less essentially) the set E are finite. If $\sigma \in \Sigma$, $\Delta \subseteq \Sigma$, the set $\mathfrak{T}(M, \sigma, \Delta)$ consisting of those $u \in F(E)$ such that $\nu_M^*(\sigma, u) \in \Delta$ is the set of words *recognized* by $\langle M, \sigma, \Delta \rangle$. The theory of finite automata studies, among other things, the structure of the class of all such sets. An alternative point of view replaces Δ by a function, called an output function, defined on $\Sigma \times E$ (or on Σ) with values in some set, say O. One then considers the function from input sequences (elements of $F(E)$) to "induced" output sequences, instead of recognition. The finite automation specializes to a *two-valued sequential circuit* if $\Sigma = \{a, b\}^n$, $E = \{a, b\}^p$ for some non-negative integers n, p, where a, b are arbitrary distinct objects. The direct transition function of the finite automaton can then be expressed by an n-tuple of Boolean polynomials (or expressions of the propositional calculus) in $n + p$ variables.

4. MACHINE SPECIES

The notion of deterministic discrete machine seems to be too general for fruitful study without some kind of restriction. One fruitful type of restriction has been indicated immediately above. The main subject of this note involves, however, a constraint of an entirely different character.

Let two non-empty sets K and C be given. To suggest the motivation, call the first set *memory states* and the second, *control states* or *instruction* (*respectively direction*) *locations*. By an *instruction* with respect to $\langle K, C \rangle$, we understand a function defined on all of $K \times C$ with values in $K \times C$. By a direction with respect to $\langle K, C \rangle$, we understand a function defined on all of K with values in $K \times C$. (The word "direction" is taken from reference 2.) Let D (respectively I) be a non-empty set of directions (respectively instructions) with respect to $\langle K, C \rangle$. By a *table of directions* (*respectively instructions*) *over* D (respectively I), we mean a function T defined on a finite subset C_T of C with values which are elements of D (respectively I) such that every value of T takes K (respectively $K \times C_T$) into $K \times C_T$. With each table of directions T (respectively instructions), we associate a function ν_T, whose domain of definition is $K \times C_T$ and whose values are also elements of $K \times C_T$, as follows:

$$\nu_T(k, c) = d(k), \quad \text{where} \quad c \in C_T \quad \text{and} \quad d = T(c)$$

(respectively $\nu_T(k, c) = i(k, c)$ where $c \in C_T$ and $i = T(c)$). Thus, $K \times C_T$ may be taken as the states of an autonomous machine whose direct transition function is ν_T. Indeed, it is convenient to *identify the machine with its direct transition function* so that ν_T is a machine. We understand the notion of function in such a way that ν_T determines $K \times C_T$ and, therefore, also K and C_T. A class $\mathfrak{M}$ of autonomous machines will be called *direction-controlled* (respectively *instruction-controlled*) if there exist non-empty sets K, C and a non-empty set D (respectively I) of directions (respectively instructions) with respect to $\langle K, C \rangle$ such that M equals the class of all ν_T, where T varies through all tables of directions (respectively instructions) over D (respectively I). We also speak of such a class $\mathfrak{M}$ as a species of direction-controlled (respectively instruction-controlled) machine or briefly, a *machine species*. (This notion evolved from an earlier one for which the same name was used and which was intended to capture the same intuitive idea.) It is clear that any set D (respectively I) of directions (respectively instructions) with respect to some non-empty sets $\langle K, C \rangle$ determines a machine species, *viz.* the class $\{\nu_T | T = \text{a table of directions (respectively instructions) over } D \text{ (respectively I)}\}$.

It is easy to see that if a class $\mathfrak{M}$ of machines is direction-controlled, then it is instruction-controlled. Indeed, if T is a table of directions over D and $D^\square$ is the set of all instructions $d^\square$, $d \in D$, defined by $d^\square(k, c) = d(k)$, $k \in K$, $c \in C$, and if $T^{\square}$ is the table of instructions defined by $T^{\square}(c') = (T(c'))^{\square}$, where $c' \in C_T$, then $T^{\square}$ is a table of instructions over $D^{\square}$ and $\nu_T = \nu_{T^{\square}}$.

On the other hand, it is *not* the case that if $\mathfrak{M}$ is instruction-controlled, it is direction controlled. Indeed, if $\mathfrak{M}$ consists of all restrictions of the identity function on $K \times C$ to $K \times C_f$, where C_f runs through all finite subsets of C, and C has more than one element, then $\mathfrak{M}$ is instruction-controlled but not direction-controlled.

Under reasonable conditions, distinct sets of directions determine distinct species. More specifically, let $\mathfrak{M}(D)$ be the species determined by D and let $\mathfrak{J}(D)$ be the set of all tables of direction over D, then: if $\mathfrak{M}(D) \subseteq \mathfrak{M}(D')$ and $Q(D)$ holds, where

$Q(D)$ = for every $d \in D$, there exist c, T, $c \in C_T$, $T \in \mathfrak{J}(D)$, such that $T(c) = d$,

then $D \subseteq D'$.

Thus, if $\mathfrak{M}(D) = \mathfrak{M}(D')$ and $Q(D)$ and $Q(D')$ hold, then $D = D'$. An *exit* of d is an element $c \in C$ such that $d(k) = \langle k', c \rangle$ for some k, $k' \in K$. Notice that $Q(D)$ holds if and only if for each $d \in D$, the set of exits of d is finite. A related point: if T, T' are tables over D and $\nu_T = \nu_{T'}$, then $T = T'$.

An analogous result does *not* hold in case of instructions rather than directions. For, if $I = D^{\square}$, where D is the set of Post directions described in the next section, and if $i(u \longrightarrow bv, n) = \langle u \longrightarrow 0v, n+1 \rangle$, then $i \notin I$ and $\mathfrak{M}(I) = \mathfrak{M}(I \cup \{i\})$.

The following remark indicates the broadness of the machine species notion. If $\mathfrak{M}$ is a class of machines and K a non-empty set, and if for each $M \in \mathfrak{M}$, the set of states of $\mathfrak{M}$ is $K \times f_{\mathfrak{M}}$, where $f_{\mathfrak{M}}$ is some finite set, then $\mathfrak{M}$ is included in some machine species.

5. POST SPECIES

We give an example of a machine species based upon the formulation of E. L. Post[2] of what is usually called a Turing machine (after A. M. Turing[3]). Turing's formulation, though somewhat similar to Post's, is rather more complicated; hence our preference here for Post's. Take the set K of memory states of a Post species to be the set of strings on the alphabet $\{0, 1, \longrightarrow\}$ of the form: $u \longrightarrow v$, where u, v are strings (possibly null) on the alphabet $\{0, 1\}$. The set C of control states is taken as the positive integers. For example, $\langle 100 \longrightarrow 01, 5 \rangle$ is a state of the Post species. (This state "corresponds" to the instantaneous description $S_1 S_0 S_0 q_5 S_0 S_1$ of reference 4.) The Post directions are described by the following formulas, where $a, b \in \{0, 1\}$, m, n are positive integers and u, v are strings on $\{0, 1\}$:

$R^n(u \longrightarrow av) = \langle (ua \longrightarrow v), n \rangle$,
$R^n(u \longrightarrow\,) = \langle u0 \longrightarrow\,), n \rangle$, (move right);
$L^n(ua \longrightarrow v) = \langle (u \longrightarrow av), n \rangle$,
$L^n(\,\longrightarrow v) = \langle (\,\longrightarrow 0v), n \rangle$, (move left);
$P^n_a(u \longrightarrow bv) = \langle (u \longrightarrow av), n \rangle$, (this is a modification of Post's "mark" and "erase" which are not always "applicable");
$J^{m,n}(u \longrightarrow 0v) = \langle (u \longrightarrow 0v), m \rangle$,
$J^{m,n}(u \longrightarrow 1v) = \langle (u \longrightarrow 1v), n \rangle$, (depending upon whether the scanned square is marked or not, follow direction n or m).

Post has a "stop" direction as well. We can achieve the effect of Post's "stop" by three directions which in effect determines whether the scanned square is 0 or 1; if it is 0 (respectively I) the machine then repeatedly prints 0 (respectively I) in that square. (In the case of tables of instructions, the effect of a "stop" can always be achieved by an identity instruction.)

The Post species is then the class of all ν_T where T varies through all tables of Post directions.

6. PARTIAL OPERATIONS OF INITIALIZED TABLES

The formulation of "Turing machines" given in reference 4* also admits a description as a machine species. The species (call it the Davis species) is determined by a set of "Davis" directions, (see reference 5, p. 127, 8). The Davis species properly includes the Post species, assuming the memory states of the Davis species are the same as in the Post species. Yet there is a sense in which both species are equivalent. To make clear what this sense is, we require additional notions.

By an operation on a set K, we mean a function on K, with values in K defined on all elements of K. If the function on K is not necessarily everywhere defined, it is called a *partial operation*. If T is a *table of operations* (respectively instructions), and $c \in C_T$, we define $[T, c]\,(k) = \nu_T^{\dagger}(\sigma)$, where $\sigma = \langle k, c\rangle$ and $\nu_T^{\dagger}$ is the stable state function of the machine ν_T. We call the ordered pair $\langle T, c\rangle$ an *initialized table*. If $[T, c]\,(k) = \langle k', c'\rangle$, we define $[T, c]^1\,(k) = k'$; $[T, c]^1$ is the partial operation on K defined by (determined by, associated with) the initialized table $\langle T, c\rangle$. The Post and Davis species are equivalent in the sense that the class of partial operations $[T, c]^1$ defined by initialized tables $\langle T, c\rangle$ is the same. More explicitly, for every initialized table $\langle T, c\rangle$ of Davis instructions, there is an initialized table $\langle T', c'\rangle$ of Post directions such that $[T, c]^1 = [T', c']^1$ and (more trivially) vice versa.

7. CELLULAR SPECIES AND MACHINES

If the set K of memory states of a machine species M with states $K \times C$ is a subset of B^A (= the set of all total functions from A into B), we call M a *cellular species*, and the elements of K content functions. Similarly, if the set of states of a single machine M is $K \times C$ and $K \subseteq B^A$, we call M cellular, so that the elements of a cellular species are cellular. If h is a total function from B into directions (respectively instructions) with respect to $\langle K, C\rangle$, call h a direction-coding (respectively instruction-coding) function, and let "h_b" denote the application of h to b. If T is a function defined on a finite subset of C with values in B, and if T_h, defined by $T_h\,(c) = h_{T(c)}$, is a table of directions (respectively instructions), then T is a *table of h-codes*, and we correlate with T and h, the machine we correlate with T_h, i.e., $\nu_{T,h}$ is defined to be ν_{T_h} and the domain of definition of this function is $K \times C_T$.

If, moreover, $C_T \subseteq A$ and $T(c) = k(c)$ for all $c \in C_T$, then we say that *k holds T*

*Following E. L. Post, "Recursive Unsolvability of a Problem of Thue," *J. Symbolic Logic*, 1947.

or that T *is stored in* k. If T is a table of h-codes, where h is direction-coding (respectively instruction-coding), if T is stored in k and $c \in C_T$, then $\nu_{T,h}(k,c) = h_{k(c)}(k)$ (respectively $= h_{k(c)}(k,c)$). These considerations suggest inquiring whether there is a reasonable notion of a single machine being direction-controlled (respectively instruction-controlled).

We entertain the following notions. Call a machine M (= the direct transition function of M) *direction-controlled* (respectively *instruction-controlled*) if M is cellular with states $K \times C$, $K \subseteq B^A$, if $C \subseteq A$, and if there exists a total function $h: B \longrightarrow D$ (respectively $h: B \longrightarrow I$), where D (respectively I) is a set of directions (respectively instructions) with respect to $\langle K, C \rangle$, such that for all $k \in K$, $c \in C$, $M(k,c) = h_{k(c)}(k)$ (respectively $= h_{k(c)}(k,c)$).

Let M be an arbitrary cellular machine, with $C \subseteq A$. Suppose M is direction-controlled. Then for all $k \in K$, $c_1, c_2 \in C$,

$$k(c_1) = k(c_2) \Longrightarrow M(k,c_1) = M(k,c_2).$$

Moreover, it this condition holds, then M is direction-controlled, for one may define $h_b(k) = M(k,c)$, where $k(c) = b$, and define $h_b(k)$ arbitrarily if no such c exists. While M may fail to be direction-controlled, there may nevertheless be some b's in B which can serve as direction codes. Let Code B be the set of $b \in B$ satisfying for all $k \in K$, $c_1, c_2 \in C$,

$$k(c_1) = b = k(c_2) \Longrightarrow M(k,c_1) = M(k,c_2).$$

Consider the class of computations

$$\langle k_0, c_0 \rangle, \langle k_1, c_1 \rangle, \ldots, \langle k_i, c_i \rangle, \ldots$$

of M, where $k_i(c_i) \in$ Code B for each i. Then this class of computations may be said to be direction-controlled in the sense that there is a function h defined on Code B with values which are directions with respect to $\langle K, C \rangle$ such that every computation $\langle k_0, c_0 \rangle, \langle k_1, c_1 \rangle, \ldots, \langle k_i, c_i \rangle, \ldots$ in this class satisfies $h_{k_i(c_i)}(k_i) = \langle k_{i+1}, c_{i+1} \rangle$ for each i. If $c_i = c_j \Longrightarrow k_i(c_i) = k_j(c_j)$, and $\{c_0, c_1, \ldots\}$ is finite, then the given computation is determined by $\nu_{T,h}$ and $\langle k_0, c_0 \rangle$, where $T(c_i) = k_i(c_i)$.

On the other hand, every cellular machine M with $C \subseteq A$ is instruction controlled! For, if $h_b = M$ for all $b \in B$, then $M(k,c) = h_{k(c)}(k,c)$ for all $k \in K$, $c \in C$. If one restricts oneself, however, to instructions with certain properties, the notion may escape degeneracy. For example, not every such machine is controlled by location independent[1] instructions.

REFERENCES

1. C. C. Elgot and A. Robinson, "Random-Access Stored-Program Machines, An Approach to Programming Languages," *J. Assoc. Comp. Mach.* **11**, 365–399 (1964).

2. E. L. Post, "Finite Combinatory Processes–Formulation I," *J. Symbolic Logic*, 1936, pp. 103–105.

3. A. M. Turing, "On Computable Numbers, with an Application to the Entscheidungs Problem," *Proc. London Math. Soc.*, **42**, Sect. 2 (1936–37).

4. M. Davis, *Computability and Unsolvability* (New York: McGraw-Hill, 1958).

5. C. C. Elgot, "A Perspective View of Discrete Automata and Their Design," *Amer. Math. Monthly*, **72**, 2, Part II, 125–134 (February 1965).

COMPUTABILITY

Martin Davis*

Belfer Graduate School of Science, Yeshiva University, New York, N. Y.

Turing's mathematical formulation of the notation of automatic computing machines is now embedded in a substantial body of mathematical theory. This theory may be thought of as the mathematics of what actual computers can do when one abstracts from considerations of space and time. It has been argued that physical computers must operate within limits imposed by just such practical considerations, and that, therefore, their mathematics is rather the theory of finite automata. However, it is maintained that just because the boundaries (though definite) are vaguely defined, Turing's theory is, in many cases, the appropriate conceptualization of computers.

I was asked to present an introduction to computability theory, and so I shall avoid technicalities. Computability theory has to do with computations in which limitations of space and time are permitted to play no role. That is, one regards the notion of computation in such an unrealistic way that one is prepared to countenance computations that may take any length of time no matter how large, and is willing to use unlimited amounts of storage, or, more accurately, any finite amount of storage not predetermined.

So computability is an abstract mathematical notion rather than a practical or an engineering notion. For the purpose of developing some of the results of computability theory, let us consider machines of the kind shown in Fig. 1.

We assume that the input to the machine is a positive integer (say as a sequence of decimal digits or binary digits, it doesn't matter), and that once this input has entered the interior of the machine, certain deterministic operations, whose detailed nature will concern us not at all, take place. The result of these operations is that an answer "yes" or "no" is determined, and what we demand is that the machine be so constructed that no matter what integer one puts in there will always be a "yes" answer or a "no" answer determined. Then we ask that if the answer is "yes," the green bulb light up at the end of the computation, while if the answer is "no," the red bulb light up at the end of the computation. To say that the machine is deterministic means that if, say, the integer 59 is fed in today or tomorrow, exactly the same steps will occur inside the machine and the same one of the two bulbs will eventually light up. Such machines we call "red-light-green-light machines."

With each red-light-green-light machine there is a certain set of positive integers that we can associate with it, namely, the set S which consists of all n such that the machine lights up green when n is the input. Now suppose we reverse matters and, instead of starting with the machine, suppose we start with a certain set of integers (say, the set of even numbers or the set of perfect squares)

*Presently at Mathematics Department, New York University, New York, N. Y.

Presented at the Symposium on System Theory
Polytechnic Institute of Brooklyn, April 20, 21, 22, 1965

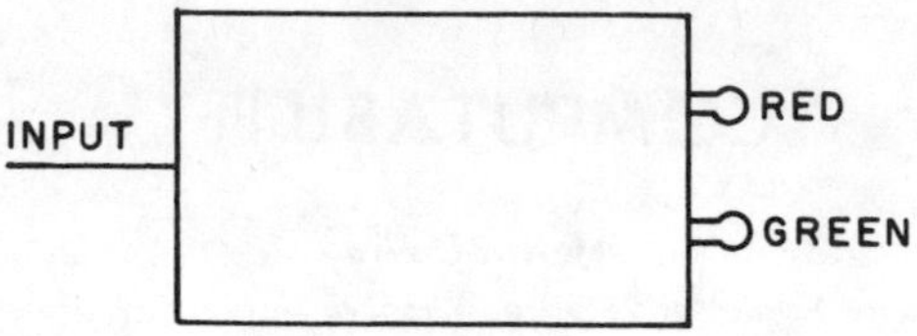

Figure 1.

and ask: can one build a red-light-green-light machine that does this job for that set? If one can, the set is called *computable* or *recursive*. So, a computable set is simply one for which we can build a red-light-green-light machine, which does this job for the set. It is easy to actually construct red-light-green-light machines for the even numbers, or the perfect squares, so that these sets are, in fact, computable.

Next we will discuss a different kind of machine—green-light machines. A green-light machine looks just like the other kind on the outside except that it has only one light bulb, a green light bulb (Fig. 2). Again, with each green-light machine we associate a set of integers; in fact we associate the set

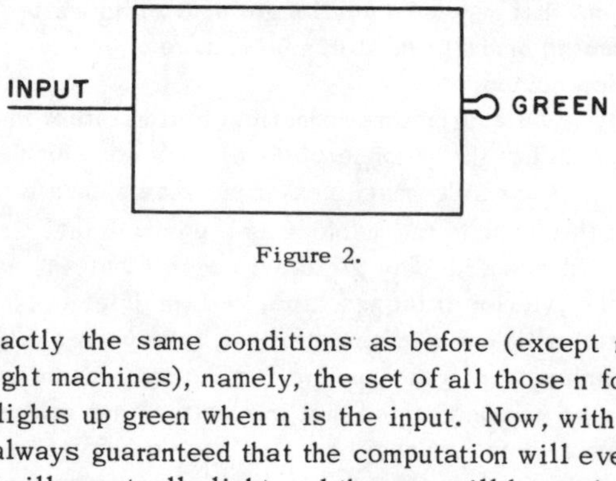

Figure 2.

determined by exactly the same conditions as before (except now with reference to green-light machines), namely, the set of all those n for which the machine eventually lights up green when n is the input. Now, with the first kind of machine you are always guaranteed that the computation will eventually come to a halt; the machine will eventually light and then we will know that the integer n belongs to the set. If, on the other hand, we put the integer 85 into a green-light machine and have been waiting 15 years and nothing has happened, it may be that if we are willing to wait another 15 years the machine will stop and the green light will light up telling us that 85 belongs to the set; it may also be that no matter how long we wait nothing will happen, that 85 doesn't belong to the set. (Heaven help us if the bulb burns out!)

Now, sets that are determined by machines of this kind are called *recursively enumerable;* so there are recursively enumerable sets of integers and recursive sets of integers. The recursive sets are determined by red-light–green-light machines, and the recursively enumerable sets by green-light machines, and there is an important and simple relationship between these notions which can be expressed in the following theorem:

S *is recursive if and only if* S *and* $\overline{S}$ *are both recursively enumerable.*

$\overline{S}$ simply means the complement of the set S, in other words the set of those integers which don't belong to S. If S is the set of even numbers, $\overline{S}$ is the set of odd numbers. On the intuitive heuristic basis that we are following here, it is very easy to see why this theorem is true. If you know that S is recursive, you have a red-light–green-light machine for it, and you are supposed to make from that a green-light machine for S and also a green-light machine for the complement of S. That is very easy to do: to make a green-light machine for S, you simply unscrew the red bulb. To make a green-light machine for the complement of S, you put the green bulb where the red one is now and leave the socket that used to have the green light in empty. What about the converse? Suppose there is a green-light machine for S and there is a green-light machine for the complement of S. How can we combine them into a red-light–green-light machine for S? Again, the answer is very easy: we first make a paralleling input device, so that if an integer n is input we make sure that it gets sent into each of the green-light machines. Secondly, we replace the green bulb in the machine for $\overline{S}$ by a red one. Now we are done, for any integer we start with will have to be found either in S or its complement, but not in both; so if an integer n is input to both of these machines, and both of the machines begin computing, then exactly one of them will come to a halt and light up the appropriate light. So it works just like a red-light–green-light machine should. That observation proves the theorem.

This theorem suggests the very obvious question: is every recursively enumerable set also recursive? Here the answer is "no"! One has the fundamental theorem:

There is a set K *which is recursively enumerable but not recursive, i.e., the complement of* K *is not recursively enumerable.*

In outlining the construction of a set K having these properties, I'll have to be even less rigorous than I have been so far, but the key ideas will be indicated. Let us agree that detailed descriptions of all possible green light machines are given in some standard form, e.g., a book written in the English language. So, for each green-light machine we can imagine that we have a certain book that tells how it is constructed, i.e., a customers' manual. Now, let us arrange to put all such customers' manuals for the green-light machines in a definite order, so there is a first book, a second book, a third book and so on. There are various ways in which this can be done in a systematic way; for example, we can just regard each book as being, as it were, a single word on an alphabet which consists of the ordinary English alphabet with small and capital letters and punctuation marks (including the space between words). So this great big book is just a very long word on this alphabet, and the books can be arranged in alphabetical order, as if they were entries in a dictionary. That means that all the recursively enumerable sets are also put in order; in general, S_n is the set determined by nth green-light machine in this order. Now the set K is simply the following set: K *is the set of* n *such that* n *belongs to* S_n. It consists of those integers n which happen to belong to the set determined by the nth green-light machine. Now, I claim that this set K is itself recursively enumerable. In order to see that this is true, I would have somehow to construct a green-light machine for determining the set K. While I cannot really do that, I can make it quite plausible that there is such a machine. This machine will consist of a man sitting on the inside (perhaps a wise old man, but a very obedient man, who does just what he is told). Now, let this man do the following: whenever an integer n is fed into him, he figures out which is the nth book of instructions, the nth customers' manual, by just using the alphabetical order. Then, once he has that book in front of him, he knows exactly how that machine works, and he simply does to the integer n exactly what the nth machine would have done. It is possible that in the process of doing that, he just goes on computing forever; well, that is all right: then he will never light his green light, and he shouldn't, because in that case n doesn't belong to S_n, and therefore n shouldn't belong to K. If, on the other hand, the computation ever does come to an end, the machine would light the green light; well, then the man lights his own green light. So the set K is recursively enumerable. On the other hand, K is not recursive, because the complement of K is not recursively enumerable, as it is very easy to see. For, suppose $\bar{K}$ were recursively enumerable; then $\bar{K} = S_k$ for some k. In that case, n belongs to $\bar{K}$, if and only if n belongs to S_k. Now, when does n belong to the complement of K? Answer: when it doesn't belong to S_n, because for n to belong to K means exactly that it belongs to the nth set, S_n. But, if we consider the possibility that n is equal to k, this is, in fact, an explicit impossibility: k belongs to S_k if and only if k doesn't belong to S_k.

Let me emphasize that in spite of the rather vague and off-hand flavor of all this, the fact is that it can all be made quite rigorous, definite and explicit at the expense of a certain amount of ugly detail; the underlying ideas are as they have been stated.

Now, what if anything does all this have to do with actual physical digital computers? In one sense very little; when once you say that the word computation is to involve no limit on the amount of time it takes nor on how much memory space it uses, you will immediately incur the impatience of practical computer people who are precisely concerned with such questions all the time. Yet there is something that one can say. Consider the following question: Everyone who has worked with actual electronic computers has faced, at one time or another, the situation of a program which he designed to do something but which, in fact, has its own ideas and is doing something different; and sometimes this rather different thing seems to involve an intention to continue computing forever. The machine is "looping." What does one mean when one says this? In fact, an actual machine can't compute forever; it is not even going to last forever. In other words, there is a sense, which is pretty clearly understood by everyone working with computers, in which these machines, if left to their own devices, as it were, would compute forever. This sense involves mentally replacing the actual machine with a mathematical abstraction which differs from the real machine in that it will follow its order code indefinitely, and that it won't ever make any mistakes. What is curious is that the statement that comes to a practical computer man's lips in this situation is the quite impractical statement, "Oh, the machine is executing an infinite 'loop'."

This is an instance of the familiar fact that it sometimes simplifies a problem, to regard it as infinite, even though it is in fact finite. One very often goes to the limit, because in the limit things become simpler and more satisfactory. For example, an actual computing machine has a definite bounded storage capacity: Is it the core? Or is it the tape? How many tapes, and what about punch cards?

In fact, if one examines an actual data processing system one sees that, while it certainly doesn't have unlimited storage, there really doesn't exist any definite integer that in some absolute sense is the maximum number of bits with which the machine can operate. Now, if we take this point of view towards computers, it may be advantageous to go to the limit and think of them as operating with indefinite time alloted and with indefinite storage alloted.

What is at issue emerges clearly in the following connection: Suppose one seeks a general algorithm for testing a given program, together with given input, to determine whether or not it will cause the machine to "loop." We would like to use such an algorithm as follows: we don't want to waste our time on a program that we know in advance is going to execute an infinite "loop," so we would first use our algorithm to test it and see whether or not the machine would execute an infinite "loop" if we ever started it. If it would, we would have better things to do with our time than to run it. However, *we can't have such an algorithm.* Why not? Because if we had such an algorithm we could do the following: We could begin with the set K which has a green-light machine associated with it. We could turn the mechanism of that green-light machine into a program and then, to find out whether an integer n belongs to the set K or not, all we would have to do is use this assumed algorithm and test the program for K, together with that particular integer n, to see whether or not there would be an infinite "loop." If not, we know that n really belongs to the set K, and if the answer is yes, we know that n belongs to the complement of K and so we could build a red light-green-light machine for the set K, if we had such an algorithm. Since K is not recursive, we know we can't build a red-light-green-light machine for the set K, so there can be no such algorithm. Of course, the fact remains that if you were really to specify a bounded memory capacity, this theorem would no longer be true and such an algorithm could be written; nevertheless, there is a sense in which something like this result is true of real machines. In fact, I have never heard of anyone actually sitting down and trying to write a practical algorithm to be used for this purpose.

ON SYSTEM MEASUREMENT AND IDENTIFICATION*

W. L. Root
University of Michigan, Ann Arbor, Mich.

Our concern in this paper is with systems for which it makes sense to talk about an input, x, and an output, y. The point of view is that the system is an ordinary or stochastic transformation between a domain of possible input functions and a range of output functions; that is, the system can be represented by an operator H (either ordinary or stochastic) such that $y = Hx$.

The first part of the paper is taken up with the definition of a fairly general class of systems, followed by a discussion of some elementary properties of these systems, particularly in connection with stochastic inputs. The latter part of the paper is devoted to some orientation on one of the basic kinds of system problem: the determination of an unknown system from a knowledge of outputs produced by certain inputs, i.e., the "identification problem." The treatment is abstract and not connected explicitly with any engineering problems; however, the author was led to the subject through problems in radio communication, which has given some bias to the discussion.

I. A CLASS OF SYSTEM OPERATORS

Let us denote the input to a system by x, the output by y, and the system operation by H, $y = Hx$. Any system to be discussed here can be represented in the form

$$\begin{aligned} y(t) = h_0(t) &+ \int h_1(t,s)x(s)ds \\ &+ \iint h_2(t,s_1,s_2)x(s_1)x(s_2)ds_1\,ds_2 \\ &+ \iiint h_3(t,s_1,s_2,s_3)\,x(s_1)\,x(s_2)\,x(s_3)\,ds_1\,ds_2\,ds_3 \\ &+ \cdots \end{aligned} \tag{1}$$

where $x(t)$, $y(t)$ and $h_n(t, s_1, \ldots, s_n)$ are real-valued functions or real-valued random functions (i.e., sample functions from stochastic processes). Most of the time, we shall be concerned with special subclasses of the class of all such systems. We note at the outset that

$$\int \cdots \int h_n(t,s_1,\ldots,s_n)x(s_1)\ldots x(s_n)ds_1\ldots ds_n = \int \cdots \int h_n(t,s_{i_1},\ldots,s_{i_n})x(s_1)\ldots x(s_n)ds_1\ldots ds_n$$

*This work was supported by the National Aeronautics and Space Administration under research grant NsG-2-59.

Presented at the Symposium on System Theory
Polytechnic Institute of Brooklyn, April 20, 21, 22, 1965

where $i_1, \ldots, i_n$ is any permutation of $1, 2, \ldots, n$. Consequently, h_n can always be replaced by its symmetrization

$$\tilde{h}_n(t, s_1, \ldots, s_n) = \frac{1}{n!} \sum h_n(t, s_{i_1}, \ldots s_{i_n}),$$

where the sum is over all permutations, without changing the value of the integral. Thus we may always assume $h_n(t, s_1, \ldots, s_n)$ is a symmetric function of the variables $s_1, \ldots, s_n$.

For convenience and because it is usually a reasonable assumption, we shall always require that $x(t)$ be of integrable square on every finite interval if it is a sure function, and that with probability one it be of integrable square on every finite interval if it is a sample from a stochastic process. If $x(t)$ is only defined on a finite interval $[a, b]$ and is of integrable square (in which case we write: $x(t)$ belongs to $L_2[a, b]$), then this condition is considered to be satisfied, as it is of course by the trivial extension of $x(t)$ to the entire real axis obtained by setting $x(t) = 0$ for $t < a$ or $t > b$. Again for convenience we shall always require, if h_n is a sure function, that

$$\int \cdots \int_{\Lambda} |h_n(t, s_1, \ldots, s_n)|^2 dt ds_1 \ldots ds_n < \infty \tag{2}$$

over any bounded $(n+1)$-dimensional rectangle Λ, and if h_n is a sample from a stochastic process, that (2) be satisfied with probability one. In case h_n is stochastic, it follows from the Fubini theorem that if

$$\int \cdots \int_{\Lambda} E|h_n(t, s_1, \ldots, s_n)|^2 dt ds_1 \ldots ds_n < \infty, \tag{3}$$

then (2) is satisfied with probability one. The notation $E(\xi)$ denotes the mathematical expectation of the random variable ξ.

For the moment let us take h_n to be a sure function and consider the (homogeneous polynomial) operator H_n defined by

$$y(t) = [H_n x](t) = \int_a^b \cdots \int_a^b h_n(t, s_1, \ldots, s_n) x(s_1) \ldots x(s_n) ds_1 \ldots ds_n, \qquad a \le t \le b, \tag{4}$$

where a and b are finite. If we denote the norm of an element of $L_2[a, b]$ by $\|\cdot\|$, then, by the Schwarz inequality,

$$\|y\|^2 \le \|x\|^{2n} \int_a^b \int_a^b \cdots \int_a^b |h_n(t, s_1, \ldots, s_n)|^2 dt ds_1 \ldots ds_n. \tag{5}$$

Furthermore, if $y = H_n x$ and $\eta = H_n \xi$,

$$\|y - \eta\|^2 \le \int_a^b \cdots \int_a^b |x(s_1) \ldots x(s_n) - \xi(s_1) \ldots \xi(s_n)|^2 ds_1 \ldots ds_n \times \int_a^b \int_a^b \cdots \int_a^b |h(t, s_1, \ldots, s_n)|^2 dt ds_1 \ldots ds_n. \tag{6}$$

Since

$$\begin{aligned}
&|x(s_1)\dots x(s_n) - \xi(s_1)\dots\xi(s_n)|^2\\
&\le [\,|x(s_1)\dots x(s_{n-1})|\;|x(s_n) - \xi(s_n)| + |x(s_1)\dots x(s_{n-2})\xi(s_n)|\\
&\quad |x(s_{n-1}) - \xi(s_{n-1})| + \dots + |\xi(s_2)\dots\xi(s_n)|\;|x(s_1) - \xi(s_1)|\,]^2\\
&\le 2n[\,|x(s_1)\dots x(s_{n-1})|^2|x(s_n) - \xi(s_n)|^2 + \dots\\
&\quad + |\xi(s_2)\dots\xi(s_n)|^2|x(s_1) - \xi(s_1)|^2]
\end{aligned}$$

one finds that the integral comprising the first factor of the right side of (6) is dominated by

$$\begin{aligned}
&2n\int_a^b\dots\int_a^b [\,|x(s_1)\dots x(s_{n-1})|^2|x(s_n) - \xi(s_n)|^2 + \dots\\
&\quad + |\xi(s_1)\dots\xi(s_{n-1})|^2|x(s_1) - \xi(s_1)|^2]\,ds_1\dots ds_n\\
&= 2n\{\|x\|^{2(n-1)}\|x - \xi\|^2 + \|x\|^{2(n-2)}\|\xi\|^2\|x - \xi\|^2\\
&\quad + \dots + \|\xi\|^{2(n-1)}\|x - \xi\|^2\}\\
&\le 2n^2\|x - \xi\|^2[\max(\|x\|, \|\xi\|)]^{2n-2}.
\end{aligned}$$

We now write

$$[\![H_n]\!]_n^2 = \int_a^b\int_a^b\dots\int_a^b |h_n(t, s_1, \dots, s_n)|^2 ds_1\dots ds_n dt, \tag{7}$$

which is finite by the condition (2). Then, from (6) and the above bound, we have

$$\|y - \eta\|^2 \le 2n^2 [\![H_n]\!]_n^2 \|x - \xi\|^2[\max(\|x\|, \|\xi\|)]^{2n-2}. \tag{8}$$

Thus H_n is a continuous operator on $L_2[a, b]$ in the sense that if

$$\lim_{k\to\infty} \|x_k - x\| = 0$$

then

$$\lim_{k\to\infty} \|H_n x_k - H_n x\| = 0.$$

$[\![H_n]\!]_n$ is a true norm for H_n, since it is just the L_2 norm of its kernel h_n as a function on $n + 1$-dimensional space. H_1 is of course a linear operator and is Hilbert-Schmidt, with Hilbert-Schmidt (*HS*) norm $[\![H_1]\!]_1$ (see Zaanen,[15] for a discussion of properties of *HS* operators).

Also the polynominal operator $H = H_1 + H_2 + \dots + H_N$, N finite, is a continuous operator on $L_2[a, b]$. In fact, if we put

$$y = y_1 + y_2 + \dots + y_N,$$
$$y_n = H_n x,\ n = 1, 2, \dots, N,$$

and

$$\eta = \eta_1 + \eta_2 + \dots + \eta_N,$$
$$\eta_n = H_n \xi,\ n = 1, 2, \dots, N,$$

then

$$\|y-\eta\|^2 = \left(\sum_1^N (y_n - \eta_n), \sum_1^N (y_m - \eta_m)\right)$$

$$= \sum_{n,m=1}^N (y_n - \eta_n, y_m - \eta_m) \le \sum_{n,m=1}^N \|y_n - \eta_n\| \, \|y_m - \eta_m\|$$

$$\le 2\|x - \xi\|^2 \sum_{n,m=1}^N nm[\max(\|x\|, \|\xi\|)]^{n+m-2} \, \|H_n\|_n \|H_m\|_m \quad (9)$$

From (9) it is clear that if $\|H_n\|_n \le$ constant not depending on n, then the infinite series $H = H_1 + H_2 + \ldots$ is a continuous operator on a closed bounded set for which $\|x\| \le \alpha$ for any α strictly less than 1.

Equation (4), which defines the operator H_n, can be written

$$y(t) = \int_{t-b}^{t-a} \cdots \int_{t-b}^{t-a} k_n(t, u_1, \ldots, u_n) x(t-u_1) \ldots x(t-u_n) du_1 \ldots du_n$$

$$a \le t \le b \quad (10)$$

where

$$k_n(t, u_1, \ldots, u_n) = h_n(t, t-u_1, \ldots, t-u_n). \quad (11)$$

Either k_n or h_n is called a *kernel* of the operator H_n. For rather obvious reasons we call the variable t, the *observation time*, and the variables u_i, the *age variables*. Now if H_n has the property that

$$k_n(t, u_1, \ldots, u_n) = 0 \text{ if any } u_i < 0, \quad (12)$$

we say H_n is *realizable* (it does not act on the future values of the input). If H_n has the property that

$$k_n(t, u_1, \ldots, u_n) = 0 \text{ if any } u_i > \gamma, \quad (13)$$

where γ is a positive constant, we say H_n has *bounded memory*. If $k_n(t, u_1, \ldots, u_n)$ does not actually depend on t we say H_n is time-invariant.* In this case, using a slightly improper notation, we write $k_n(u_1, \ldots, u_n)$ for the kernel. To avoid later confusion it may be noted that, if H_n is realizable, the lower limits on the integrals in eq. (10) may be taken to be 0 without changing the value; if $x(t)$ is extended by being set equal to zero outside $[a, b]$, the upper limits on the integrals may be taken to be b-a without changing the value. Finally, if H_n is realizable, time-invariant, and has bounded memory γ, and if b-$a > \gamma$, we may replace eq. (7) by

$$y(t) = \int_0^{\gamma} \cdots \int_0^{\gamma} k_n(u_1, \ldots, u_n) x(t-u_1) \ldots x(t-u_n) du_1 \ldots du_n, \; a \le t < b. \quad (14)$$

A (non-homogeneous) polynomial operator $H = H_0 + H_1 + \ldots + H_N$ where the H_n

*The operator H_n is not actually time-invariant, of course, unless $a = -\infty$, $b = \infty$, but the term should not be confusing.

are as in eq. (4) will be said to be realizable, time-invariant, or to have bounded memory, respectively, if each of the H_n has the property in question.

If h_n is a stochastic kernel and satisfies the inequality (3), then the integral

$$\int_a^b \cdots \int_a^b |h_n(t, s_1, \ldots, s_n)|^2 ds_1 \ldots ds_n \tag{15}$$

exists for a.e. t with probability one, and $y(t)$ is defined by eq. (4) for any $x \in L_2[a, b]$ for a.e. t, with probability one. Furthermore, the inequalities (5) and (8) hold with probability one (the right-hand sides are random variables), so the stochastic homogeneous polynomial operator H_n defined by eq. (4) is continuous with probability one. We say the stochastic kernel k_n or stochastic operator H_n is *realizable*, has *bounded memory*, or is *time-invariant* if the conditions already specified in the definitions of these terms are satisfied with probability one. To avoid confusion, it will sometimes be necessary to refer to the integral operators with real-valued functions as kernels as *ordinary operators* to distinguish them from the stochastic operators just introduced.

There is an obvious generalization of the class of operators being considered to operators on spaces of vector-valued functions. Equation (4) can be changed to read

$$y_i(t) = \int_a^b \cdots \int_a^b \sum_{i_1,\ldots,i_n=1}^{N} h_n^{(i,i_1,\ldots,i_n)}(t, s_1, \ldots, s_n) x_{i_1}(s_1) \ldots x_{i_n}(s_n) ds_1 \ldots ds_n$$

$$a \leq t \leq b, \; i = 1, \ldots, n, \tag{16}$$

and all the comments that have been made thus far can be extended without difficulty to cover this case of vector-valued $x(t)$ and $y(t)$. Although it is essential in many control problems and communications data-processing problems to consider vector-valued inputs and outputs, we shall not work at this level of generality here.

II. SYSTEMS WITH STOCHASTIC INPUTS

In this section $x(t)$ is to denote a sample function from a real-valued stochastic process.* A system operator H is to be an ordinary operator of the type of eq. (1). Then the system output $y(t) = [Hx](t)$ is a sample function from a stochastic process, the statistics of which are determined by H and the statistics of $x(t)$.

We shall assume throughout, obviously without any real loss of generality, that $Ex(t) = 0$ for all t. We shall further assume that $Ex^2(t) < C$ for all t, where C is a constant.

*More properly, $x = x(\cdot, \cdot)$ is to be a separable, measurable stochastic process with linear parameter set T and probability space (Ω, B, μ), B a Borel field and μ a probability measure. $x(t, \cdot)$, $t \in T$, is a random variable on (Ω, B, μ), and $x(\cdot, \omega)$, $\omega \in \Omega$, is a sample function. See, e.g., reference 5.

By the Fubini theorem, with a and b finite or infinite, if

$$\int_a^b \cdots \int_a^b |h_n(t, s_1, \ldots, s_n)| \; E\,|x(s_1)\ldots x(s_n)|\, ds_1 \ldots ds_n < \infty \tag{17}$$

for every t, then

$$y(t) = \int_a^b \cdots \int_a^b h_n(t, s_1, \ldots, s_n) x(s_1)\ldots x(s_n)\, ds_1 \ldots ds_n \tag{18}$$

exists for each t and for every sample function $x(s)$, except possibly an exceptional set of sample functions of probability zero, and furthermore

$$Ey(t) = \int_a^b \cdots \int_a^b h_n(t, s_1, \ldots, s_n) E\{x(s_1)\ldots x(s_n)\}\, ds_1 \ldots ds_n. \tag{19}$$

With the conditions already imposed on $x(t)$, it is obviously sufficient that

$$\int_a^b \cdots \int_a^b |h_n(t, s_1, \ldots, s_n)|\, ds_1 \ldots ds_n < \infty \tag{20}$$

for each t in order that (17) be satisfied. In general (20) is a further hypothesis beyond the condition (2). However, in the important special case where the kernel h_n is time-invariant and a and b are finite, (2) implies (20).

We denote the autocorrelation function of a stochastic process $z(t)$ by $R_z(t', t'')$,

$$R_z(t', t'') = Ez(t')z(t'').$$

For $y(t)$ as given by eq. (18), with the condition (20) satisfied,

$$R_y(t, t') = \int_a^b \cdots \int_a^b h_n(t, s_1, \ldots, s_n) h_n(t', s_1', \ldots, s_n') \cdot E[x(s_1)\ldots x(s_n) x(s_1')\ldots x(s_n')]\, ds_1 \ldots ds_n'. \tag{21}$$

More generally, if $n_1, \ldots, n_p$ is a set of positive integers and $y_{n_i} = H_{n_i}x$, $i = 1, \ldots, p$,

$$Ey_{n_1}(t) y_{n_2}(t') \ldots y_{n_p}(t^{(p-1)})$$

$$= \int_a^b \cdots \int_a^b h_{n_1}(t, s_1, \ldots, s_n) h_{n_2}(t', s_1' \ldots, s_{n_2}') \ldots h_{n_p}(t^{(p-1)}, s_1^{(p-1)}, \ldots, s_{n_p}^{(p-1)})$$

$$E[x(s_1)\ldots x(s_{n_1})\ldots x(s_1^{(p-1)}) \ldots x(s_{n_p}^{(p-1)})]\, ds_1 \ldots ds_{n_p}^{(p-1)}. \tag{22}$$

Thus, in principle, any characterization of the output process $y(t)$ by its moments can be expressed in terms of moments of the input process by formulas of the type of eq. (22).

So far, $x(t)$ has been an arbitrary stochastic process. We now require that it be Gaussian; this permits the expression of all moments of any order in terms of second moments, and the reduction of the polynomial operators to a certain canonical form. In order to establish this canonical form we start with a well-known and basic property of sets of jointly-Gaussian random variables. Let $x_1, x_2, \ldots, x_{2n}$ be a set of real random variables which have a Gaussian joint distribution, and each of which has mean zero. The distribution may have a singular covariance matrix, in fact any number of the $2n$ variables may be identical. Let $R_{i_j} = Ex_i x_j$. Then

$$Ex_1 x_2 \ldots x_{2n} = \sum^{(2n)*} R_{i_1 i_2} R_{i_3 i_4} \ldots R_{i_{2n-1} i_{2n}} \tag{23}$$

where $i_1, i_2, \ldots, i_{2n}$ is a permutation of the numbers $1, 2, \ldots, 2n$, and where the sum,

$$\sum^{(2n)*},$$

is over all permutations which lead to distinct products (i.e., one summand cannot have factors which are just a re-arrangement of the factors in another summand and $R_{i_j} = R_{j_i}$). There are n factors in each term and

$$1 \cdot 3 \cdot 5 \cdot 7 \ldots (2n-1) = \frac{(2n)!}{2^n n!}$$

terms. For example,

$$Ex_1 x_2 x_3 x_4 = R_{12}R_{34} + R_{13}R_{24} + R_{14}R_{23}.$$

On the other hand, if there are an odd number of variables, $x_1, x_2, \ldots, x_{2n-1}$, real, jointly Gaussian, and each with mean zero, then

$$Ex_1 x_2 \ldots x_{2n-1} = 0 \tag{24}$$

The relations given by eqs. (23) and (24) we shall refer to as the *combinatoric property of Gaussian moments*; each may be derived in an elementary fashion by expanding the characteristic function of the $2n$ or $(2n-1)$-variate Gauss distribution and differentiating to obtain the moments.

Using this combinatoric property we can establish classes of orthogonal polynomials of Gaussian random variables. These particular orthogonal polynomials were apparently first described by Barrett[2] as a generalization of n-dimensional Hermite polynomials described by Grad.[7] Wiener (see reference 13 and earlier references quoted there) implicitly used these polynomials in setting up his canonical form for nonlinear functionals of Brownian motion. Cameron and Martin[4] used products of Hermite polynomials of linear functionals of Brownian motion for the same purpose; their procedure is related, but does not explicitly involve the Grad-Barrett-Hermite polynomials.

We now define these polynomials and prove their orthogonality as a corollary of the combinatoric property of Gaussian moments. Let $\{x_\alpha\}$, $\alpha \in A$, where A is an arbitrary index set (perhaps uncountably infinite), be a family of random variables such that any finite subcollection is jointly Gaussian. Let $Ex_\alpha = 0$ for all α. $P^{(n)}_{\alpha_1,\ldots,\alpha_n}$ is an nth degree polynomial in the random variables $x_{\alpha_1}, \ldots, x_{\alpha_n}$ defined as follows (for simplicity in the notation we replace $\alpha_1, \ldots, \alpha_n$ with $1, \ldots, n$):

for n even:
$$P^{(n)}_{1,\ldots,n} = x_1 x_2 \ldots x_n - \sum_{(\beta_1<\beta_2)} R_{\beta_1\beta_2} x_{i_1} x_{i_2} \ldots x_{i_{n-2}}$$
$$+ \sum_{(\beta_1<\beta_2,\beta_3<\beta_4)} R_{\beta_1\beta_2} R_{\beta_3\beta_4} x_{i_1} \ldots x_{i_{n-4}}$$
$$-(-1)^{n/2} \sum_{(\beta_1<\beta_2,\ldots,\beta_{n-1}<\beta_n)} R_{\beta_1\beta_2} R_{\beta_3\beta_4} \ldots R_{\beta_{n-1}\beta_n} \tag{25}$$

for n odd: same expression, except last term is
$$(-1)^{\frac{n-1}{2}} \sum_{(\beta_1<\beta_2,\ldots,\beta_{n-2}<\beta_{n-1})} R_{\beta_1\beta_2} R_{\beta_3\beta_4} \ldots R_{\beta_{n-2}\beta_{n-1}} x_{i_n} \tag{26}$$

The summation convention can be inferred from a typical one:
$$\sum_{(\beta_1<\beta_2,\beta_3<\beta_4)},$$

for example, is to denote summation over all pairs (β_1, β_2) and (β_3, β_4) where the β_i run from 1 to n, where each of the β_i is distinct from each other β_i, where $\beta_1 < \beta_2$, $\beta_3 < \beta_4$, and where no term is just a permutation of another (for example, if there is a term $R_{12}R_{34}$, there is no term $R_{34}R_{12}$). The i_k are the remaining integers from $1, \ldots, n$ in any order, which are not used as indices for the R's. The first five polynomials are of the form:

$$\begin{aligned}
P^{(0)} &= 1 \\
P^{(1)}_{1} &= x_1 \\
P^{(2)}_{12} &= x_1x_2 - R_{12} \\
P^{(3)}_{123} &= x_1x_2x_3 - (R_{12}x_3 + R_{23}x_1 + R_{13}x_2) \\
P^{(4)}_{1234} &= x_1x_2x_3x_4 - (R_{12}x_3x_4 + R_{13}x_2x_4 + R_{14}x_2x_3 \\
&\quad + R_{23}x_1x_4 + R_{24}x_1x_3 + R_{34}x_1x_2) \\
&\quad + (R_{12}R_{34} + R_{13}R_{24} + R_{14}R_{23}).
\end{aligned}$$

It is clear that any product $x_1x_2 \ldots x_n$ can be expressed as a sum of $P^{(n)}_{12\ldots n}$ and polynomials of lower degree. For example,
$$x_1x_2x_3 = P^{(3)}_{123} + R_{12}P^{(1)}_{3} + R_{23}P^{(1)}_{1} + R_{13}P^{(1)}_{2}.$$

Consequently, an arbitrary polynomial of degree n can be expressed as a sum of the orthogonal polynomials $P^{(k)}$ with $k \leq n$. This expansion in the $P^{(k)}$ is unique. It follows that the orthogonality condition for the polynomials,
$$E\,[P^{(n)}_{\alpha_1\ldots\alpha_n} P^{(m)}_{\gamma_1\ldots\gamma_m}] = 0, \quad n \neq m, \quad \alpha_k, \gamma_k \in A, \tag{27}$$
is equivalent to the condition
$$E\,[x_{\gamma_1} \ldots x_{\gamma_m} P^{(n)}_{\alpha_1\ldots\alpha_n}] = 0 \text{ for all } m < n, \ \alpha_k, \gamma_k \in A. \tag{28}$$

We now prove eq. (28). Suppose first that n is an even integer. Then if m is odd, each term in the brackets in eq. (28), after the expression is multiplied out, contains the product of an odd number of x's. Hence, by eq. (24), the expected value is zero. Therefore, we need only look at the case m even, $m \leq n-2$. Now, according to eq. (25), eq. (28) is equivalent to

$$E[x_{\gamma_1}\dots x_{\gamma_m} x_{\alpha_1}\dots x_{\alpha_n}] = \sum_{(\beta_1<\beta_2)} R_{\beta_1\beta_2} E(x_{i_1}\dots x_{i_{n-2}} x_{\gamma_1}\dots x_{\gamma_m})$$

$$-\sum_{(\beta_1<\beta_2,\beta_3<\beta_4} R_{\beta_1\beta_2} R_{\beta_3\beta_4} E(x_{i_1}\dots x_{i_{n-4}} x_{\gamma_1}\dots x_{\gamma_m})$$

$$+\dots+(-1)^{n/2} \sum_{(\beta_1<\beta_2,\dots,\beta_{n-1}<\beta_n)} R_{\beta_1\beta_2}\dots R_{\beta_{n-1}\beta_n}$$

$$\times E(x_{\gamma_1}\dots x_{\gamma_m}) \quad (29)$$

where the β_k indexing the summations range only over the indices $\alpha_1, \dots, \alpha_n$ and the i_k are the remainder of the indices $\alpha_1, \dots, \alpha_n$ not used up by the β_k, as in eq. (25). Consequently, it is sufficient to verify eq. (29). The expansion of the left side of eq. (29) according to the combinatoric property of Gaussian moments will yield a sum of terms, each a product of $(m+n)/2$ different correlations. Each of these terms will also appear in the expansion of the first sum on the right. Conversely, each term in the expansion of the first sum on the right appears in the expansion of the left side. However, terms may be repeated in the first sum on the right. Precisely, all terms of the form

$R_{\beta_1\beta_2}$ {Product of R_{pq}'s such that at least one of the indices of each R_{pq} is a γ_i}

occur exactly once (if $m = n-2$) or not at all (if $m < n-2$). All terms of the form

$R_{\beta_1\beta_2} R_{\beta_3\beta_4}$ {Product of R_{pq}'s such that at least one of the indices of each R_{pq} is a γ_i}

occur exactly twice (if $m \geq n-4$) or not at all (if $m < n-4$). All terms of the form

$$R_{\beta_1\beta_2} R_{\beta_3\beta_4} R_{\beta_5\beta_6} \{\quad\},$$

where $\{\quad\}$ indicates a product with the same conditions as above, occur exactly three times, or not at all, etc. Now all terms in the expansion of the second sum in eq. (29) occur in the expansion of the first, but there are no terms of the form $R_{\beta_1\beta_2}\{\quad\}$; terms of the form $R_{\beta_1\beta_2} R_{\beta_3\beta_4}\{\quad\}$ occur exactly once or not at all; terms of the form $R_{\beta_1\beta_2} R_{\beta_3\beta_4} R_{\beta_5\beta_6}\{\quad\}$ occur exactly $\binom{3}{2} = 3$ times or not at all, etc. In general, the kth sum will contain a term of the form $R_{\beta_1\beta_2} R_{\beta_3\beta_4}\dots R_{\beta_{\mu-1}\beta_\mu}\{\quad\}$ no times if $m < n-\mu$ or $\mu < 2k$, exactly once if $m \geq n-\mu$ and $\mu = 2k$ and exactly $\binom{\mu/2}{k}$ times if $m \geq n-\mu$ and $\mu > 2k$. Such a term will then appear on the right side of eq. (29) exactly

$$\binom{\frac{\mu}{2}}{1} - \binom{\frac{\mu}{2}}{2} + \binom{\frac{\mu}{2}}{3} - \cdots \pm \binom{\frac{\mu}{2}}{\frac{\mu}{2}} = 1$$

time if $\mu > n - m$. Thus each term in the expansion of the left side of eq. (29) occurs once on the right side; there are no other terms on the right side, and eq. (29) is verified (for n even). For n odd, a similar argument shows that eq. (28) is satisfied.

In order to evaluate $E[P^{(n)}_{\alpha_1 \dots \alpha_n} P^{(n)}_{\beta_1 \dots \beta_n}]$ we have only to modify slightly the above argument. First, since the lower degree terms in $P^{(n)}_{\gamma_1 \dots \gamma_n}$ are orthogonal to $P^{(n)}_{\alpha_1 \dots \alpha_n}$,

$$E[P^{(n)}_{\gamma_1 \dots \gamma_n} P^{(n)}_{\alpha_1 \dots \alpha_n}] = E[x_{\gamma_1} \cdots x_{\gamma_n} P^{(n)}_{\alpha_1 \dots \alpha_n}]. \tag{30}$$

Now eq. (29) is no longer valid when $m = n$, but only because the right side does not contain any of the terms of the form $\prod^n R_{\alpha_p \gamma_q}$; the remainder of the terms in the expansion of the left side occur exactly once on the right, as just argued above. Hence,

$$E[P^{(n)}_{\gamma_1 \dots \gamma_n} P^{(n)}_{\alpha_1 \dots \alpha_n}] = \sum_{(\beta)} R_{\gamma_1 \beta_1} R_{\gamma_2 \beta_2} \cdots R_{\gamma_n \beta_n} \tag{31}$$

where the sum is over all permutations $\beta_1, \dots, \beta_n$ of $\alpha_1 \dots \alpha_n$. For example,

$$\begin{aligned} EP^{(3)}_{123} P^{(3)}_{456} &= R_{14}R_{25}R_{36} + R_{14}R_{26}R_{35} + R_{15}R_{24}R_{36} \\ &\quad + R_{15}R_{26}R_{34} + R_{16}R_{24}R_{35} + R_{16}R_{25}R_{34}. \end{aligned}$$

We can now use the orthogonal polynomials to put the polynomial integral operators in a canonical form when the input, $x(t)$, is a Gaussian process with mean zero. This form will necessarily depend on the autocorrelation function of the process. We illustrate this with a special case. Let

$$\begin{aligned} y(t) &= h_0(t) + \int_a^b h_1(t,s)x(s)ds + \int_a^b\!\!\int h_2(t,s_1,s_2)x(s_1)x(s_2)ds_1\,ds_2 \\ &\quad + \int_a^b \int_a^b \int_a^b h_3(t,s_1,s_2,s_3)x(s_1)x(s_2)x(s_3)ds_1 ds_2 ds_3. \end{aligned}$$

Write

$$\begin{aligned} x(s_1)x(s_2)x(s_3) &= P^{(3)}(s_1,s_2,s_3) + R(s_1,s_2)x(s_3) \\ &\quad + R(s_2,s_3)x(s_1) + R(s_1,s_3)x(s_2) \end{aligned}$$

and

$$x(s_1)x(s_2) = P^{(2)}(s_1,s_2) + R(s_1,s_2)$$

and substitute in the integrals above. This yields

$$y(t) = \int_a^b \int_a^b \int_a^b h_3(t, s_1, s_2, s_3) P^{(3)}(s_1, s_2, s_3) ds_1 ds_2 ds_3$$
$$+ \int_a^b \int_a^b h_2(t, s_1, s_2) P^{(2)}(s_1, s_2) ds_1 ds_2$$
$$+ \int_a^b g_1(t, s_1) x(s_1) ds_1 + g_0(t) \tag{32}$$

where

$$g_1(t, s_1) = h_1(t, s_1) + 3 \int_a^b \int_a^b h_3(t, s_1, s_2, s_3) R(s_2, s_3) ds_2 ds_3$$

$$g_0(t) = h_0(t) + \int_a^b h_2(t, s_1, s_2) R(s_1, s_2) ds_1 ds_2.$$

If we put $y(t) = y_3(t) + y_2(t) + y_1(t) + y_0(t)$, where $y_3(t)$, $y_2(t)$, $y_1(t)$ are the first, second and third terms on the right side of eq. (32), and $y_0(t) = g_0(t)$, then

$$E\, y_i(t) y_j(t') = 0, \quad i \neq j, \quad \text{for any} \quad t, t'. \tag{33}$$

Further,

$$E\, y_3(t) y_3(t') = 3! \int_a^b \cdots \int_a^b h_3(t, s_1, s_2, s_3) h_3(t', s_1', s_2' s_3') R(s_1, s_1') R(s_2, s_2')$$
$$\times R(s_3, s_3') ds_1 \ldots ds_3'$$

$$E\, y_2(t) y_2(t') = 2 \int_a^b \cdots \int_a^b h_2(t, s_1, s_2) h_2(t', s_1', s_2') R(s_1, s_1') R(s_2, s_2') ds_1 \ldots ds_2' \tag{34}$$

$$E\, y_1(t) y_1(t') = \int_a^b \int_a^b g_1(t, s) g_1(t', s') R(s, s') ds ds'$$

$$E\, y_0(t) y_0(t') = g_0(t) g_0(t').$$

The technique for writing an arbitrary nth degree polynomial integral operator on a Gaussian process as a sum of orthogonal polynomial operators is clear, and we do not write a general formula.

It perhaps is of some interest to write general expressions for the stationary Gaussian case. Let $x(t)$ be a stationary Gaussian process, with mean zero, and let H be a time-invariant polynomial operator acting on functions defined on the real line. We suppose this operator to be in canonical form for the process $x(t)$, so

$$y(t) = \sum_{n=1}^{N} \int_{-\infty}^{\infty} \cdots \int_{-\infty}^{\infty} g_n(u_1, \ldots, u_n) P^{(n)}(t - u_1, \ldots, t - u_n) du_1 \ldots du_n \tag{35}$$

where the constant zero'th term has been deleted. To guarantee the validity of the operations to follow without the requirement of any subtle arguments, we ask that each g_n be bounded and be absolutely integrable for $-\infty < u_1, \ldots, u_n < \infty$; we also ask that $R(\tau)$, the autocorrelation function of $x(t)$, be absolutely integrable on the real line. This guarantees that the spectrum of $x(t)$ is absolutely continuous. We write for the spectral density of x(t), $S(f)$; it is given by

$$S(f) = \int_{-\infty}^{\infty} e^{i2\pi ft} R(t)dt. \tag{36}$$

The autocorrelation function of $y(t)$ is

$$\begin{aligned} Ey(t)y(t+\tau) &= \sum_{n=1} \int_{-\infty}^{\infty} \cdots \int_{-\infty}^{\infty} g_n(u_1, \ldots, u_n) g_n(u_1', \ldots, u_n') \sum_{(j)} R(\tau + u_1' - u_{j_1}) \\ &\quad \times R(\tau + u_2' - u_{j_2}) \ldots R(\tau + u_n' - u_{j_n}) du_1 \ldots du_n du_1' \ldots du_n'. \\ &= \sum_{n=1}^{N} n! \int_{-\infty}^{\infty} \cdots \int_{-\infty}^{\infty} g_n(u_1, \ldots, u_n) g_n(u_1 + \eta_1, \ldots, u_n + \eta_n) \\ &\quad \times R(\tau + \eta_1) R(\tau + \eta_2) \ldots R(\tau + \eta_n) du_1 \ldots du_n d\eta_1 \ldots d\eta_n \end{aligned} \tag{37}$$

when the sum,

$$\sum_{(j)},$$

is over all permutations $j_1, \ldots, j_n$ of $1, 2, \ldots, n$. The autocorrelation function of $y(t)$ is stationary, and we denote it by $R_y(\tau)$. It is also absolutely integrable, so $y(t)$ has a completely continuous spectrum with density $S_y(f)$. Then

$$\begin{aligned} S_y(f) &= \int_{-\infty}^{\infty} e^{i2\pi f\tau} R_y(\tau) d\tau \\ &= \sum_{n=1}^{N} n! \int_{-\infty}^{\infty} \cdots \int_{-\infty}^{\infty} g_n(u_1, \ldots, u_n) g_n(u_1 + \eta_1, \ldots, u_n + \eta_n) \\ &\quad \int_{-\infty}^{\infty} e^{i2\pi f\tau} R(\tau + \eta_1) \ldots R(\tau + \eta_n) d\tau d\eta_1 \ldots d\eta_n du_1 \ldots du_n \\ &= \sum_{n=1}^{N} n! \int_{-\infty}^{\infty} \cdots \int_{-\infty}^{\infty} S(f') S(f'' - f') \ldots S(f^{(n-1)} - f^{(n-2)}) \\ &\quad S(f - f^{(n-1)}) \left| G_n(f', f'' - f', \ldots, f - f^{(n-1)}) \right|^2 df' \ldots df^{(n-1)} \end{aligned} \tag{38}$$

where

$$G_n(f_1, \ldots, f_n) = \int_{-\infty}^{\infty} \cdots \int_{-\infty}^{\infty} e^{i2\pi(f_1 u_1 + \cdots + f_n u_n)} g_n(u_1, \ldots, u_n) du_1 \ldots du_n. \tag{39}$$

Equation (38) is a nonlinear generalization of the well-known formula for the spectral density of the output of a time-invariant linear filter with stationary input. G_n is a "nonlinear transfer function."

III. A DISCUSSION OF TYPES OF PROBLEMS

It seems natural, given the triple of symbols, x, y, H, to classify all problems pertaining to the kind of system being considered into the following categories:

Type I. The analysis problem: with known x, H, find $y = Hx$.
Type II. The inversion problem: with known H, y, find x so that $Hx = y$.
Type III. The synthesis and identification problem: with known x and $y = Hx$, find H.

If H is a mapping in the usual sense and x belongs to the domain of H, a problem of type I is well defined. Usually H will be fixed and x will vary over the domain of H or some subset of its domain. If H has an inverse (is 1 : 1) and y belongs to the range of H, a problem of type II is well defined; even if H is not 1 : 1, one may ask for the entire inverse-image of y under H, or for some particular element of it (as, e.g., the pseudo-inverse). Again, usually H will be fixed and y will vary over the range of H, or some subset thereof.

The type III category is subject to more varied interpretation than the first two. If x is allowed to take any value in some specified set, if corresponding to each x there is assigned a y, and if an admissible class of possible H's is specified, then there results a *synthesis problem*: find an admissible H which will carry each x into the assigned y. There may be no solution, one solution, or many. Usually there is no concern about the uniqueness of a solution, unless a cost has been assigned to each H and an optimum (minimum cost) solution is desired.

On the other hand, if H represents an existing system, and an input x and corresponding output y, or perhaps several x's and corresponding y's, are known from observation, and if one wants to find H so as to predict future operation, then one wants the exact operator H, or at least a class of operators H which have identical effect on all the inputs of interest. This is a problem of *system identification*. Usually some freedom is allowed in choosing x in order to probe or test the system effectively. The basic difficulty in a system identification problem is, of course, lack of uniqueness. Roughly speaking, it isn't good enough to find an H that might have produced the observed result; one needs to know the H that did produce it, so as to be able to account for the future behavior of the system with other inputs. In order to get uniqueness, or uniqueness, say, modulo some parameter that is irrelevant, it is necessary to have prior knowledge suitably restricting the class of admissible H's.

An example that illustrates the basic difficulty is the following trivial one: let x, y be vectors of length 2, and H be any 2×2 matrix. Then it is impossible to determine H from a knowledge of x and $y = Hx$ for any choice of x whatsoever (i.e., there are infinitely many solutions). H must be restricted to a subclass of

2×2 matrices with two degrees of freedom removed in a suitable way before an identification of H is possible.

The problem of system identification is the concern of the remainder of the paper, and more especially the problem of characterizing classes of operators for which identification is possible, as contrasted with that of establishing efficient measurement procedures and calculational algorithms for carrying out the identification in particular cases.

Before looking at examples, we wish to broaden the notion of what is meant by the system problem classification. It is intended that each type also include situations in which it is not intended to find the actual solution, output, input, or system operator as the case may be, but only to find characteristics of the solution or approximations to it. Further, in the case where some of the elements of the problem are stochastic, the given data are partly, at least, statistical and the required answer is a statistical characterization of the unknown quantity. For example, in an analysis problem in which $x(t)$ is a stochastic process fully described as a known probability measure on a Borel field of subsets of a function space, the best answer one can hope for is the probability measure induced by H on the space of output functions. Thus when we talk about characterizing classes of operators for which identification is possible, the term "identification" may have various connotations, ranging from strict to rather weak, and being either deterministic or probabilistic in nature. In particular, the term *determinable class* which is introduced in the next section with a precise meaning is to be regarded as one formal specialization of the idea of an "identifiable class."

IV. DETERMINABLE CLASSES OF LINEAR SYSTEMS

The material of this section is a fragmentary summary of some work originating in statistical radio communication theory, and it seems worthwhile first to take a quick look at the background.

In many radio communication and measurement problems the total received signal is of the form

$$y(t) = (Hx_\alpha)(t) + n(t), \quad a \leq t \leq b$$

when $x_\alpha(t)$ is a known transmitted signal for each α in some parameter set, $n(t)$ is random noise, and H is a linear operation which is imperfectly known. The detection theory problem is to devise processing for the total received signal $y(t)$ that will yield a good statistical decision as to which of the possible signals $x_\alpha(t)$ was actually transmitted. In order to provide good data for the detection theory problem, H should be determined as well as practicable, either by initial measurements with a known transmitted signal $x(t)$, or by a learning procedure which accompanies the statistical decision. In general H is a time-varying linear operator. If its kernel, $k(t, u)$, varies too rapidly with t and there is not sufficient additional information about its behavior, it is impossible to determine H as an ordinary operator, much less extrapolate its behavior into the future. In this case one may perhaps be able to measure certain time-invariant averages; that is, one can treat H as a stochastic operator and estimate some useful statistic, usually its autocorrelation function. A result pertaining to this situation is given later, in the next section.

If, however, $k(t, u)$ varies slowly enough with t, it may be possible to approximate it satisfactorily by a succession of time-invariant kernels which can be determined from measurement,* there may be additional information available as to the nature of $k(t, u)$ which can supplement a measurement to permit a determination of $k(t, u)$. To treat situations such as these latter ones, the notion of "determinable classes of channels" was introduced.[11] Here, however, we briefly discuss this notion in an abstract setting (see especially reference 10), and disregard the connections with statistical communication theory.

Let $\mathfrak{H}$ be the class of Hilbert-Schmidt (*HS*) operators on $L_2[a, b]$ for some a, b (finite or infinite). An operator $H \in \mathfrak{H}$ is then a linear operator of the general type given by eq. (1),

$$y(t) = [Hx](t) = \int_a^b h(t, s)\,x(s)\,ds, \quad a \leq t \leq b,$$

where

$$\int_a^b \int_a^b |h(t, s)|^2\,dt\,ds = \|H\|^2 < \infty$$

is the *HS* norm of H. (We drop the subscript "1" in this section). Let $\mathfrak{D}$ be a subset of $\mathfrak{H}$. We assume that $\mathfrak{D}$ is bounded, i.e., if $H \in \mathfrak{D}$, $\|H\| < C =$ constant independent of H.

By a *measurement* on $\mathfrak{D}$ is meant a bounded continuous functional μ defined on $\mathfrak{D}$ of the particular form, $\mu(H) = m(Hx)$ for some x in $L_2[a, b]$, $H \in \mathfrak{D}$. By a *linear measurement* on $\mathfrak{D}$ is meant a measurement of the particular form, $\mu(H) = (p, Hx)$ where $p \in L_2[a, b]$. We shall sometimes refer to the x in the measurement as the *test signal*. A class of operators $\mathfrak{D}$ is said to be *uniformly determinable* if, for every $\varepsilon > 0$, there is a single test signal x, a finite set of linear measurements $\{(p_1, Hx), \ldots, (p_K, Hx)\}$, where K depends on ε, and a function f from K-dimensional Euclidean space to $\mathfrak{H}$ which is continuous with respect to the *HS* norm, such that for each $H \in \mathfrak{D}$, $\hat{H} = f((p_1, Hx), \ldots, (p_K, Hx))$ satisfies $\|H - \hat{H}\| < \varepsilon$.

This definition of a determinable class of operators is suggested by a direct formalization of actual measurement procedures in radio engineering (the restriction to a single x reflects the fact that everything transmitted in a given measurement interval comprises one test signal; the linear measurements represent the outputs at fixed times of linear filters whose inputs are the received signal; the continuous function f represents the computation made from the reduced data from the linear filters to estimate the channel). However, there turns out to be an equivalent coordinate-free characterization of determinable class (10):

Theorem. Let $\mathfrak{D}$ be a bounded class of *HS* operators. It is uniformly determinable if and only if (i) its closure is compact (in *HS* norm), and (ii) for each

*Kailath's result in reference 9 on channels for which the band-spread memory product is less than one is interesting in connection with this point, but there is not space here to go into it properly.

$\varepsilon > 0$ there exists an x in $L_2[a, b]$ such that for all pairs of operators H' and H'' satisfying $\|H' - H''\| > \varepsilon$, $\|H'x - H''x\| > 0$.

The compactness condition (i) reflects the fact that a finite number of measurements must characterize $\mathfrak{D}$ uniformly well; the condition (ii) says that the correspondence between operators in $\mathfrak{D}$ and measurements must be almost 1 : 1. In the case of operators with time-invariant kernels, $k(t, u) \equiv k(u)$, the condition (ii) is satisfied automatically, as can be seen by taking for x a suitably good approximation to a δ-function, depending upon ε. The condition (i), which is compactness in $L_2([a, b] \times [a, b])$, is satisfied if the kernels form a compact set in $L_2[a, b]$. A necessary and sufficient condition that a subset of a separable Hilbert space be compact (see reference 6, p. 338) is as given in the statement to follow, and we have:

Let $\{\phi_k\}$ be a complete orthonormal set in $L_2[0, T]$. Let $M > 0$, and let $N(\varepsilon)$ be an arbitrary positive, integer-valued function of ε, defined for $\varepsilon > 0$, and monotone increasing as $\varepsilon \longrightarrow 0$. Let $k(u)$ be a real-valued function of integrable square on $[0, T]$ whose Fourier coefficients $a_n = (k, \phi_n)$ satisfy

$$\sum_{n=1}^{\infty} a_n^2 \leq M < \infty, \qquad \sum_{n=N(\varepsilon)}^{\infty} a_n^2 \leq \varepsilon.$$

Then the class $\mathfrak{D}'$ of all Hilbert-Schmidt operators H of the form

$$[Hx](t) = \int_0^t k(u)x(t-u)\,du, \quad 0 \leq t \leq T, \quad x \in L_2[0, T], \tag{40}$$

with $k(u)$ as specified, is a uniformly determinable class.

A direct proof of this, not involving the theorem quoted above, as in the plausibility argument just given, is in reference 11. The $\{\phi_k\}$ might be sines and cosines, in which case the criterion is a statement about the frequency response of the channel operator; in any case, the (k, ϕ_n) correspond roughly to "frequency components" and the criterion is that the tails of the frequency response pattern be uniformly dominated.

Characterizing particular determinable classes of linear operators with time-varying kernels in a way that might fit practical measurement problems is much more awkward. The "degrees of freedom" of the operators must be restricted in some way, and although it is easy to give sufficient conditions to accomplish this, they are not in general such as would apply to any realistic problem. One way to restrict the degrees of freedom that might prove useful is to require that all the channel operator kernels change in time according to a known trend, and one way to make this condition precise is as follows[11]:

For each s in an interval I, let ψ_s be a bounded linear transformation with domain and range contained in $L_2[0, \gamma]$, which satisfies

i) Domain ψ_s = Domain $\psi_{s'}$ for all $s, s' \in I$
ii) For all $h \in$ Domain ψ_s and a.e. $t \in [0, \gamma]$

$$|(\psi_s h - \psi_{s'} h)(t)| \leq \eta(s, s')\|h\|$$

where $0 \leq \eta(s, s') = \eta(s', s) \longrightarrow 0$ as $s' \longrightarrow s$ and η is a continuous function of both variables for $s, s' \in I$.

iii) For any $h, \tilde{h} \in$ Domain ψ_s

$$\| \psi_s h - \psi_s \tilde{h} \| \leq \zeta(s) \| h - \tilde{h} \|$$

where $0 \leq \zeta(s)$, $\zeta(s) \longrightarrow 1$ as $s \longrightarrow 0$ and $\zeta(s)$ is of integrable square on any finite interval $\subset I$.

We shall call $\{\psi_s\}$ a *continuous trend*; $\{\psi_s\}$ defines a class of channel operator kernels of *known trend* as follows: for any $h_0 \in$ Domain ψ_s, put $h(t, 0) \equiv h_0(t)$ and then define

$$h(t, s) \equiv [\psi_s h_0](t - s), \; s \in I, \; t \in [s, s + \gamma]. \tag{41}$$

It can now be shown that if the class of functions $h_0(t)$ is suitably restricted, the class of all $h(t, s)$ as defined by eq. (41) will be a determinable class. In particular, it is sufficient that the $h_0(t)$ belong to $\mathfrak{D}'$ where $\mathfrak{D}'$ is a determinable class of the kind defined above. A specific example is the set of all

$$h(t, s) = [\psi_s g](t - s) = g(\alpha(s) + \beta(s)(t - s))$$

where $\alpha(s)$, $\beta(s)$ are arbitrary fixed functions continuous in $[0, T]$ with $\alpha(0) = 0$, $\beta(0) = 1$ and $\beta(s)$ bounded away from zero, and where $g(u)$ is any function vanishing outside $[0, \gamma]$, $\gamma < T$, which satisfies the conditions:

a) $|g(u) - g(u')| \leq C_1 \|g\| \cdot |u - u'|$,

b) $\|g\| \leq C_2$,

C_1, C_2 independent of g.

The author feels that perhaps the most useful direction in which to carry this theory is toward characterizing classes of operators which are determinable in essentially the sense defined, but only with respect to particular classes of input functions which are subsets (not in general linear) of L_2. At present not much has been accomplished in this direction.

V. IDENTIFIABILITY OF A CLASS OF LINEAR STOCHASTIC SYSTEMS

We consider a result from communication theory that ties in with the material of the previous section, and illustrates some of the general comments made about system identification rather well. This result, which is due to Bello,[3] following work of Spilker,[12] is obtained by a simple but ingenious argument.

It was pointed out that ordinary identification of time-varying linear operators is difficult, because unless the rate of variation is slow enough to permit approximation by time-invariant kernels over a useful period of time, additional information to that obtained from measurements must be provided. It was further pointed out that sometimes in radio communications rapidly varying linear transmission channels do exist. Such transmission channels (or systems) may occur when the mode of radio wave propagation involves a complicated scattering mechanism. This mechanism may, however, exhibit long term average properties which remain invariant, and if so, it is appropriate to represent the channel as a realization of a linear stochastic operator. One then attempts to make a statistical identification of the channel of some sort; practically about the most one can hope for is to determine the autocorrelation of the kernel of the channel operator. This autocorrelation is useful information, because, if it is available, the autocorrelation of a received signal corresponding to any known transmitted signal can be computed.

The following class of linear stochastic operators, which is wide sense stationary in the observation time, corresponds to a physical situation in which the physical mechanism, though random, is not changing with time. Let

$$y(t) = (Hx)(t) = \int_{-\infty}^{\infty} h(t, s)x(s)ds$$

$$= \int_{-\infty}^{\infty} k(t, u)x(t-u)du \tag{42}$$

where H is a realizable stochastic operator with finite memory, as specified in Section I. In addition we shall ask that

$$Ek(t, u) = 0 \text{ for all } t, u,$$

and that

$$Ek(t, u_1)k(t+\tau, u_2) \equiv \Gamma(\tau;\ u_1, u_2) \tag{43}$$

be continuous in all its variables, and depend on the observation-time variables t and $t+\tau$ only through their difference, as indicated. We shall also ask that the fourth moments of $k(t, u)$ be stationary in the first variable. The problem is to make measurements yielding time averages which can be used as estimates of $\Gamma(\tau;\ u_1, u_2)$; the difficulty is isolating the variables τ, u_1, u_2 in any such measurement.

In fact it is not necessary to estimate $R(\tau;\ u_1, u_2)$ for all values of the variables, for it is sufficient that the sum $\Gamma(\tau;\ u, u+\tau-\gamma) + \Gamma(\tau;\ u-\gamma, u+\tau)$ be known for all values of τ, u, γ in order to calculate any output correlation function. From eq. (43), the autocorrelation function of the output is

$$R(t, t+\tau) = Ey(t)y(t+\tau)$$

$$= \int_{-\infty}^{\infty}\int_{-\infty}^{\infty} \Gamma(\tau;\ u_1, u_2)x(t-u_1)x(t+\tau-u_2)du_1du_2$$

$$= \int_{-\infty}^{\infty}\int_{-\infty}^{\infty} \Gamma(\tau;\ t-\eta, t+\tau-\xi)x(\eta)x(\xi)d\eta d\xi.$$

$\Gamma(\tau;\ t-\eta, t+\tau-\xi)$ can now be replaced by its symmetric part in the variables η, ξ without changing the value of the integral; thus,

$$R(t, t+\tau) = \frac{1}{2}\int_{-\infty}^{\infty}\int_{-\infty}^{\infty} x(\eta)x(\xi)[\Gamma(\tau;\ t-\xi,\ t+\tau-\eta) + \Gamma(\tau;\ t-\eta,\ t+\tau-\xi)]\,d\eta d\xi$$

$$= \frac{1}{2}\int_{-\infty}^{\infty}\int_{-\infty}^{\infty} x(t+\gamma-u)x(t-u)[\Gamma(\tau;\ u, u+\tau-\gamma) + \Gamma(\tau;\ u-\gamma,\ u+\tau)]\,du d\gamma \tag{44}$$

by the substitutions $\xi \longrightarrow t-u$, $\eta \longrightarrow t+\gamma-u$.

Now, the sum $\Gamma(\tau; u, u+\tau-\gamma)+\Gamma(\tau; u-\gamma, u-\tau)$ can be estimated by the following procedure. First, if $x(t)=\delta(t-t_0)$, then $y(t)=k(t, t-t_0)$ and

$$\rho(t, t_0, \tau)=y(t)y(t+\tau)$$

is an unbiased estimator of $\Gamma(\tau; t-t_0, t-t_0+\tau)$ since

$$\begin{aligned} Ey(t)y(t+\tau) &= Ek(t, t-t_0)k(t+\tau, t+\tau-t_0) \\ &= \Gamma(\tau, t-t_0, t-t_0+\tau). \end{aligned}$$

It follows then that the average of a sequence of measurements $\rho(t_i+t, t_i+t_0, \tau)$, which, because of the finite memory, can be taken at intervals $(t_{i+1}-t_i)$ large enough so that there is no interference from one measurement to the next, will converge in mean square to $\Gamma(\tau, t-t_0, t-t_0+\tau)$, by a law of large numbers. Second, if $x(t)=\delta(t-t_0)+\delta(t-t_0-\gamma)$, then $y(t)=k(t, t-t_0)+k(t, t-t_0-\gamma)$ and the product $y(t)y(t+\tau)$ is an unbiased estimator of $\Gamma(\tau; t-t_0, t-t_0+\tau)+\Gamma(\tau; t-t_0, t-t_0+\tau-\gamma)+\Gamma(\tau; t-t_0-\gamma, t-t_0+\tau)+\Gamma(\tau; t-t_0-\gamma, t-t_0+\tau-\gamma)$.

In principle, then, one can obtain estimates, arbitrarily good in the mean square sense, of the quantities $\Gamma(\tau; u, u+\tau)$, $\Gamma(\tau; u-\gamma, u-\gamma+\tau)$ from a succession of measurements of the first kind, and of $[\Gamma(\tau; u, u+\tau)+\Gamma(\tau; u, u+\tau-\gamma)+\Gamma(\tau; u-\gamma, u+\tau)+\Gamma(\tau; u-\gamma, u+\tau-\gamma)]$ from a succession of measurements of the second kind. Subtracting the first two of these estimates from the third yields an unbiased estimate, with arbitrarily small mean square error, of

$$\Gamma(\tau; u, u+\tau-\gamma)+\Gamma(\tau; u-\gamma, u+\tau)$$

as desired. Finally, we make the almost trivial observation that the impulse inputs, $x(t)=\delta(t)$, can be replaced by inputs of integrable square and still yield arbitrarily good estimates. In fact, if $\{\delta_n(t)\}$ is a sequence of approximate δ-functions (see, e.g., reference 6, p. 219) and

$$y_n(t)=\int_{-\infty}^{\infty} k(t, u)\delta_n(t-u)\,du,$$

then, with the conditions we have imposed on $\Gamma(\tau; u_1, u_2)$, it follows that

$$Ey_n(t)y_n(t+\tau) \longrightarrow \Gamma(\tau; t, t+\tau)$$

for every t and τ.

VI. DETERMINABLE CLASSES OF NONLINEAR OPERATIONS

The definition of determinable class given previously to apply to Hilbert-Schmidt linear operators can be extended with very little change to apply to certain nonlinear operators. We do that here, and describe one general example.

Let H_n be a time-invariant, realizable, homogeneous polynomial operator on

$L_2[0, T]$, as specified in eq. (10). That is,

$$
\begin{aligned}
y(t) &= [H_n x](t) \\
&= \int_0^T \cdots \int_0^T h_n(t, s_1, \ldots, s_n)\, x(s_1) \ldots x(s_n)\, ds_1 \ldots ds_n \\
&= \int_0^T \cdots \int_0^T k_n(u_1, \ldots, u_n)\, x(t - u_1) \ldots x(t - u_n)\, du_1 \ldots du_n, \quad 0 \le t \le T,
\end{aligned} \tag{45}
$$

where $x(s)$ is set equal to zero for $s < 0$.

We recall that

$$k_n(u_1, \ldots, u_n) = h_n(t, t - u_1, \ldots, t - u_n) \tag{46}$$

where, because of the hypothesis of time-invariance, the right side of eq. (46) is not actually a function of t. Further,

$$k_n(u_1, \ldots, u_n) = 0 \text{ for any } u_i < 0.$$

We let $\mathcal{H}_n$ be the class of all such operators H_n satisfying the condition, $\| H_n \|_n < \infty$. We let $\mathcal{H}$ be the class of all operators

$$H = H_0 + H_1 + H_2 + \ldots + H_N$$

where each $H_n \in \mathcal{H}_n$. Then the definition of a uniformly determinable class $\mathfrak{D}_n C \mathcal{H}_n$ is taken to read word for word the same as the definition of a determinable class $\mathfrak{D}_1 C \mathcal{H}_1$ except that $\mathfrak{D}_n$ replaces $\mathfrak{D}_1, \mathcal{H}_n$ replaces $\mathcal{H}_1$ and $\| \cdot \|_n$ replaces $\| \cdot \|_1$. Similarly, the definition of a determinable class $\mathfrak{D} C \mathcal{H}$ is the same except that $\mathfrak{D}$ replaces $\mathfrak{D}_1$, $\mathcal{H}$ replaces $\mathcal{H}_1$ and

$$\sum_{n=1}^{N} \| \cdot \|_n$$

replaces $\| \cdot \|_1$.

We now construct a uniformly determinable class $\mathfrak{D}_n(x)\, C \mathcal{H}_n$ corresponding to any $x \in L_2[0, T]$, which is also a continuous function on $[0, T]$. We have for $k_n \in \mathcal{H}_n$,

$$y(t) = \int_0^T \cdots \int_0^T k_n(u_1, \ldots, u_n)\, x(t - u_1) \ldots x(t - u_n)\, du_1 \ldots du_n, \quad 0 \le t \le T$$

$$\| y \|^2 = \int_0^T \int_0^T \cdots \int_0^T k_n(u_1, \ldots, u_n) k_n(u_1', \ldots, u_n')\, x(t - u_1) \ldots x(t - u_n) \cdot x(t - u_1') \ldots x(t - u_n')\, du_1 \ldots du_n'\, dt$$

Let $L_2[0, T]^n$ denote the L_2-space of functions of n variables u_i, $0 \le u_i \le T$. Consider the symmetric integral operator G on $L_2[0, T]^n$ with kernel

$$g(u_1, \ldots, u_n; u_1', \ldots, u_n') = \int_0^T x(t - u_1) \ldots x(t - u_n)\, x(t - u_1') \ldots x(t - u_n')\, dt. \tag{47}$$

G is a compact operator; in fact it is Hilbert-Schmidt:

$$\int_0^T \cdots \int_0^T \left| \int_0^T x(t-u_1)\ldots x(t-u_n)x(t-u_1')\ldots x(t-u_n')\,dt \right|^2 du_1\ldots du_n' < \infty$$

since $x(t)$ is bounded on $[0, T]$. Let $\{\phi_i(u_1, \ldots, u_n)\}$ be an orthonormal set of eigenfunctions of G with corresponding eigenvalues λ_i, $G\phi_i = \lambda_i\phi_i$. Note that the ϕ_i are symmetric functions of their n arguments. We denote inner products in $L_2[0, T]^n$ by $(\cdot\,,\cdot)_n$; then,

$$\lambda_i = (\phi_i, G\phi_i)_n = \int_0^T \cdots \int_0^T \phi_i(u_1, \ldots, u_n)$$

$$\int_0^T \cdots \int_0^T g(u_1, \ldots, u_n; u_1', \ldots, u_n')\phi_i(u_1', \ldots, u_n') \cdot du_1' \ldots du_n' du_1 \ldots du_n$$

$$= \int_0^T \left\{ \int_0^T \cdots \int_0^T \phi_i(u_1, \ldots, u_n)x(t-u_1)x(t-u_n)du_1 \ldots du_n \right\}^2 dt \geq 0.$$

Hence G is positive definite. Now put

$$\psi_i(t) = \int_0^T \cdots \int_0^T \phi_i(u_1, \ldots, u_n)x(t-u_1)\ldots x(t-u_n)du_1 \ldots du_n. \tag{48}$$

Then, from the preceding calculation, $\|\psi_i\|^2 = \lambda_i$. Further,

$$(\psi_i, \psi_j)_1 = (\phi_i, G\phi_j)_n = 0 \text{ if } i \neq j,$$

so $\{\psi_i(t)\}$ is an orthogonal set in $L_2[0, T]$ induced by the orthonormal set $\{\phi_i(u_1, \ldots, u_n)\}$. We note that changes of order of integration in the preceding expressions can all be justified in routine fashion by using the facts that $x(t)$ is bounded and that $\phi_i(u_1, \ldots, u_n) \in L_2[0, T]^n$, and hence to $L_1[0, T]^n$ since the base space has finite measure.

Now we let

$$k_n(u_1, \ldots, u_n) = \sum_i a_i\phi_i(u_1, \ldots, u_n), \; \sum_i a_i^2 < \infty \tag{49}$$

and take for $\mathfrak{D}_n$ a compact set of such k_n's. In fact, let $N(\varepsilon)$ be an arbitrary, positive, integer-valued function of ε defined for $\varepsilon > 0$ and monotone non-decreasing as $\varepsilon \longrightarrow 0$. Then let $\mathfrak{D}_n$ be the set of all $k_n(u_1, \ldots, u_n)$ such that

$$\sum_1 a_i^2 \leq B,$$

a fixed constant, and

$$\sum_{N(\varepsilon)}^{\infty} a_i^2 \leq \varepsilon.$$

Then

$$y(t) = \int_0^T \cdots \int_0^T \sum_1^\infty a_i\phi_i(u_1, \ldots, u_n)x(t-u_1)\ldots x(t-u_n)\,du_1\ldots du_n, \quad (50)$$

and we put

$$y_N(t) = \sum_1^N a_i \int_0^T \cdots \int_0^T \phi_i(u_1, \ldots, u_n)x(t-u_1)\ldots x(t-u_n)du_1\ldots du_n$$

$$= \sum_1^N a_i\psi_i(t). \quad (51)$$

Now $\Sigma_1^N a_i\phi_i$ converges in $L_2[0,T]^n$ to $\Sigma_1^\infty a_i\phi_i$ and, *a fortiori*, $\Sigma_1^N a_i\psi_i$ converges in $L_2[0,T]$ to $\Sigma_1^\infty a_i\psi_i$ (since $\|\psi_i\| \longrightarrow 0$). Also

$$y(t) = \left(\sum_1^\infty a_i\phi_i, X_t\right)_n$$

and

$$y_N(t) = \left(\sum_1^N a_i\phi_i, X_t\right)_n$$

where $X_t \equiv x(t-u_1)\ldots x(t-u_n)$; so, by continuity of the inner product, $y_N(t) \longrightarrow y(t)$ for each t. Consequently, since y_N converges in $L_2[0,T]$,

$$\|y_N - y\| \longrightarrow 0.$$

$\mathfrak{D}_n$ is indeed a determinable class, for, given $\varepsilon > 0$, take $x(t)$ as test signal, $N = N(\varepsilon)$, and $p_k = \psi_k$, $k = 1, 2, \ldots, N$. Then,

$$(y, p_k) = a_k,$$

$$\hat{k}_n(u_1, \ldots, u_n) = \sum_1^N (y, p_k)\phi_k(u_1, \ldots, u_n), \quad \|k_n - \hat{k}_n\|_n^2 \le \varepsilon$$

and

$$\|H_n - \hat{H}_n\|_n^2 \le T\|k_n - \hat{k}_n\|_n^2 \le T\varepsilon.$$

We now consider nonhomogeneous polynomial operators of degree M, with the zero degree term omitted,

$$y(t) = \sum_{n=1}^M \int_0^T \cdots \int_0^T k_n(u_1, \ldots, u_n)x(t-u_1)\ldots x(t-u_n)du_1\ldots du_n.$$

The symbols ψ_i, a_i used above associated with the kernel k_n we now write as $\psi_i^{(n)}$, $a_i^{(n)}$. Then,

$$y(t) = \sum_{n=1}^{M} \sum_{i=1}^{\infty} a_i^{(n)} \psi_i^{(n)}(t). \tag{52}$$

If each $\psi_i^{(n)}$ is not contained in the closed linear span of all the $\psi_i^{(m)}$, $i = 1, 2, \ldots,$ $m \neq n$, then the $a_i^{(n)}$ can be found and $\mathfrak{D} = \{\mathfrak{D}_1, \ldots, \mathfrak{D}_M\}$ is a determinable class in $\mathcal{H}$ with test signal $x(t)$. However, nothing in the above construction appears to shed light on when this condition is satisfied. An analogous, but more complicated construction can be made which gives a determinable class in $\mathcal{H}$ directly.

We note that the classes $\mathfrak{D}_n$ are maximal with respect to the determination, i.e., given $x(t)$, $N(\varepsilon)$, $\{p_k'\}$ and the function k_n, then $\mathfrak{D}_n$ cannot be enlarged. The description of a determinable class $\mathfrak{D}_n$ just given will be recognized as a kind of restricted extension to time-invariant polynomial operators of a description of determinable classes of time-invariant linear operators given in Section IV.

There is not space here to go into the matter, but the material of this section is closely related to work of Balakrishman[1] and Hsieh[8] on the method of steepest descent applied to the problem of finding unknown time-invariant, nonlinear system operators (and was in fact partly motivated by it). The algorithm for finding a steepest descent approximation truncated to a fixed number of stages is actually a determination in the sense the word has been used here. We emphasize again, however, that it is not a purpose of the present paper to discuss efficient numerical procedures, but rather to characterize situations where an identification is possible.

VII. STOCHASTIC IDENTIFICATION OF NONLINEAR SYSTEMS

We shall confine ourselves to polynomial integral operators of the same kind as permitted in the previous section: time-invariant, realizable operators operating on functions defined on a finite interval, $[0, T]$. We suppose the kernels each satisfy the condition (20). The idea is to test the system with a sample function $x(t)$ of a stationary Gaussian process with mean zero and known, continuous, autocorrelation function and to use the orthogonality of a canonical representation, such as that in eq. (35), to obtain the kernel functions in the canonical representation. This is of course a weaker notion of system identification than that embodied in the determinable class concept of the Section VI. An unknown operator in a determinable class can be found to within an arbitrary ε in some suitable measure of distance by a sufficiently elaborate procedure occupying a fixed, finite time. An unknown operator can only be estimated statistically by the stochastic identification procedure, and, in general, the best situation that can obtain is that the estimates are consistent, so that a long sequence of estimates will converage in some sense to the true value. Thus one would expect that much larger classes of operators are accessible to stochastic identification than to determination in the strict technical sense.

Let us now sketch a procedure for stochastic identification of an arbitrary operator of the type specified in the preceding paragraph. We have,

$$y(t) = k_0 + \sum_{n=1}^{N} \int_0^T \cdots \int_0^T k_n(u_1, \ldots, u_n) x(t - u_1) \ldots x(t - u_n) du_1 \ldots du_n$$

$$= g_0 + \sum_{n=1}^{N} \int_0^T \cdots \int_0^T g_n(u_1, \ldots, u_n) P^{(n)}(t - u_1, \ldots, t - u_n) du_1 \ldots du_n \tag{53}$$

where the g_n's are of the form:

$$g_N(u_1, \ldots, u_N) = k_N(u_1, \ldots, u_N)$$

$$g_{N-1}(u_1, \ldots, u_{N-1}) = k_{N-1}(u_1, \ldots, u_{N-1})$$

$$g_n(u_1, \ldots, u_n) = k_n(u_1, \ldots, u_n) + [\text{known functions of } k_{n+2}, \ldots, k_N \text{ and } R(\tau)],\ n = 0, 1, \ldots, N-2 \tag{54}$$

We suppose that $x(t)$ is chosen so that the positive-definite *HS* operator on $L_2[0, T]$ defined by

$$[Rz](t) = \int_0^T R(t - s) z(s) ds, \quad 0 \leq t \leq T$$

has a complete set of eigenfunctions, $\{\phi_j(t)\}$, which we assume orthonormal, with associated eigenvalues λ_j, $R\phi_j = \lambda_j \phi_j$. Then $\{\phi_{j_1}(t_1) \ldots \phi_{j_n}(t_n)\}_j$ is a cons in $L_2[0, T]^n$, and we write

$$g_n(u_1, \ldots, u_n) = \sum_{j_1, \ldots, j_n} a^{(n)}_{j_1 \ldots j_n} \phi_{j_1}(u_1) \ldots \phi_{j_n}(u_n). \tag{55}$$

The identification of g_n is accomplished by forming products of the form

$$\hat{\alpha}_{m_1 \ldots m_n} = y(T) \int_0^T \cdots \int_0^T \phi_{m_1}(u_1') \ldots \phi_{m_n}(u_n') P^{(n)} \cdot (T - u_1', \ldots, T - u_n') du_1'; \ldots du_n'. \tag{56}$$

By the orthogonality properties of the Grad-Barrett-Hermite polynomials, one has

$$E\, \hat{\alpha}_{m_1 \ldots m_n} = \int_0^T \cdots \int_0^T g_n(u_1, \ldots, u_n) \phi_{m_1}(u_1') \ldots \phi_{m_n}(u_n')$$

$$\Sigma\, R(u_1 - u_{i_1}') \ldots R(u_n - u_{i_n}') du_1' \ldots du_n' du_1 \ldots du_n$$

$$= \lambda_{m_1} \ldots \lambda_{m_n} a^{(n)}_{m_1 \ldots m_n}$$

(The expected value of the estimator $\hat{\alpha}_{m_1 \cdots m_n}$ appears at first glance not to depend on the observation instant, chosen to be $t = T$. However, this is not correct; we have assumed in our integral operator representation (in order to get fixed upper limits) that $x(t)$ is zero for $t < 0$, hence the stationarity of the autocorrelation function of $x(t - u)$, $0 \leq u \leq T$, holds only for $t = T$.) Thus,

$$\frac{\hat{\alpha}_{m_1 \ldots m_n}}{\lambda_{m_1} \ldots \lambda_{m_n}}$$

is an unbiased estimator of $a^{(n)}_{m_1 \ldots m_n}$. Under our assumptions it certainly has finite variance, which in principle can be calculated, but which we shall not attempt to calculate because of the tremendous complexity of the expression for the second moment of $(\hat{\alpha}_{m_1 \ldots m_n})/(\lambda_{m_1} \ldots \lambda_{m_n})$. Consequently it is a consistent estimator; by the strong law of large numbers the average of repeated estimates will converge with probability one to $a_{m_1 \ldots m_n}$. In principle one can simultaneously estimate any finite number of the $a^{(n)}_{m_1 \ldots m_n}$'s and thus determine approximations to the g_n's. This gives approximations for k_N and k_{N-1} directly, and, by an iterated calculation, the k_n's for $n \leq N - 2$.

REFERENCES

1. A. V. Balakrishnan, "Determination of Nonlinear Systems from Input-Output Data," *Proc. Princeton Conf. Identification Problems in Communication and Control* (New York: Academic Press, 1963).
2. J. F. Barrett, "Application of the Theory of Functionals to Communication Problems," Eng. Lab. Report, Cambridge Univ. (1955).
3. P. Bello, "On the Measurement of a Channel Correlation Function," *IEEE Trans. on Info. Theory*, IT-10, 4, 381–383 (1964).
4. R. H. Cameron and W. T. Martin, "The Orthogonal Development of Nonlinear Functionals in Series of Fourier-Hermite Functionals," *Ann. Math.*, **48**, 385–392 (1947).
5. J. L. Doob, *Stochastic Processes* (New York: John Wiley and Sons, 1953).
6. N. Dunford and J. T. Schwartz, *Linear Operators*, Part I (New York: Interscience, 1958).
7. H. Grad, "Note on n-dimensional Hermite Polynomials," *Commun. Pure Appl. Math.*, 2, 325–330 (1949).
8. H. C. Hsieh, "The Least Squares Estimation of Linear and Nonlinear Weighting Function Matrices," *Info. and Control*, 7, 84–115 (1964).
9. T. Kailath, "Sampling Methods for Linear Time-Variant Filters," M.I.T. Res. Lab. of Electronics Tech. Rep. No. 352 (1959).
10. R. T. Prosser and W. L. Root, "Determinable Classes of Channels" (submitted for publication).
11. W. L. Root, "On the Measurement and Use of Time-Varying Communication Channels," (to be published in *Info. and Control*).
12. J. J. Spilker, "On the Characterization and Measurement of Randomly-Varying Filters," Comm. Sciences Dept., Philco Western Development Labs., Tech. Memo No. 72(1963).
13. N. Wiener, "Nonlinear Problems in Random Theory" (Technology Press, M.I.T., 1958).
14. R. Deutsch, *Nonlinear Transformations of Random Processes* (Englewood Cliffs, N.J.: Prentice-Hall, 1962).
15. A. C. Zaanen, *Linear Analysis* (Amsterdam: North-Holland, 1956).
16. L. A. Zadeh, "On the Representation of Nonlinear Operators," *IRE Wescon Convention Record*, Part 2, pp. 105–113 (1957).

DISCUSSION ON

ON SYSTEM MEASUREMENT AND IDENTIFICATION

by

W. L. ROOT

G. Adomian, Pennsylvania State University, University Park, Pa.

I would like to add that it appears desirable to me to emphasize more the *stochastic system* case. This includes the deterministic as a special case and gives the results for a deterministic system with random input. Physical problems arise both in a formulation where the system is specified or the operator is given—so, given an input and the operator, we ask for the statistics of the transformed processes, and also, in a differential equation formulation—(a stochastic differential equation with random coefficients)—where we ask for the statistics of the dependent variable in terms of the statistics of the forcing function and a "stochastic Green's function" (see, e.g., Vol. 16, AMS Annual Symposia in *Applied Math.* or *Rev. Mod. Phys.*, January (1963) to be obtained from the statistics of the random coefficients of the stochastic differential operator. Physical problems, particularly in the systems theory area—in control, communications, measurement—fall into this context. Also, problems involving propagation or scattering by random media give rise to such equations and it is clear that one cannot get answers by reasoning from the deterministic case. The state of the theory and many interesting applications are in a UCLA Dept. of Physics Technical Report dated 1963 and representing the 1961 thesis of Adomian, which gives an indication of relevant work also by Zadeh, Samuels, Rosenbloom, as well as by people more in the probabilistic functional analysis area.

Root:

I certainly agree with Professor Adomian that the stochastic system case is very important and I am interested in stochastic systems. Two of the chief reasons for not discussing stochastic systems more extensively here were simply lack of space and lack of knowledge on my part. I do feel, of course, that many systems are more appropriately modeled as deterministic than stochastic; and I also feel that it is not sufficient to say they are special cases of stochastic systems and hence need no individual attention—any more than one could say trigonometric Fourier series are special cases of series of orthogonal functions and hence need no individual attention.

Let me refer to a rather specialized interest of my own where I want to consider deterministic systems.

In radio communication theory there seems to me to be a gray area (where channels are time varying, but where statistics are hardly known) where it is not clear whether a deterministic or stochastic channel model is more useful. I have some personal interest in exploring in such cases what can be done with deterministic models (allowing error tolerances all along the line) and the resulting sure-signal-in-noise type detection problems, as opposed to stochastic models and the resulting noise-in-noise type detection problems.

THE WOLD DECOMPOSITION PROBLEM

David Lee Hanson
Department of Statistics, University of Missouri, Columbia, Mo.

This paper will deal with the Wold decomposition problem, its relation to causality, and the progress that has been made on the problem. Particular topics will include: the tail field of a sequence of random variables; the interpretation of the tail field and of trivial tail fields; the fact that a causal system acting on a sequence of independent and identically distributed inputs produces a tail trivial output sequence; the Wold decomposition problem (i.e., Is every tail trivial process the output of a causal system acting on an independent and identically distributed sequence of random variables?); some partial solutions to the decomposition problem; the role of conditional probabilities in the decomposition problem; and some examples.

1. THE LINEAR WOLD DECOMPOSITION

Let $\{X_n\}$ for $n = 0, \pm 1, \ldots$ be a sequence of real valued random variables such that $EX_n^2 < \infty$ for all n. Let $\mathcal{H}_n$ be the Hilbert space generated by the X_k's for $k \leq n$, that is, the collection of linear combinations of X_k's with $k \leq n$ and all mean square limits of these linear combinations; $\mathcal{H}_n$ is the collection of all random variables which can be approximated arbitrarily closely by sums of the form

$$\sum_{i=1}^{N} c_i X_{k_i} \quad k_i \leq n \quad \text{for} \quad i = 1, \ldots, N, \tag{1}$$

that is, by finite linear combinations of observations on the process up through time n. Define $\mathcal{H}_{-\infty} = \cap \mathcal{H}_n$. Thus, $\mathcal{H}_{-\infty}$ is the collection of random variables which can be approximated arbitrarily closely by sums of the form (1) of random variables from the arbitrarily remote past of the process. Intuitively speaking, we can say that $\mathcal{H}_n$ contains the linear information in the process through time n, and $\mathcal{H}_{-\infty}$ contains the linear information in the infinite past of the process. Let X_n^* be the projection of X_n on $\mathcal{H}_{n-1}$ (i.e., the best approximation to X_n by a member of $\mathcal{H}_{n-1}$) and define $\xi_n = X_n - X_n^*$. Note that ξ_n is orthogonal to every member of $\mathcal{H}_{n-1}$. We may think of ξ_n as the linear portion of X_n which is new at time n in the sense that the remainder of X_n (that is, $X_n^* = X_n - \xi_n$) is a linear function of the past, while none of ξ_n can be linearly approximated using the past. It is well known that there exist constants $c_{i,j}$ with $i = 0, \pm 1, \ldots$ and $j = 0, 1, \ldots$ such that we can write

$$X_n = \sum_{k=0}^{\infty} c_{n,k} \xi_{n-k} + V_n \tag{2}$$

Presented at the Symposium on System Theory
Polytechnic Institute of Brooklyn, April 20, 21, 22, 1965

with $V_n \in \mathcal{H}_{-\infty}$. (Note that $\{\xi_n\}$ is an orthogonal sequence which is orthogonal to everything in the linear infinite past $\mathcal{H}_{-\infty}$.) This is an explicit expression of X_n in terms of the linear information about X_n contained in the infinite past (i.e., in terms of V_n) and the explicit additional linear information (that is, $c_{n,n-k}\,\xi_k$) obtained about X_n at each time point k up through time n. The decomposition (2) is a linear Wold decomposition of the process $\{X_n\}$. If $\{X_n\}$ is weakly stationary in the sense that $EX_m X_{m+n} = \rho_n$ is independent of m for all n, then (see chapter XII of reference 1) the constants $c_{n,k}$ are independent of n, so that we can write

$$X_n = \sum_{k=0}^{\infty} c_k\,\xi_{n-k} + V_n. \tag{3}$$

In case the original process $\{X_n\}$ is Gaussian with $EX_n \equiv 0$, one obtains more (from the fact that the entire distribution of a Gaussian process with zero means is determined by the second moments). The ξ_n's are all Gaussian with zero means and are orthogonal to each other and the infinite past $\mathcal{H}_{-\infty}$; hence they form an independent sequence which is independent of the infinite past.

Now let $\mathcal{F}_n$ be the smallest σ-field with respect to which X_k is measurable for all $k \leq n$ (that is, $\mathcal{F}_n$ is the collection of events described in terms of the X_k's for $k \leq n$). Let $\mathcal{F}_{-\infty} = \cap\, \mathcal{F}_n$ so that $\mathcal{F}_{-\infty}$ is the collection of events in the arbitrarily remote past of the process $\{X_n\}$ or, more intuitively, $\mathcal{F}_{-\infty}$ is the collection of events in the infinite past of the process $\{X_n\}$. We call $\mathcal{F}_{-\infty}$ the *tail field* of the process $\{X_n\}$ and say that $\mathcal{F}_{-\infty}$ is trivial (synonomously, that the process $\{X_n\}$ is *tail trivial*) if $\mathcal{F}_{-\infty}$ contains no events whose probabilities are different from zero and one. A reasonable interpretation of the condition "$\mathcal{F}_{-\infty}$ is trivial" is that the infinite past of the process $\{X_n\}$ contains no information (linear or otherwise) about the process.

In the Gaussian case, $\mathcal{F}_n$ is (in addition to its definition given above) the smallest σ-field containing all events in $\mathcal{F}_{-\infty}$, and all events described in terms of the ξ_k's for $k \leq n$; and all the events in $\mathcal{F}_n$ are independent of the events described in terms of the ξ_k's for $k > n$. In addition, the events in $\mathcal{F}_{-\infty}$ are independent of the events described in terms of the ξ_k's, and the V_n's are measurable with respect to $\mathcal{F}_{-\infty}$ so that events described in terms of the V_n's are events in the infinite past of the process $\{X_n\}$. Since the ξ_k's are independent of $\mathcal{F}_{-\infty}$, we conclude that V_n contains all the information (not just all the linear information) about X_n which is contained in the infinite past of the process; and since ξ_k is independent of $\mathcal{F}_{k-1}$, we conclude that $c_{n,n-k}\,\xi_k$ contains all the information about X_n which is available at time k but was not available previous to time k. The representation (2) is still valid, but in the Gaussian case, eq. (2) shows when information about X_n is first available, not just when it is first available in linear form.

For the Gaussian process $\{X_n\}$ satisfying $EX_n \equiv 0$, weak stationarity is equivalent to strong stationarity (i.e., for all m, $n_1, \ldots, n_m$ the joint distribution of $X_{n_1+k}, \ldots, X_{n_m+k}$ is independent of k). Thus if one assumes $\{X_n\}$ is Gaussian and weakly stationary, one is in reality making the assumption that $\{X_n\}$ is strongly stationary. In this case the sequence $\{(\xi_n, V_n)\}$ of pairs is strictly stationary.

One would hope to obtain a nonlinear stationary Wold decomposition, the nonlinear analog of (3), by replacing weak stationarity by strong stationarity, by replacing orthogonality of the sequence $\{\xi_n\}$ and $\mathcal{H}_{-\infty}$ by independence of $\{\xi_n\}$ and $\mathcal{F}_{-\infty}$, and by replacing the linear relationship (3) by some nonlinear relationship. The nonlinear problem is, of course, much harder than the linear one, and only partial solutions have been obtained.

2. CAUSALITY AND THE NONLINEAR REPRESENTATION PROBLEM

Let $\{\xi_n\}$ be an independent sequence of real random variables, let $\{f_n\}$ be a sequence of real valued functions of infinitely many real variables, and define

$$X_n = f_n(\ldots, \xi_{n-1}, \xi_n) \tag{4}$$

so that X_n is a function of the ξ_k's for $k \leq n$. The ξ_k's may be thought of as a sequence of independent inputs and the f_n's as describing the action of a "black box" on the present and past inputs into the box. Often the f_n's are all the same. If they are different it could be due to degradation of the "black box" due to time, or maybe to some inherent dependence of the action of the box on time. In any case, the output X_n depends only on the present (that is, ξ_n) and past (that is, $\ldots, \xi_{n-2}, \xi_{n-1}$) of the ξ process, so the f_n's can be thought of as describing a causal system and the X_n's as being the output of a causal system acting on a sequence of independent inputs. It is known (see for example lemma 1 of reference 2) that the tail field of the sequence $\{X_n = f_n(\ldots, \xi_{n-1}, \xi_n)\}$ is trivial. The nonlinear Wold decomposition problem is essentially the converse problem: "Can each tail trivial process be considered to be the output of a causal system acting on independent inputs?" As noted by Rosenblatt,[2] there are actually two interpretations of this problem:

i) Is X_n actually the output of a causal system acting on an independent sequence of inputs in the sense that one can obtain, on the same probability space, ξ_k's and f_n's such that $X_n = f_n(\ldots, \xi_{n-1}, \xi_n)$?

ii) Do there exist ξ_k's and f_n's on some other probability space such that the sequences $\{X_n\}$ and $\{f_n(\ldots, \xi_{n-1}, \xi_n)\}$ have the same probability structure, i.e., such that for all $m, n_1, \ldots, n_m$, the random variables $X_{n_1}, \ldots, X_{n_m}$ have the same joint distribution as do the random variables $f_{n_1}(\ldots, \xi_{n_1-1}, \xi_{n_1}), \ldots, f_{n_m}(\ldots, \xi_{n_m-1}, \xi_{n_m})$?

Most of the results obtained have been for the second problem and have been for Markov processes. All the published results known to me have been for strictly stationary processes, although it is not difficult to state some sets of sufficient conditions that a not necessarily stationary Markov chain have a representation of type (ii).

It should be pointed out that given any real valued stochastic process $\{X_n\}$, one can obtain from it a Markov process of the form $\{Y_n = g(\ldots, X_{n-1}, X_n)\}$ such that $X_n = h(Y_n)$, that is, such that X_n can be recovered from Y_n. If the $\{Y_n\}$ process has a representation, say $\{f_n(\ldots, \xi_{n-1}, \xi_n)\}$, then the $\{X_n\}$ process has the representation $\{hf_n(\ldots, \xi_{n-1}, \xi_n)\}$. Thus it is reasonable to concentrate one's attention on Markov processes, since it suffices to solve the problem for Markov processes.

3. A STATEMENT OF RESULTS OBTAINED TO DATE

Throughout most of this section, $\{X_n\}$ will be a strictly stationary tail trivial stochastic process, and $\{\xi_n\}$ will be an independent sequence of random variables, each of which is uniformly distributed on $[0, 1]$. (This type of random variable is not essential to the problem but is easy to work with. Any random variable with a continuous distribution will do.) The sequence $\{X_n\}$ will be said to have a representation if there exists a real valued function f of infinitely many random variables such that the sequences $\{X_n\}$ and $\{f(\ldots, \xi_{n-1}, \xi_n)\}$ have the same probability structure. Note that obtaining a representation of this type for $\{X_n\}$ solves problem (ii) for $\{X_n\}$.

The first concrete results on this problem were obtained in 1959 by M. Rosenblatt.[2] He worked with Markov chains and obtained some results for problem (i) as well as some partial results for problem (ii). Rosenblatt completely solved the problem for Markov chains one year later[3] with a version of the following theorem:

Theorem 1: If $\{X_n\}$ is a stationary Markov chain with finite or denumerable state space, the following three conditions are equivalent

i) $\{X_n\}$ is ergodic and aperiodic;

ii) $\{X_n\}$ is tail trivial;

iii) $\{X_n\}$ has a representation.

In reference 4, Rosenblatt's results were extended to a more general class of Markov processes which includes some Markov processes with nondenumerable state spaces. Let $P_x(A) = P\{X_{n+1} \epsilon A | X_n = x\}$ and $\overline{P}(A) = P\{X_n \epsilon A\}$. The theorem obtained is:

Theorem 2: Let $\{X_n\}$ be a real valued stationary Markov process such that

i) It has a trivial tail field;

ii) There exist Borel subsets A and C of the real line and a non-negative measure ψ on the real line such that $\overline{P}(C) > 0$, $\psi(A) > 0$, and for all $x \epsilon C$ and $A' \subset A$ we have $P_x(A') \geq \psi(A')$.

Then $\{X_n\}$ has a representation.

Condition (ii) of Theorem 2 is satisfied if the state space of $\{X_n\}$ has an atom, i.e., if there exists a point x_0 such that $P\{X_n = x_0\} > 0$. Thus, in particular, condition (ii) is satisfied for all Markov chains with finite or denumerable state space so that the results of Theorem 1 are contained in Theorem 2. The method of proof used in Theorem 2 is a generalization of, but no radical departure from, the proof of Theorem 1. If it is true that every stationary tail trivial process has a representation, then Theorem 2 can be proved without the condition (ii). This will take some new insights into the problem.

In references 5 and 6, work is done on 0–1 processes (i.e., on processes $\{X_n\}$ which can take on only the values 0 and 1). The process $\{X_n\}$ is not required to be a Markov process. Define

$$Y_n = \cdot X_n X_{n-1} \cdots \quad \text{(binary)} \tag{5a}$$

or

$$Y_n = \frac{X_n}{2} + \frac{X_{n-1}}{4} + \dots \tag{5b}$$

so that $\{Y_n\}$ is a Markov process taking on values in the interval [0, 1]. Further define

$$\phi(y) = P\{X_{n+1} = 0 \mid Y_n = y\}. \tag{6}$$

It is clear that

$$Y_{n+1} = \frac{1}{2} + \frac{Y_n}{2} \quad \text{or} \quad Y_{n+1} = \frac{Y_n}{2}.$$

We see that $\phi(y)$ is the conditional probability that $Y_{n+1} = Y_n/2 = y/2$ given $Y_n = y$. If two numbers x and y in [0, 1] agree in the first m places of their binary expansion, we will write $x \overset{m}{\equiv} y$. (Note that a rational binary number has two expansions, $\frac{1}{2} = .1000\dots$ and $\frac{1}{2} = .0111\dots$ for example. This fact causes minor problems. For our purposes here it suffices to say that these can be overcome.)

Let $\varepsilon_m = \sup\{\,|\phi(x) - \phi(y)|\,\big|\, 0 \le x,\ y \le 1 \text{ and } x \overset{m}{\equiv} y\}$. The following theorem is obtained by Rosenblatt:[5]

Theorem 3: If $\{X_n\}$ is a stationary 0–1 stochastic process such that

i) either $0 < \Delta \le \phi(x)$ or $\phi(x) \le 1 - \Lambda < 1$ for all $0 \le x \le 1$;

ii) $\Sigma\, \varepsilon_m < \infty$,

then $\{X_n\}$ has a representation.

Both the conditions of Theorem 3 are weakened in reference 6, but not in such a way as to give much additional insight into the problem. Another theorem of a slightly different nature that appears in reference 5 is:

Theorem 4: If $\{X_n\}$ is a stationary 0–1 stochastic process such that

i) $|\phi(x) - \phi(y)| \le 1 - \Delta < 1$ for all $x, y \in [0, 1]$;

ii) ϕ is non-decreasing;

then $\{X_n\}$ has a representation.

I have succeeded in proving (but have not yet published a proof of) the following theorem:

Theorem 5: If $\{X_n\}$ is a stationary 0–1 stochastic process such that

i) ϕ is of bounded variation;

ii) $0 < \alpha \le \phi(x) \le 1 - \alpha$ for all $x \in [0, 1]$;

then $\{X_n\}$ has a representation.

In reference 6, a representation is obtained for a type of process $\{Z_n\}$ called a "chain of almost finite order." The trick in this case is to obtain from $\{Z_n\}$ a tail trivial Markov chain from which $\{Z_n\}$ can be recovered. Again, this result gives no real insight into the general representation problem.

All the work mentioned so far in this section has dealt with the case when the tail field of the process $\{X_n\}$ is trivial. Even if $\mathcal{F}_{-\infty}$ is not trivial, there still exists the mathematical problem of obtaining a representation for $\{X_n\}$. This representation is obtained for stationary Markov chains in reference 7; however, a process $\{X_n\}$ with non-trivial tail field is not causal, so there seems to be no point in delving further into this type of representation here.

4. REMARKS ON THE METHOD OF PROOF

If $\{X_n\}$ is a stationary Markov process, it is possible to define a probability space, a real valued function h of two variables, and random variables $\{\xi_n\}$ and $\{Y_n\}$ such that

i) the sequences $\{X_n\}$ and $\{Y_n\}$ have the same probability structure;

ii) $\{\xi_n\}$ is an independent sequence of random variables uniformly distributed on $[0, 1]$;

iii) $Y_{n+1} = h(\xi_{n+1}, Y_n)$.

Then we see that

$$\begin{aligned} Y_{n+1} &= h[\xi_{n+1}, h(\xi_n, Y_{n-1})] \\ &= h[\xi_{n+1}, h(\xi_n, h(\xi_{n-1}, \ldots h(\xi_{n-k+1}, Y_{n-k}) \ldots]. \end{aligned}$$

Thus Y_{n+1} can be made a function of some ξ's, and one Y_{n-k} in the arbitrarily remote past. Of course this does not guarantee that the dependence on Y_{n-k} drops out as one goes back further and further into the past, as it must if Y_{n+1} is to be a function only of the ξ_k's for $k \leq n+1$. There clearly exists some optimal theorem giving necessary and sufficient conditions (in terms of the process $\{X_n\}$) for the existence of a function h of the type mentioned above such that the process $\{Y_n\}$ is strictly a function of the $\{\xi_n\}$ process. However, even when a "good" h exists it is still possible to choose a "bad" h. For example, suppose $\{X_n\}$ represents a sequence of tosses of a fair coin so that $P\{X_n = 0\}$ $P\{X_n = 1\} = \frac{1}{2}$ and the X_n's are independent. If we define h_g (for good h) by

$$h_g(\xi, y) = h_g(\xi) = \begin{cases} 0 & 0 \leq \xi \leq \frac{1}{2} \\ 1 & \frac{1}{2} < \xi \leq 1, \end{cases}$$

then the sequence $\{Y_n = h_g(\xi_n, Y_{n-1}) = h_g(\xi_n)\}$ clearly represents a sequence of independent coin tosses, and just as clearly Y_n is a function of $\ldots, \xi_{n-1}, \xi_n$ only (since it is strictly a function of ξ_n). Now suppose we define h_b (for bad h) by

$$h_b(\xi, y) = \begin{cases} 0 & \text{if } 0 \leq \xi \leq \frac{1}{2} \text{ and } y = 0 \\ 0 & \text{if } \frac{1}{2} < \xi \leq 1 \text{ and } y = 1 \\ 1 & \text{if } \frac{1}{2} < \xi \leq 1 \text{ and } y = 0 \\ 1 & \text{if } 0 \leq \xi \leq \frac{1}{2} \text{ and } y = 1. \end{cases}$$

If $Y_{n+1} = h_b(\xi_{n+1}, Y_n)$, then the observation of ξ_{n+1} tells whether $Y_{n+1} = Y_n$ or $Y_{n+1} \neq Y_n$. One easily convinces himself that the observation of $\xi_{n-k+1}, \ldots, \xi_{n+1}$ tells for all $\alpha = n - k, \ldots, n$, whether $Y_{\alpha+1} = Y_\alpha$ or not, and also tells whether $Y_{n-k} = Y_{n+1}$ or $Y_{n-k} \neq Y_{n+1}$, but does not tell the values of any Y_k unless a value is given for Y_{n-k} (or any other Y_j with $n - k \leq j \leq n$ for that matter). It follows that in this instance Y_{n+1} is not a function of $\ldots, \xi_n, \xi_{n+1}$ only. One notices immediately that the function h_b was "unnaturally" chosen so that $h_b(\xi, 0)$ is non-decreasing, while $h_b(\xi, 1)$ is non-increasing. (In a sense the function h_g was "scrambled" to get h_b.) However, $h_g(\xi, y)$ is non-decreasing in ξ for $y = 0$ *and* for $y = 1$. We note that h_g has a simple and "natural" relationship to $P(Y_{n+1} \leq y | Y_n = x)$ in that

$$Y_{n+1} = h_g(\xi_{n+1}, x) = \inf \{y | P(Y_{n+1} \leq y | Y_n = x) > \xi_{n+1}\}. \tag{7}$$

Unfortunately, the "natural" choice of h given by (7) does not always work. (See the example in Section 4 of reference 6.) However, a "reasonable" conjecture is that if a Markov process has a representation, then after a suitable permutation of its state a "natural" representation can be found for the process.

The tricky part(s) of all the work done to date have been choosing a good h, showing that the chosen h works, or both.

5. CONCLUDING REMARKS

One can only speculate about the eventual practical applications which might come from this representation theory. One would hope that it might eventually be useful in nonlinear prediction.

If a causal system is divided into the three parts—input, "black box", and output—then insights into the representation problem might well be used to provide information about one or more parts of the system based on information about the remainder of the system. It would seem that a great deal of work will have to be done in this area before any of the results obtained can be used in practical applications.

REFERENCES

1. J. L. Doob, *Stochastic Processes*, (New York: Wiley, 1953).
2. M. Rosenblatt, "Stationary Processes as Shifts of Functions of Independent Random Variables," *J. Math. and Mech.*, **8**, 665–681 (1959).
3. M. Rosenblatt, "Stationary Markov Chains and Independent Random Variables," *J. Math. and Mech.*, **9**, 945–949 (1960).
4. D. L. Hanson, "On the Representation Problem for Stationary Stochastic Processes with Trivial Tail Field," *J. Math. and Mech.*, **12**, 293–301 (1963).
5. M. Rosenblatt, "The Representation of a Class of Two State Stationary Processes in Terms of Independent Random Variables," *J. Math. and Mech.*, **12**, 721–730 (1963).
6. J. R. Blum and D. L. Hanson, "Further Results on the Representation Problem for Stationary Stochastic Processes with Trivial Tail Field," *J. Math. and Mech.*, **12**, 935–943 (1963).
7. D. L. Hanson, "A Representation Theorem for Stationary Markov Chains," *J. Math. and Mech.*, **12**, 731–736 (1963).

A GROUP-THEORETIC APPROACH TO CAUSAL SYSTEMS

Roe Goodman

Department of Mathematics, Massachusetts Institute of Technology, Cambridge, Mass.

We consider a classification of multiparameter Hilbert systems (continuous unitary representations of $\mathbf{R}^n$ or $\mathbf{Z}^n$ on a Hilbert space of states) as nondeterministic or deterministic in terms of the existence of proper *causal manifolds* of states.

Every one-parameter Hilbert system splits into deterministic plus nondeterministic parts.

Hyperbolic equations of evolution such as those occurring in relativistic quantum mechanics are considered from this point of view and it results that the equations describing massless particles (e. g., wave equation, Maxwell's equations) generate nondeterministic systems, while the equations describing particles of nonzero mass (e. g., Dirac equation, Klein-Gordon equation) generate deterministic systems.

1. INTRODUCTION

For the purposes of this paper, we shall define a *multiparameter Hilbert system* to be a system whose inputs and outputs are functions on the parameter group G (either $\mathbf{R}^n$—the continuous case—or $\mathbf{Z}^n$—the discrete case—where $\mathbf{R}$ = real numbers, $\mathbf{Z}$ = integers) with values in a complex, separable Hilbert space $\mathcal{H}$. We assume that the collection $\mathcal{S}$ of inputs and outputs is

1) linear: $f, g \in \mathcal{S}$, λ a complex number implies $f(t) + \lambda g(t) \in \mathcal{S}$;

2) translation invariant: $f \in \mathcal{S}$, $s \in G$ implies $U(s) f \in \mathcal{S}$, where $(U(s)f)(t) = f(s + t)$;

3) stationary: $\| f(t) \|_{\mathcal{H}} = \| f(s) \|_{\mathcal{H}}$ for all $s, t \in G$, where $\| \cdot \|_{\mathcal{H}}$ is the norm in $\mathcal{H}$.

In the continuous case, we also assume

4) $t \longrightarrow \| f(t) \|_{\mathcal{H}}$ is a continuous function on G for each $f \in \mathcal{S}$.

It follows from the assumptions above that we may define an inner product on $\mathcal{S}$ by setting

$$(f, g) = (f(0), g(0))_{\mathcal{H}}.$$

Thus

$$(U(t)f, U(t)g) = (f, g),$$

*Research reported here was supported in part by the Air Force Office of Scientific Research and the National Science Foundation.

Presented at the Symposium on System Theory
Polytechnic Institute of Brooklyn, April 20, 21, 22, 1965

so for each t, the linear operator $U(t)$ is unitary, while $U(s+t)f(x) = f(x+s+t) = U_s U_t f(x)$, that is,

$$U(s+t) = U(s)U(t),$$

so $t \longrightarrow U(t)$ is a unitary representation of G on $\mathfrak{H}$, which by assumption (4) is strongly continuous, that is, $t \longrightarrow \|U(t)f\|$ is a continuous function.

It is thus evident that from one point of view a multiparameter Hilbert system is simply a continuous unitary representation of the parameter group G, the theory of which is highly developed. The aspect we are interested in here, however, is a notion of causality in Hilbert systems, and its application to some concrete Hilbert systems associated with hyperbolic partial differential equations and the "elementary particles" of relativistic quantum theory. The definition of Hilbert system that we have given is a modification of that given by Fourès and Segal in reference 2. (The Fourès and Segal article,[2] together with Segal's paper,[6] were the starting point of the present article.)

2. SPECTRAL MEASURES

We shall briefly indicate the facts about unitary representations that shall be used in the sequel (cf., e.g., reference 5). If U is a unitary representation of G on a Hilbert space $\mathfrak{H}$, then for each $f \in \mathfrak{H}$ there exists a positive Baire measure μ_f on the dual group $\hat{G}$ ($\mathbf{R}^n$ in the continuous case, $\mathbf{T}^n$—the n-torus— in the discrete case), such that

$$(U_t f, f) = \int_{\hat{G}} e^{ix \cdot t} d\mu_f(x).$$

We shall call μ_f the spectral measure for f. There exist $f_1, f_2, \ldots$ in $\mathfrak{H}$ such that the representation U is unitarily equivalent to the representation $\hat{U}$ on $\sum_{k=1}^{\infty} \oplus L_2(d\mu_k)$, where $\mu_k = \mu_{f_k}$, and $\hat{U}(t)$ is the operator multiplication by $e^{it \cdot x}$ on each summand $L_2(d\mu_k)$. If each measure μ_k is equivalent to Lebesgue measure on $\hat{G}$, then we say that U has *homogeneous Lebesgue spectrum.* If U is the representation determined by a Hilbert system $\mathfrak{H}$, we say in this case that $\mathfrak{H}$ has homogeneous Lebesgue spectrum.

In the special case $G = \mathbf{R}^1$, every unitary representation is of the form $U(t) = \exp[itH]$ for a self-adjoint operator H on $\mathcal{H}$, and conversely. (For the representation $\hat{U}$ above, H is the operator "multiplication by x" on each summand $L_2(d\mu_k)$). We shall say that a self-adjoint operator H has homogeneous Lebesgue spectrum if the representation $t \longrightarrow \exp[itH]$ does.

3. CAUSALITY

To discuss causality in the context of Hilbert systems, we assume G is "causally-oriented" by means of a subset C with the properties

i) $C + C \subset C$

ii) if $K \subset G$ is compact, there exists $s, t \in C$ such that: a) $K \subset C - s$; and b) $K \subset C' + t$.

[For example, in case $\mathbf{G} = \mathbf{R}^1$ or $\mathbf{Z}$, we take $\mathbf{C}$ = negative axis or $\mathbf{C}$ = negative integers, respectively. When $\mathbf{G} = \mathbf{R}^n$, any proper convex cone with interior, e.g., the "backward light cone", satisfies (i) and (ii).] The cone $\mathbf{C}$ gives a partial ordering of $\mathbf{G}$: $t \leq s \iff t - s \in \mathbf{C}$, and we shall refer to the points $s \leq t$ as being "earlier" than t.

Now define a *causal manifold* to be a closed linear subspace $\mathfrak{M}$ in $\mathfrak{S}$ with the property (1): $U(t)\,\mathfrak{M} \subseteq \mathfrak{M}$ for all $t \in \mathbf{C}$. If $\mathfrak{L}$ is any collection of functions in $\mathfrak{S}$, the causal manifold generated by $\mathfrak{L}$ consists of all functions in $\mathfrak{S}$ which can be approximated (in the Hilbert space norm of $\mathfrak{S}$) by linear combinations of functions $U(t)f$, with $t \in \mathbf{C}$ and $f \in \mathfrak{L}$. In case a causal manifold $\mathfrak{M}$ satisfies $U(t)\,\mathfrak{M} \subseteq \mathfrak{M}$ for *all t*, we say $\mathfrak{M}$ is *trivial*, otherwise $\mathfrak{M}$ is called *proper*. A causal manifold $\mathfrak{M}$ is *maximal* if (2a): $\bigcap_{t \in \mathbf{C}} \mathfrak{M}_t = 0$, and (2b): $\bigcup_{t \in \mathbf{C}} \mathfrak{M}_{-t}$ is dense in $\mathfrak{S}$. Finally, we say a Hilbert system is *deterministic* if every causal manifold is trivial. If there exists a maximal causal manifold, we say that the system is *non-deterministic*. [In a deterministic system, the value $f(t)$ can be approximated arbitrarily well by linear combinations $\sum'_{t_k \in \mathbf{C}} a_k f(t_k)$, so that the "past history" of f, that is, the values of f on $\mathbf{C}$, determines f completely in this sense.]

The simplest example of a non-deterministic Hilbert system is obtained by taking $\mathcal{H} = L_2(\mathbf{G};\ \mathcal{K})$. This is the space of all functions φ on $\mathbf{G}$ with values in a Hilbert space $\mathcal{K}$ such that

$$||\varphi||^2_{\mathcal{H}} \equiv \int |\varphi(t)|^2_{\mathcal{K}}\, dt < \infty,$$

$|\cdot|_{\mathcal{K}}$ denoting the norm in $\mathcal{K}$, and dt the invariant measure on $\mathbf{G}$ (volume measure on $\mathbf{R}^n$, discrete measure on $\mathbf{Z}^n$). The space $\mathfrak{S}$ of inputs and outputs consists of the functions $f(t) = \varphi_t$, where $\varphi \in \mathcal{H}$ and $\varphi_t(s) = \varphi(s+t)$. If $\mathfrak{M}$ = all functions φ_t, where $\varphi = 0$ on $\mathbf{C}$, then properties (i), (iia), and (iib) of $\mathbf{C}$ imply that $\mathfrak{M}$ satisfies the corresponding properties (1), (2a), and (2b). $\mathfrak{M}$ is thus a maximal causal manifold (cf. reference 2 for further properties of this system).

Remark: One may interpret the definition of a maximal causal manifold as follows: the condition (2a) says that the "infinite past" of the system is 0, while condition (2b) says that any input can be approximated by inputs depending on only a "finite portion" of the past.

Given a Hilbert system $\mathfrak{S}$, we consider here the question of finding criteria for the existence of proper causal manifolds in $\mathfrak{S}$. In this respect the one-parameter systems differ fundamentally from the multiparameter systems. In case $\mathbf{G} = \mathbf{R}^1$ or $\mathbf{Z}^1$, every causal manifold $\mathfrak{M}$ in $\mathfrak{S}$ defines a resolution of the identity on a subsystem of $\mathfrak{S}$. Specifically, let $\mathfrak{M}_t = U(t)\,\mathfrak{M}$. Then $\mathfrak{M}_t \subseteq \mathfrak{M}$ for $t < 0$ implies $\mathfrak{M}_s \subseteq \mathfrak{M}_t$ if $s \leq t$. Let $\mathfrak{M}_{+\infty} = \left(\bigcup_{t \geq 0} \mathfrak{M}_t\right)^-$ and $\mathfrak{M}_{-\infty} = \bigcap_{t<0} \mathfrak{M}_t$. When $\mathfrak{M}$ is trivial, $\mathfrak{M}_{\pm\infty} = \mathfrak{M}$, while when $\mathfrak{M}$ is maximal $\mathfrak{M}_{-\infty} = 0$ and $\mathfrak{M}_{+\infty} = \mathfrak{S}$. In any case, if

$$\mathfrak{S}_1 = \mathfrak{M}_\infty \cap (\mathfrak{M}_{-\infty})^\perp$$

$$\mathfrak{N}_t = \mathfrak{M}_t \cap (\mathfrak{M}_{-\infty})^\perp$$

($\perp$ = orthogonal complement), then $\mathfrak{N}_0$ is a maximal causal manifold in the subsystem $\mathcal{S}_1$, and $\mathfrak{N}_t$ is a resolution of the identity in $\mathcal{S}_1$. Furthermore, $U(s)\mathfrak{N}_t = \mathfrak{N}_{t+s}$. Now, if $\mathcal{S}_1 \neq 0$, the theorem of Stone and von Neuman on the uniqueness of the Schrödinger operators (as generalized by Mackey[4]) states that the subsystem $\mathcal{S}_1$ must be of the special type $L_2(\mathbf{G}; \mathcal{K})$ discussed above, with the maximal causal manifold $\mathfrak{N}_0$ consisting of all functions $\{\varphi_t\}$ with φ vanishing on $\mathbf{C}$.

The above facts, together with well-known facts in the theory of decompositions of representations, lead immediately to Theorem 1.

Theorem 1. Let $\mathcal{S}$ be a one-parameter Hilbert system. Then $\mathcal{S}$ is non-deterministic if and only if the associated representation U has homogeneous Lebesgue spectrum.

Every one-parameter Hilbert system is the direct sum of a deterministic system and a non-deterministic system.

(See reference 3 for further details.)

Remarks. 1. Our definitions of deterministic and non-deterministic systems differ from the more restrictive notions used in the theory of stationary stochastic processes, in that we are only concerned with the classification of systems up to unitary equivalence. Thus, e.g., in the case $\mathbf{G} = \mathbf{R}^1$, if $f \in \mathcal{S}$, then f will generate a proper causal manifold whenever $d\mu_f/dt$ (the density function for the absolutely continuous part of μ_f) is nonzero almost everywhere. The integrability of $(\log d\mu_f/dt)/(1 + t^2)$ is irrelevant, since by a unitary transformation we can obtain an equivalent system in which the function $\hat{f}$ corresponding to f has $d\mu_{\hat{f}}/dt = 1$. [The Wiener prediction theory can be derived from the above theorem, however.[1]]

2. It follows from Theorem 1 that in a one-parameter Hilbert system, any two causal manifolds are equivalent, ignoring spectral multiplicities. This is definitely false for multiparameter Hilbert systems, as there exist maximal causal manifolds which are not equivalent to the special form discussed above, and the corresponding Hilbert systems are non-deterministic but do not have homogeneous Lebesgue spectrum.

3. Theorem 1 does yield information even for a multiparameter system $\mathcal{S}$, however, if we consider the functions in $\mathcal{S}$ only along a line lying interior to $\mathbf{C} \cup (-\mathbf{C})$, thus obtaining a one-parameter system. If any of these one-parameter systems have no Lebesgue spectrum, then certainly $\mathcal{S}$ is deterministic (any proper causal manifold in $\mathcal{S}$ would define a proper causal manifold in such a one-parameter system). As yet there exists no classification of all non-deterministic multi-parameter Hilbert systems, however.

4. HILBERT SYSTEMS AND WAVE EQUATIONS

A continuous one-parameter Hilbert system $\mathcal{S}$, i.e., a unitary representation U of $\mathbf{R}^1$, is determined by its infinitesimal generator H, where $U(t) = \exp[itH]$ (cf. Sec. 2). An interesting class of systems, in connection with relativistic quantum mechanics, arises when H is a differential operator on a Hilbert space $\mathcal{H}$ of vector-valued (generalized) functions on $\mathbf{R}^n$. The elements of $\mathcal{S}$ are then (weak) solutions of the partial differential equation,

$$\frac{\partial u}{\partial t} = iHu. \tag{1}$$

The Dirac equation, for example, is of this form, where $\mathcal{H}$ consists of functions on $\mathbf{R}^3$ ("space") with values in four-dimensional "spin-space", and the operator H is a first-order differential operator. The associated Hilbert system is the "one-particle" space for the electron (cf. reference 7 for further details). Also reducible to the form of eq. (1), however, are wave equations which are not of first order in $\partial/\partial t$. For example, the scalar wave equation

$$\Box\, \varphi = 0 \tag{2}$$

where $\Box = \Delta - \partial^2/\partial t^2$, Δ being the Laplacian operator on $\mathbf{R}^3$, can be written as a pair of equations and put in the form of eq. (1) by taking

$$H = \begin{pmatrix} 0 & -\Delta \\ I & 0 \end{pmatrix}, \quad u = \begin{pmatrix} \varphi \\ \partial\varphi/\partial t \end{pmatrix}.$$

Now a natural Hilbert space norm in this case is the "energy norm"

$$||u||_{\mathcal{H}}^2 = \int_{\mathbf{R}^3} |\nabla \varphi|^2 + |\partial \varphi/\partial t|^2 \, dx.$$

This norm is translation invariant, and the collection of all solutions of eq. (1) with finite norm comprises a one-parameter Hilbert system. Other norms, similar to the energy norm but involving fractional powers of the Laplacian, are relevant in quantum field theory. One obtains the Maxwell equations for free space or the Klein-Gordon equation by taking φ vector-valued or by adding $m^2\varphi$ to the right hand side of eq. (2), respectively, and changing the energy norm appropriately.[7] From the differential equation point of view, the solutions of eq. (1) which constitute a Hilbert system are "wave packets"; we exclude "plane-waves" by requiring that $u(t)$ for each t be in the Hilbert space $\mathcal{H}$. We shall refer to the functions in $\mathcal{S}$ as *normalizable* solutions of (1). Thus from Sec. 3 follows Theorem 2.

Theorem 2. The Hilbert system of normalizable solutions of (1) is non-deterministic $\Longleftrightarrow$ the generator H has homogeneous Lebesgue spectrum. (For further properties of this class of Hilbert systems, and for the relationship between causal manifolds and the set of solutions of (1) which vanish on $\mathbf{C}$, cf. reference 8.).

Remarks. This theorem sheds considerable light on the extent to which the "systems theory" approach to causality described here is applicable to the systems arising in relativistic quantum mechanics. For such systems the spectrum of the non-quantized generator H for translations in time will exclude the interval $(-m, m)$, where all the elementary particles described by the system have mass $\geq m$. Now when $m > 0$, it follows that such a system is always deterministic, in our definition. (For example, the normalizable solutions to the Dirac or Klein-Gordon equations comprise deterministic systems.) Furthermore, quantum mechanical systems in general are non-deterministic, in our definition, only to the extent that they contain massless particles, e.g., involve interactions with electromagnetic radiation. (The normalizable solutions of the Maxwell equations comprise a non-deterministic system.)

REFERENCES

1. P. Cartier, *Analyse spectrale et théorème de prédiction statistique de Wiener*, Seminaire Bourbaki 1960/61, fascicule 3.
2. Y. Fourès and I. E. Segal, "Causality and Analyticity," *Trans. Amer. Math. Soc.*, **78**, (385–405) (1955).
3. R. Goodman, "Invariant Subspaces for Normal Operators," *J. Math. Mech.* (to appear).
4. G. W. Mackey, "A Theorem of Stone and Von Neuman," Duke Math. J., **16**, 313–326 (1949).
5. G. W. Mackey, "Group Representations in Hilbert Space," Appendix to ref. 7.
6. I. E. Segal, "Direct formulation of causality requirements on the S-operator," *Phys., Rev.*, **109**, 2191–2198 (1958).
7. I. E. Segal, *Mathematical Problems of Relativistic Physics* (Providence: American Math. Soc., 1962).
8. R. Goodman, *On Domains of Uniqueness* (to appear).

APPLICATIONS OF FUNCTION SPACE INTEGRALS TO NONLINEAR DIFFERENTIAL EQUATIONS

Monroe D. Donsker
Courant Institute of Mathematical Sciences,
New York University, New York, N. Y.

ABSTRACT*

Theorems on the asymptotic behavior of function space integrals are applied to function space integral solutions of certain differential equations. In particular, one treats the viscous flow equation as the viscosity approaches zero.

*The full text of Professor Donsker's paper was not available at the time of publication of these *Proceedings*.

Presented at the Symposium on System Theory
Polytechnic Institute of Brooklyn, April 20, 21, 22, 1965

STOCHASTIC STABILITY AND THE DESIGN OF FEEDBACK CONTROLS*

H. Kushner

Division of Applied Mathematics, Center for Dynamical Systems
Brown University, Providence, R.I.

Some recent results in stochastic stability, and in the theory of diffusion, are applied to the design of feedback controls for some stochastic control problems, where the system is represented by a stochastic differential equation.

Basically, the procedures for choosing the controls are the same as in the deterministic case. A total cost of control $V(x_0, t_0)$ (a stochastic Liapunov function) is decided upon, where (x_0, t_0) is the initial point. A corresponding control and target set are then derived. The controls obtained by such means have certain useful properties—such as giving stable trajectories (in an appropriate sense), and, in some cases, are optimum for some error criteria.

Theorems are given and applied to several problems in the choice of a feedback control. Part of the interest in the technique is that, at present, it gives information of practical consequence for a variety of problems in an area in which such information is hard to obtain in any other way.

Probability estimates of the form

$$P[\sup V(x, t) \geq q] \leq V(x, 0)/q$$
$$T \geq t \geq 0$$

are available and, since $V(x, t)$ is often at our disposal, give useful information on the trajectory.

Similar methods can be used to analyze the behavior, and eventual convergence, of the random trajectories of some types of adaptive and hill-climbing systems.

1. INTRODUCTION

The object of this paper is to describe the stochastic extensions of the various techniques for using the second method of Liapunov to aid the construction and analysis of feedback controls.[1-8] The method appears to be useful for design and analysis, although it is too early to make a final judgment. Much depends on future success in finding suitable Liapunov functions, and understanding the relationship between the loss function and the desired behavior of the control system.

The deterministic methods have been motivated by considerations of the following nature. Consider the optimal control problem with control u, and system

$$\dot{x} = f(x, u)$$

*This research was supported in part by National Aeronautics and Space Administration under Grant No. NGR-40-002-015 and in part by the United States Air Force through the Air Force Office of Scientific Research under Grant No. AF-AFOSR-693-64.

Presented at the Symposium on System Theory
Polytechnic Institute of Brooklyn, April 20, 21, 22, 1965

and cost

$$C^u(x) = \int_0^\tau k(x,u)\,dt, \quad C^u(\partial S) = 0$$

where τ is the first time of contact with ∂S, the boundary of a target set S. The minimum cost,

$$\underline{C}(x) = \min_u C^u(x),$$

is achieved by $u = w$. If $\underline{C}(x)$ is sufficiently differentiable, then the Hamilton-Jacobi equation

$$d\underline{C}(x)/dt = \underline{C}'_x(x)\,f(x,w) = -k(x,w)$$

is satisfied (where $'$ is transpose and $\underline{C}_x$ is the gradient of C), and w is the u *minimizing*

$$[\underline{C}'_x(x)\,f(x,u) + k(x,u)].$$

In lieu of attempting to solve this problem, an alternative procedure has suggested itself to many authors (e.g., references 1–8). Choose a Liapunov function $V(x)$, and some $u(x)$ so that the system has suitable stability properties, and compute

$$V'_x(x)\,f(x,u) = -k_1(x,u),$$

where $k_1(x,u) \geqq 0$ in $X + \partial S$. X is the state space.

A comparison of $k_1(x,u)$ and $k(x,u)$ can yield useful information, e.g., whether $V(x)$ is greater or less than $\underline{C}(x)$, or stability properties of the controlled system, the nature of the problem for which $V(x)$ and u are optimum, and whether some other calculable control would minimize the cost $C^u(x)$, etc.

Similar results are achievable in the stochastic situation. Stochastic stability seems to be a more complicated subject than its deterministic counterpart, since the corresponding Liapunov functions do not decrease monotonically for each sample function. The effect of controls on the statistical behavior of the system can be made rather explicit in terms of a reduction of a bound on the probability of arbitrary deviations in the sample paths before hitting ∂S.

In Part II several comparison and optimality theorems are proved. In Part III the theorems are applied to the problem of choosing and analyzing the effect of feedback controls for several stochastic systems.

2. THE SYSTEM TO BE CONTROLLED

The object to be controlled is represented by the vector stochastic differential (Ito) equation

$$dx = f(x,u)\,dt + \sigma(x,u)\,dz, \tag{1a}$$

by which is meant (using the Ito[9] interpretation of the stochastic integral)

$$x_t = x_0 + \int_0^t f(x_t, u(x_t))\,dt + \int_0^t \sigma(x_t, u(x_t))\,dz_t. \tag{1b}$$

z is a vector Wiener process with independent components, $\dot{z}$ is commonly called white Gaussian noise;

$$\dot{x} = f(x, u) + \sigma(x, u)\,\dot{z}. \tag{1c}$$

f is a vector with components f_i, and σ is a matrix with components σ_{ij}. The process x_t is confined to X.

Without the control parameter u, the meaning of (1b) and the conditions under which a solution (a stochastic process) exists and is unique is discussed in references 9 and 10. To be secure in the mathematical development we assume these conditions. Let $\| \ \|$ be the Euclidean norm. For some finite positive K, let

$$\begin{aligned} \| f(x+\alpha, u+\beta) - f(x,u) \| &\leqq K \| \alpha \| + K \| \beta \| \\ \| \sigma(x+\alpha, u+\beta) - \sigma(x,u) \| &\leqq K \| \alpha \| + K \| \beta \| \end{aligned} \tag{2}$$

$$\begin{aligned} \| f(x,u) \| &\leqq K[1 + \| x \|^2 + \| u \|^2]^{1/2} \\ \| u(x+\alpha) - u(x) \| &\leqq K \| \alpha \| \end{aligned} \tag{3}$$

A control satisfying (3) is termed *admissible*. (3) implies continuity of $u(x)$. Note that $u = \text{sign } x$ is not admissible. Since the K in (3) can be large, admissibility is probably not a serious restriction.

In certain cases, our results are valid if (2) and (3) are replaced by local Lipshitz conditions. This is the case when the trajectories have appropriate stability properties (e.g., when the origin is stable with probability one (w.p.1) in the sense of reference 15).

The primary attractions of the model (1) are that it represents a rather large class of Markov processes with continuous sample paths, there is a large body of theory concerning it, and it seems that many physical problems can be modelled by it. The question of modelling will not be discussed. The identification of particular forms of (1) with particular physical problems is still an open problem in general (especially in the nonlinear case). (Some interesting results in reference 11 clarify some of the questions of modelling.)

For each integer r, define the stochastic process

$$x^r_{n+1} = x^r_n + f(x^r_n, u(x^r_n))\,\Delta + \sigma(x^r_n, u(x^r_n))\,\delta z_n, \tag{4}$$

where $\delta z_n = z((n+1)\Delta) - z(n\Delta)$, and define $x^r(t) = x^r_n$ in the interval $(n+1)\Delta > t \geqq n\Delta$. Then, for a suitable sequence of $\Delta \longrightarrow 0$, we have $x^r(t) \longrightarrow x(t)$ with probability one for each t, where $x(t)$ is the solution to (1).

Some facts, to be used later, will be quoted. If $u(x)$ is admissible, x_t is continuous with probability one, and is a Markov process; i.e., for any measurable set A in X,

$$P[x_{t+s} \in A \mid x_\sigma, \sigma \leqq t] = P[x_{t+s} \in A \mid x_t], \tag{5}$$

where the bar | denotes conditional probability. A major, relatively recent, development in probability theory is the analysis and extensive use of the concept of *random time* (see references 10, 12, 13 for details). An example of a random time is the first time that x_t leaves an open set A; $\tau = \min\{t: x_t \notin A\}$. τ is a random variable. Loosely speaking, whether or not the event $\{\tau < t\}$ has occurred (in the example, whether x_s has left A by time t) can be determined by observations on the x_s process up to and including time t. (The set $\{\tau < t\}$ is in the σ-field determined by x_s, $s \leqq t$.)

The significance, to control applications, of the concept of random time, will be seen in the sequel. If the process x_t is confined to a set X which is compact, and if u is admissible, the process x_t is, in fact, a *strong Markov process*. A strong Markov process has the Markovian property relative to random times. Let τ be a random time, then

$$P[x_{\tau+s} \in A \mid x_\delta, \delta \leqq \tau] = P[x_{\tau+s} \in A \mid x_\tau].$$

For example, let x_t start in an open set B, let τ be the least time of leaving B, then for any nonrandom s the probability that $x_{\tau+s} \in A$, given x_τ and the paths up to τ, equals the probability given only x_τ. The strong Markov property is proved in reference 10.

3. THE CONTROL PROBLEM

The process x_t is defined in a set X in a Euclidean space. There is a set S in X given, and the main object of the control is to transfer $x_0 = x$ to ∂S in finite average time. In certain cases, infinite average times will be allowed. The proofs of the theorems we require assume that X is compact (e.g., the proof of (8) for the operator L^u). This does not seem to be a restriction from the practical point of view, since X may be as large as desired. We may stop the process upon leaving some very large set, and estimate the probability of this event by (10). Also, to each u and initial point $x_0 = x$, there is the associated cost

$$C^u(x) = E_x^u \int_0^{\tau_u} k(x_t, u_t)\, dt. \tag{6}$$

E_x^u is the expectation and τ_u is the random time of arrival at ∂S, (provided that it is defined), and $k(x, u)$ is continuous and non-negative, and is referred to as the loss.

Define $\underline{C}(x) = \min\limits_u C^u(x)$, provided that the minimizing u is admissible. Part of the control problem is the comparison of $C^u(x)$ and $E_x^u\ \tau_u$ for various controls. Various restrictions may be placed on the control; it may be bounded, or its functional form may be restricted, e.g., it may be allowed to be a function of some, but not all, components of x. Some stability properties may also be of interest, e.g., an estimate of the probability that x_t ever leaves some set X', if x_0 is in X', or some other qualitative information on the random paths.

A number of relevant results and examples of stability are in references 14–16. Reference 17 is concerned with ergodic properties of the processes and utilizes certain properties of stochastic Liapunov functions.

4. OTHER MATHEMATICAL PRELIMINARIES

Let u be admissible. Define the operator

$$L^u = \frac{\partial}{\partial t} + \sum_i f_i(x, u) \frac{\partial}{\partial x_i} + \frac{1}{2} \sum_{i,j} S_{ij}(x, u) \frac{\partial^2}{\partial x_i \partial x_j}$$

$$S_{ij} = \sum_k \sigma_{ik} \sigma_{jk} \tag{7}$$

L^u is the differential generator of the x_t process, with control u. We say that $V(x)$ is in the domain of L^u $(V(x) \in D(L))$ if $V(x)$ is a non-negative, scalar-valued function with continuous second derivatives, and the sets $\{x: V(x) \leqq c\}$ are compact and connected,* for all c less than some $c_0 > 0$. Such a $V(x)$ will also be called a Liapunov function, or a Liapunov function in a region R, if $L^u V \leqq 0$ in R for the given u. Note that $L^u V(x) = dV(x)/dt = V_x'(x) f(x, u)$ in the deterministic case.

Since X is compact and x_t is a strong Markov process, Dynkin's formula[10]

$$E_x^u\, V(x_\tau) - V(x) = E_x^u \int_0^\tau L^u V(x_s)\, ds \tag{8}$$

holds for all random times τ with $E_x^u\, \tau < \infty$. (8) underlies many of the results of the sequel. It says, in effect, that $V(x)$ is the average value of the integral of the "stochastic derivative" $L^u V(x)$. The compactness of X and the finiteness of $E_x^u\, \tau$ are useful in establishing its validity. Eq. (8) is actually valid under more general conditions, but this is beyond our purpose.

Let $V(x)$ be in $D(L^u)$ in the region $R \in X$,

$$R = \{x: V(x) < \lambda\} - \{x: V(x) \leqq \lambda_0\}, \quad \lambda > \lambda_0$$
$$\partial R = \{x: V(x) = \lambda, \quad V(x) = \lambda_0\}.$$

Let $L^u V < 0$ in R and $L^u V(x) \leqq 0$ on ∂R. Let τ_u be the random time to ∂R, starting at $x \in R$. It can be proved, using the continuity of x_t and $L^u V(x)$, and the compactness of X, that τ_u will exist (although $E_x^{\tau u}$ may not be finite), and that the integral in (8) is defined and finite, and that (8) is valid. (See reference 22.) Since x_t is continuous with probability one, x_t cannot leave R without touching ∂R (with probability one). We have

$$E_x^u\, V(x_\tau) = \lambda_0\, P\left[\sup_{\tau_u \geqq t \geqq 0} V(x_t) \leqq \lambda_0\right] + \lambda\, P\left[\sup_{\tau_u \geqq t \geqq 0} V(x_t) \geqq \lambda\right]. \tag{9}$$

Letting $\lambda_0 = 0$, and noting that the integral in (8) is nonpositive in $R + \partial R$,

$$P\left[\sup_{\tau_u \geqq t \geqq 0} V(x_t) \geqq \lambda\right] = (V(x) - E_x^u \int_0^{\tau_u} L^u V(x)\, dt)/\lambda \leqq V(x)/\lambda. \tag{10}$$

*The domain of L^n is obviously larger than our $D(L)$, but $D(L)$ suffices.

(10) can also be derived by showing that $V(y_t)$ is a non-negative super martingale, where y_t is the x_t process stopped at time τ_u; then the inequality (10) is the non-negative super martingale inequality. The latter method must be used when time is discrete. If $L^u V^n(x) \leqq 0$ in R for any real number $n \geqq 1$, then

$$P\left[\sup_{\tau_u \geqq t \geqq 0} V(x_t) \geqq \lambda\right] \leqq V^n(x)/\lambda^n, \tag{11}$$

which is an improvement over (10).

In general, we will try to improve (10) by finding the maximum n for which $L^u V^n(x) \leqq 0$ in R. This method is not generally the best for obtaining probability bounds on the behavior of components of x.

5. COMPARISON AND OPTIMALITY THEOREMS

It is always assumed that X is compact, $k(x, u) \geqq 0$ and continuous, and that (2), (3) are satisfied. The purpose of the theorems is to allow a comparison of the costs and stability properties resulting from the use of different controls, and to obtain upper and lower bounds on $\underline{C}(x)$ without actually solving the minimization problem. The symbols τ_0, τ_u are the random times to transfer $x_0 = x$ (in some given initial set) to ∂S, the boundary of the target set S, in the cases of no control, and control u, respectively.

The theorems use the assumption $E_x^u \tau_u < \infty$. When $L^u V(x) < 0$ in $X - S$ and $L^u V(x) \leqq 0$ on ∂S and does not depend on time, the finiteness assumption may be dropped. The modification will be used occasionally in the examples. It is usually of little consequence, since a slight enlargement of the target set will usually assure that $E_x^u \tau_u < \infty$.

Theorem 1. *Assume that there is an optimal admissible control w with* $E_x^w \tau_w < \infty$. *Let u be admissible and* $E_x^u \tau_u < \infty$. *Let* $V_1(x)$ *be in* $D(L)$ *and* $V_1(\partial S) = 0$, *and*

$$L^u V_1(x) + k(x, u) < 0 \tag{12}$$

in $X - S$. *Then*

$$V_1(x) > \underline{C}(x). \tag{13}$$

Also, for any $\lambda > 0$,

$$P\left[\sup_{\tau_u \geqq t \geqq 0} V_1(x_t) \geqq \lambda\right] \leqq EV_1(x)/\lambda. \tag{14}$$

If there is a $V_2(x)$ *in* $D(L)$ *with* $V_2(\partial S) = 0$ *and, for all admissible u,*

$$L^u V_2(x) + k(x, u) > 0, \tag{15}$$

in $X - S$, *then*

$$V_2(x) < \underline{C}(x). \tag{16}$$

(In the event that there is a nonadmissible control for which the problem has a meaning, and which minimizes $\underline{C}^u(x)$, then the first part of the theorem still holds.)

Proof: Equation (8) may be applied to $V_1(x)$ and τ_u. Thus,

$$V_1(x) - E_x^u V_1(x_{\tau_u}) > E_x^u \int_0^{\tau_u} k(x, u)\,dt \geqq \underline{C}(x).$$

Since $E_x^u \tau_u < \infty$, x_{τ_u} is on ∂S w.p. 1. Since X is bounded and $V_1(\partial S) = 0$, we have $E_x^u V_1(x_{\tau_u}) = 0$, and (13) follows.

Since w is admissible, and $V_2(x)$ is in $D(L)$ and $E_x^w \tau_w < \infty$, the application of (8) to $V_2(x)$ and τ_w yields

$$V_2(x) - E_x^w V_2(x_{\tau_w}) < E_x^w \int_0^{\tau_w} k(x, w)\,ds = \underline{C}(x),$$

$E_x^w V_2(x_{\tau_w}) = 0$ by a repetition of a former argument. (14) follows from (10).

Corollary 1. *Let the optimal admissible control exist, and let $V(x)$ satisfy the conditions on $V_1(x)$. Let u and w be admissible controls, $E_x^w \tau_w < \infty$, $E_x^u \tau_u < \infty$, and, for all such u,*

$$L^u V(x) + k(x, u) \geqq 0$$

with equality when $u = w$. Then

$$V(x) = \underline{C}(x)$$

and w is optimal.

Proof: The statement follows from Theorem 1, by setting $V(x) = V_1(x) = V_2(x)$ and replacing all $>$ by $\geq$.

Remark: If there is an admissible control which is optimal and a $V(x)$ satisfying the conditions of the corollary is available, then the corollary partially justifies the usual result of dynamic programming, i.e., that the optimum control minimizes (17) and that the solution of (17) is $V(x) = \underline{C}(x)$.

$$\min_u \, [L^u V(x) + k(x, u)] = 0 \tag{17}$$

Corollary 2. Equation (10) *is valid and τ_u is defined with probability one, when $k(x, u) > 0$ in $X - S$. Under this condition, the condition on finiteness of the average arrival times can be dropped, and we have a true optimality theorem (the stochastic counterpart of the Hamilton-Jacobi equation theorem in reference 20).*

Theorem 2. *Let*

$$C^u(x) = E_x^u \int_0^{\tau_u} [k(x) + \ell(x, u)]\,dt$$

where $k \geqq 0$, $\ell \geqq 0$ and $\ell(x, 0) = 0$. Let L^0 correspond to $u = 0$. Let $E_x^0 \tau_0 < \infty$, $V(x)$ in $D(L)$ and $V(\partial S) = 0$ and

$$L^0 V(x) + k(x) = 0.$$

For some u, let $E_x^u \tau_u < \infty$, *and*

$$L^u V(x) + k(x) + \ell(x, u) < 0. \tag{18}$$

Then

$$C^0(x) = E_x^0 \int_0^{\tau_0} k(x)\,dt > E_x^u \int_0^{\tau_u} [k(x) + \ell(x, u)]\,dt = C^u(x). \tag{19}$$

If $\geqq$ *replaces* $>$ *in (18), it does so in (19).*

Proof: The proof is essentially that of Theorem 1. From (8)

$$E_x^u \int_0^{\tau_u} [L^u V(x) + k(x) + \ell(x, u)]\,dt < 0 = E_x^0 \int_0^{\tau_0} [L^0 V(x) + k(x)]\,dt,$$

$$-V(x) + E_x^u V(x_{\tau_u}) + C^u(x) < -V(x) + E_x^0 V(x_{\tau_0}) + C^0(x).$$

Since x_{τ_u} and x_{τ_0} are on ∂S w.p. 1, and $V(x)$ is bounded in $X - S$, the theorem follows.

Remark: Consider the special case

$$dx = f(x, u)\,dt + \sigma(x)\,dz,$$

where σ does not depend on u, and where (with $V(\partial S) = 0$)

$$k(x) = -L^0 V(x) = -V_x'(x) f(x, 0) - \frac{1}{2} \sum_{i,j} \frac{\partial^2 V(x)}{\partial x_i \partial x_j} S_{ij}(x). \tag{20}$$

With $u \neq 0$,

$$-L^u V(x) = -V_x'(x) f(x, u) - \frac{1}{2} \sum_{i,j} \frac{\partial^2 V(x)}{\partial x_i \partial x_j} S_{ij}(x). \tag{21}$$

By Theorem 2, for any u such that

$$L^u V(x) - L^0 V(x) + \ell(x, u) \leqq 0$$

or

$$V_x'(x)\,[f(x, u) - f(x, 0)] + \ell(x, u) < 0, \tag{22}$$

we have

$$C^u(x) < C^0(x).$$

Although the theorem states that a control will decrease the cost under certain conditions, accurate estimates of the decrease are usually difficult to obtain. Estimates of the effect of the control on the probability (14) are readily available (see the examples). We obtain the best improvement of the value of (14) with the u which minimizes (18). Otherwise, the problem of selecting one, from among the many controls which may satisfy (22), is open.

Theorem 3 gives a condition under which $E_x^u \tau_u < \infty$ is assured.

Theorem 3. *Let $V(x)$ be in $D(L)$. If, for some $\varepsilon > 0$,*

$$L^u V(x) = -k_1(x, u) \leqq -\varepsilon$$

in $X - S$, then τ_u exists w.p. 1 and

$$E_x^u \tau_u \leqq V(x)/\varepsilon < \infty.$$

Let there exist an optimum w and $\underline{C}(x)$ with loss function $k(x, u)$. Let $k(x, u) \leqq k_1(x, u)$ and

$$\inf_{x,u} k(x, u) \geqq \varepsilon > 0.$$

Then

$$E_x^w \tau_w \leqq V(x)/\varepsilon < \infty.$$

Proof: Let τ be any random time with $E_x^u \tau < \infty$. The first statement follows from

$$V(x) - E_x^u V(x_\tau) = E_x^u \int_0^\tau k_1(x, u)\, dt \geqq \varepsilon\, E_x^u \tau$$

and from the boundedness of $V(x)$ in X. (If $E_x^u \tau_u = \infty$, we could increase τ until $\varepsilon\, E_x^u \tau > V(x)$ in X.)

Now, by Theorem 1,

$$V(x) \geqq \underline{C}(x) = E_x^w \int_0^{\tau_w} k(x, u) \geqq \varepsilon\, E_x^w \tau_w$$

and the second statement follows. The existence of a τ_w is part of the statement on the existence of an optimum w.

Theorem 4 gives a method of selecting S so that the corresponding problem can be studied by means of Liapunov functions.

Theorem 4. *Let u be admissible and let $V(x)$ be in $D(L)$. Define the sets $R^u = \{x : L^u V(x) \geqq 0\}$ and $S_\gamma = \{x : V(x) \leqq \gamma\}$.*

Let the sets be non-empty and let R^u be a proper subset of S_γ.

Let $x_0 = x$ be in $X - S_\gamma$ and define τ_u as the random time of arrival at ∂S_γ. Then

$$E_x^u \tau_u < \infty, \tag{23}$$

$$P\left[\sup_{\tau_u \geqq t \geqq 0} V(x_t) - \gamma \geqq \lambda\right] \leqq E[V(x) - \gamma]/\lambda. \tag{24}$$

If w minimizes $L^u V(x)$ in $X - S_\gamma$, and $L^w V(x) = -k(x) \leqq -\varepsilon < 0$ in $X - S_\gamma$, then w is the optimal control for the loss $k(x)$ and target set S_γ. The cost is

$$\underline{C}(x) = V(x) - \gamma = E_x^w \int_0^{\tau_w} k(x)\, dt. \tag{25}$$

Also, if $L^u V(x) + k(x) \leqq 0$ in $X - S_\gamma$, then

$$V(x) - \gamma \geqq C^u(x) = E_x^u \int_0^{\tau_u} k(x)\, dt. \tag{26}$$

Proof: Since $L^uV(x)$ is continuous, and R^u is a proper subset of S_γ, $L^uV(x) \leqq -\varepsilon < 0$, for some ε, in $X - S_\gamma$. Consequently, (23) follows from Theorem 3.

Since $V(x) - \gamma \geqq 0$ in $X - S_\gamma$ and $L^u[V(x) - \gamma] \leqq 0$ in $X - S_\gamma$, (24) follows from (10). The fact that the u which minimizes $L^uV(x)$ is an optimal control for loss $k(x) = -\min_u L^uV(x)$ and target ∂S_γ follows from Corollary 1. Equations (25) and (26) follow from Theorem 1 and Corollary 1, by using $V(x) - \gamma$ in their proofs.

Discussion: For a given Liapunov function $V(x)$, the control problem may be studied in several ways.

Let the loss be $k(x, u)$. Now compute $R^u = \{x : L^uV \geqq 0\}$. Now choose a γ such that $S_\gamma \supset R^u$ and check that $X - S_\gamma$ is not empty. Check that $L^uV(x) + k(x, u) \leqq 0$ in $X - S_\gamma$. Then, Theorem 4 says that, starting from a point in $X - S_\gamma$, the total cost, $C^u(x)$, of transferring $x_0 = x$ to a point on ∂S_γ, is no greater than $V(x) - \gamma$. If $L^uV(x) + k(x, u) = 0$, then the cost is $V(x) - \gamma = C^u(x)$.

Now let u_1 and u be given and check that $S_\gamma \supset (R^u \cup R^{u_1})$ and that $X - S_\gamma$ is not empty. If $L^uV(x) + k(x, u) \leqq L^{u_1}V(x) + k(x, u_1) = 0$, then the theorem says that the cost of transferring $x = x_0$ in $X - S_\gamma$ to ∂S_γ is no greater with u than with u_1. Theorem 2 may be used to try to find improved controls, provided that $V(x)$ and $k(x)$ are given.

If, for some S, two Liapunov functions, $V_1(x)$ and $V_2(x)$, are given with the properties $V_i(\partial S) = \gamma_i$, and $L^uV_1(x) + k(x, u) \leqq 0$, $L^uV_2(x) + k(x, u) \geqq 0$, $L^uV_i(x) < 0$ in $X - S$, then the cost of transferring $x_0 = x$ to ∂S is bounded by

$$V_2(x) - \gamma_2 \leqq C^u(x) \leqq V_1(x) - \gamma_1.$$

Obviously, the cost of transferring to a point interior to S is no less than the cost of transferring to S (by the continuity of x_t). The cost of transferring to a set enclosing S is no greater than the cost of transferring to S. The observation yields bounds for terminal sets other than the S.

Other forms of boundary conditions and loss functions are possible (for example, in case of instability we may minimize the probability of being lost) and will be considered in the examples. Choosing suitable $V(x)$ is, of course, no easier in the stochastic case than in the deterministic case. We have the double problem of finding $V(x)$ so that both $k(x, u)$ and S are suitable.

In the (homogeneous) deterministic case when $\dot{V}(x) \leqq 0$ with equality implying $\dot{x} = 0$, it is possible to transfer $x_0 = x$ to the origin. This is possible in the stochastic case (with probability one) if $L^uV(x) \leqq 0$ with equality only when $x = 0$.

The following theorem is useful for obtaining probability bounds on the rate of convergence of x_t to ∂S. The quantity α may depend on the control.

Theorem 5. *Let $V^n(x)$ be in $D(L)$ and*

$$L^uV^n(x) \leqq -\alpha V^n(x), \quad \alpha > 0,$$

in $X - S$. Let $t(\tau) = \min[t, \tau]$, for t nonrandom. Then

$$P\left[\sup_{\tau_u \geqq t \geqq s(\tau_u)} V(x_t) \geqq \lambda\right] \leqq e^{-\alpha s} V^n(x)/\lambda^n,$$

where $x = x_0$.

***Proof*:** Modify the system in S only, so that $L^u V^n(x) \leqq - \alpha V^n(x)$ in X. Let x' be the modified trajectory and τ' the time to the origin for the modified trajectory. By the continuity of the paths

$$P\left[\sup_{\tau' \geqq t \geqq s(\tau')} V^n(x'_t) \geqq \lambda^n\right] \geqq P\left[\sup_{\tau_u \geqq t \geqq s(\tau_u)} V^n(x_t) \geqq \lambda^n\right]$$

By Theorem 5 of reference 15, the left side is less than $e^{-s\alpha} V^n(x)/\lambda^n$, if $x_0 = x$, and the proof is concluded.

6. EXAMPLES

Example 1. Let*

$$\begin{aligned} dx_1 &= x_2\, dt \\ dx_2 &= (-x_1 - x_2 + u)\, dt + \sigma(x)\, dz \end{aligned} \tag{27}$$

with

$$\sigma^2(x) = x_1^2 \sigma^2, \quad \sigma^2 < 2$$
$$k(x, u) = x_1^2 + x_2^2 + u^2.$$

If $\sigma^2 < 2$ and $u = 0$, then $x_t \longrightarrow 0$ with probability one.[15] Owing to this, the target set may be the origin. Theorem 2 will be applied to the computation of a control. With $u = 0$, there is a positive definite quadratic form[15]

$$\begin{aligned} V(x) &= b_{11}x_1^2 + 2b_{12}x_2x_1 + b_{22}x_2^2 \\ b_{11} &= \tfrac{1}{2} + (2 + \sigma^2)/(2 - \sigma^2) \\ b_{12} &= \tfrac{1}{2} + \sigma^2/(2 - \sigma^2) \\ b_{22} &= 2/(2 - \sigma^2) \end{aligned}$$

so that

$$L^0 V(x) = -k(x, 0) = -x_1^2 - x_2^2$$

$$C^0(x) = E_x^0 \int_0^{\tau_0} (x_1^2 + x_2^2)\, dt = V(x).$$

By Theorem 2 (eq. (22)), for any u such that

$$u(\partial V/\partial x_2) + u^2 < 0, \tag{28}$$

we have

$$C^u(x) - C^0(x) < 0. \tag{29}$$

In particular,

$$u = -(\partial V/\partial x_2)/2 = -(b_{11}x_1 + b_{22}x_2) \tag{30}$$

*The spaces X of the examples are not compact. However, by letting $\sigma^2 = 0$ for large $\|x\|$, and confining $x_0 = x$ to some large, but compact, set, the space may be made compact with little loss in generality.

satisfies (28). Although the improvement (29) is difficult to estimate, an estimate of the stability improvement may be obtained with the use of (11). Now, with (30), and any real number $n \geqq 1$,

$$L^u V^n = nV^{n-1} \left[\frac{\partial V}{\partial x_1} x_2 + \frac{\partial V}{\partial x_2}(-x_1 - x_2 + u)\right] + \frac{\sigma^2 x_1^2}{2}\left[nV^{n-1}\frac{\partial^2 V}{\partial x_2^2} + n(n-1)V^{n-2}\left(\frac{\partial V}{\partial x_2}\right)^2\right]$$

$$= nV^{n-1}\left[-x_1^2 - x_2^2 - 2(b_{12}x_1 + b_{22}x_2)^2 + 2(n-1)\sigma^2(b_{12}x_1 + b_{22}x_2)^2(x_1^2/V)\right]. \quad (31)$$

The middle entry, $-2(b_{12}x_1 + b_{22}x_2)^2$, is due to the control. The noise contributes to all other terms. Also, $(x_1^2/V) \leqq (b_{11} - b_{12}^2/b_{22})^{-1}$.

Since the control contribution is proportional to the term containing σ^2, and is of opposite sign, some cancellelation occurs; this cancellation increases the maximum value of n for which $L^u V^n$ is nonpositive in X. As n increases, the estimate

$$P\left[\sup_{\tau_u \geqq t \geqq 0} V(x_t) \geqq \lambda\right] \leqq V^n(x)/\lambda^n \quad (32)$$

improves. With properly chosen $V(x)$, estimates of the form of (32) can yield useful information on the effect of the particular controls. By Theorem 3, if S is a set containing the origin as an interior point, then the average time to S is finite. In any case, $x_t \longrightarrow 0$ w.p. 1.

A useful general form is

$$L^u V^n = nV^{n-1}\left[L^0 V + (L^u - L^0)V + (n-1)\sum_{i,j}\frac{(\partial V/\partial x_i)(\partial V/\partial x_j)}{2V} S_{ij}\right]$$

$$S_{ij} = \sum_k \sigma_{ik}\sigma_{jk}$$

In our case,

$$(L^u - L^0)V = u(\partial V/\partial x_2) = 2(b_{12}x_1 + b_{22}x_2)u.$$

Let numbers $\delta > 0$ and $\varepsilon < \lambda$ be given, and assume that $x_0 = x$ is in $\{x: V(x) \leqq \varepsilon\}$. We will compute the "smallest" control which guarantees (according to our estimates and method) that $x_t \longrightarrow 0$ w.p. 1 and

$$P\left[\sup_{\tau_u \geqq t \geqq 0} V(x) \geqq \lambda\right] \leqq \delta$$

First compute the least $n \geqq 1$ such that

$$\sup_x V^n(x)/\lambda^n = (\varepsilon/\lambda)^n = \delta.$$

Then $L^u V^n \leqq 0$ in X if

$$-x_1^2 - x_2^2 + 2u(b_{12}x_1 + b_{22}x_2) + 2(n-1)\sigma^2(b_{12}x_1 + b_{22}x_2)^2(x_1^2/V) \leqq 0. \quad (33)$$

A suitable control can be determined from

$$2u(b_{12}x_1 + b_{22}x_2) = \min[0, x_1^2 + x_2^2 - 2(n-1)\sigma^2(b_{12}x_1 + b_{22}x_2)^2(x_1^2/V)],$$

which always yields a bounded control (in any compact set) (if $b_{12}x_1 + b_{22}x_2 = 0$, then $u = 0$).

Example 2. Same as Example 1, but let $\sigma^2(x) = \sigma^2$, a constant. We would prefer a $V(x)$ such that $L^0V(x) = -k(x, 0)$. Not being able to find such a $V(x)$, we select one which yields an approximation. If

$$V(x) = 3/2\, x_1^2 + x_1x_2 + x_2^2,$$

then

$$L^0V(x) = -x_1^2 - x_2^2 + \sigma^2.$$

To satisfy the conditions of Theorem 4, let

$$S \supset \{x: x_1^2 + x_2^2 \leqq \sigma^2\} = R^0.$$

$L^0V(x) < 0$ in the complement of R^0. Although R^u can be made smaller than R^0, the minimum eigenvalue will be the same, and the allowable reduction in the size of the target set may not be appreciable. Following the procedure of Theorem 4,

$$C^0(x) = E_x^0 \int_0^{\tau_0} (x_1^2 + x_2^2 - \sigma^2)\, dt = V(x) - \gamma, \tag{34}$$

where τ_0 is the random time to the assumed target set

$$S = \{x: V(x) \leqq \lambda\} \supset R^0.$$

$C^u(x) < C^0(x)$ if

$$u^2 + (\partial V/\partial x_2)u < 0,$$

which is satisfied (and is minimum) if

$$u = -(x_1/2 + x_2). \tag{35}$$

Also,

$$L^uV^n(x) = nV^{n-1}(x)[-x_1^2 - x_2^2 + \sigma^2 - 2(x_1/2 + x_2)^2 + 2\sigma^2(n-1)(x_1/2 + x_2)^2/V(x)],$$

The $-2(x_1/2 + x_2)^2$ term is contributed by the control (35). As in Example 1, the control improves stability—in the sense that the probability of an arbitrary increase in $V(x_t)$ (before absorption on ∂S) is decreased.

The method may be used to obtain bounds on moments.

Replace τ_0 in (34) by a nonrandom variable t, let $\sigma^2 = 0$ for very large $\|x\|$ (so that X is compact), and *assume* that each $E\, x_1^2$ converges to a constant as $t \longrightarrow \infty$. Since $x_1^2 + x_2^2$ is bounded in X, the order of integration may be changed for any finite t. Then, (34) and the boundedness of $V(x)$ in X yield that

$$\lim_{t\to\infty} E(x_1^2 + x_2^2) \leq \sigma^2.$$

Example 3. Assume the system of Example 2 and a positive definite quadratic form $V(x)$. We consider another type of criteria by which $V(x)$ may be chosen. Let $x_0 = x = (0, x_{20})$. Then $V(x_0) = b_{22}x_{20}^2$. Find a u which will transfer x_2^2 to some small value β^2 and such that, for a given δ and $\varepsilon > x_{20}^2$,

$$P\left[\sup_{\tau_u \geqq t \geqq 0} x_{2t}^2 \geqq \varepsilon\right] \leqq \delta.$$

Let $L^u V^n(x) < 0$ for $x_2^2 > \beta^2$, and let τ_u be well defined.

Any positive definite quadratic form in two variables may be written as

$$\begin{aligned} V(x) &= b' x_2^2 + (b_{11}x_1 + b_{12}x_2)^2/b_{11} \\ b' &= (b_{22} - b_{12}^2/b_{11}), \end{aligned} \tag{36}$$

where the first term of $V(x)$ is positive definite, and the second is positive semidefinite. Since

$$P\left[\sup_{\tau_u \geqq t \geqq 0} b' x_2^2 \geqq \lambda\right] \leqq P\left[\sup_{\tau_u \geqq t \geqq 0} V(x) \geqq \lambda\right] \leqq (b_{22}x_{20}^2)^n/\lambda^n, \tag{37}$$

where $\lambda/b' = \varepsilon$, it seems reasonable to use the positive-definite quadratic form with the maximum value of

$$b'/b_{22} = 1 - b_{12}^2/b_{11}b_{22},$$

provided, of course, that

$$L^u V^n(x) < 0 \quad \text{for} \quad x_2^2 > \beta^2 \tag{38}$$

and a suitable n. The problem suggests that we seek a $V(x)$ such that $L^0 V(x) = -x_2^2 + \text{constant}$. Thus, let

$$\begin{aligned} V(x) &= (x_1^2 + x_2^2)/2, \\ L^u V(x) &= -x_2^2 + \sigma^2/2 + ux_2. \end{aligned}$$

If $\beta^2 < \sigma^2/2$, then the use of

$$\begin{aligned} u &= -x_2(\sigma^2/2 - \beta^2)/\beta^2, \quad && \beta^2 \leqq x_2^2 \leqq \sigma^2/2 \\ &= 0 && \text{otherwise} \end{aligned} \tag{39}$$

assures that (38) is satisfied for $n = 1$. Thus, there is a control for which $x_2^2 = \beta^2$ is attainable. Note also that b'/b_{22} is maximum. If b'/b_{22} were not maximum, then either some systematic procedure for maximization would be followed, or else several $V(x)$ would be tried and compared.

To complete the analysis, find the least $n \geqq 1$ for which

$$(b_{22}x_{20}^2/\varepsilon b')^n = \delta$$

and choose the most convenient u for which

$$L^u V^n(x) = nV^{n-1}\left[-x_2^2 + \sigma^2 + \frac{(n-1)\,\sigma^2 x_2^2}{(x_1^2 + x_2^2)} + ux_2\right]$$

is negative in the desired region $x_2^2 \geqq \beta^2$.

There are, of course, similar procedures for more general initial conditions. The quadratic forms may be chosen by selecting the nonconstant, nonpositive quadratic part of $L^0 V(x)$, and solving for $V(x)$.

Other forms of experimentation with the type of quadratic form is possible, e.g., choose a control first (say, of an arbitrary linear form with coefficients to be determined), then choose $x'Bx$, so that the target $\{x : x'Bx \leq \lambda\}$ is of some useful shape, and, finally, compute the control coefficients.

Remark: Generally, the Liapunov functions $V^n(x)$ do not give the best probability bounds on, say, the excursions of some component $|x_i|$, since it couples the effects of the various components of x more than is necessary. For example, instead of choosing $n = 2$, a suitably chosen homogeneous positive-definite quartic form will usually yield better estimates on the probabilistic behavior. The powers of the quadratic form are used here purely for numerical simplicity.

Example 4. Let

$$dx = (Ax + Cu)\,dt + \sigma dz$$

$$k(x, u) = F(x) + g(u)$$

$$F(x) = \sum_1^n F_{2i}(x),$$

where $F_{2i}(x)$ is a homogeneous positive-definite form of order $2i$, and A is stable. By a theorem of Liapunov,[18] if $\sigma = 0$, and $u = 0$, there is a homogeneous positive-definite function $V_{2i}(x)$ of $2i$th order, with $\dot{V}_{2i}(x) = -F_{2i}(x)$. When σ is a constant matrix not identically zero,

$$L^0 V_{2i}(x) = -F_{2i}(x) + Q_{2(i-1)}(x)$$

$$Q_{2(i-1)}(x) = \frac{1}{2} \sum_{j,m} \frac{\partial^2 V_{2i}}{\partial x_j \partial x_m} S_{jm}$$

$$Q_0 = \text{constant.}$$

$$S_{jm} = \sum_i \sigma_{ji}\sigma_{mi}$$

Q_{2i}, $i \neq 0$, is a homogeneous non-negative definite form of order $2i$. A Liapunov function

$$V(x) = \sum_1^n V_{2i} \tag{40}$$

with

$$L^0 V(x) = -F(x) + Q_0 \tag{41}$$

is easily determined: set $\sigma = 0$ and solve, by Liapunov's theorem,

$$\dot{V}_{2n}(x) = -F_{2n}(x),$$

and, in general, for the case $0 < i < n$,

$$\dot{V}_{2i} = -F_{2i}(x) - Q_{2i}(x).$$

If the target set $S = \{x : V(x) \leq \gamma\}$ includes $\{x : F(x) \leq Q_0\}$, then

$$C^0(x) = E_x^0 \int_0^{\tau_0} (F(x) - Q_0)\,dt = V(x) - \gamma.$$

By Theorem 2, if

$$L^u V(x) + g(u) < L^0 V(x),$$

then

$$C^u(x) = E_x^u \int_0^{\tau_u} (F(x) + g(u) - Q_0)\,dt < C^0(x).$$

For the deterministic problem, this approach was investigated in considerably more detail in reference 8.

***Example* 5.** Let

$$\begin{aligned} dx &= (Ax + u)\,dt + \sigma dz \\ k(x, u) &= -\rho \\ A' + A &= 0, \quad \sigma_{ij} = \sigma^2 \delta_{ij}, \end{aligned} \tag{42}$$

and $u'u = \rho^2$. The target set is to be a sphere about the origin, with radius $r > 0$. The deterministic part of (42) has been termed "norm-invariant." Let the components of z be independent. The Liapunov function which is the minimal cost of transferring $x = x_0$ to the origin, for the deterministic problem, is

$$V_1(x) = \|x\| = (x'x)^{1/2}.$$

We have

$$L^u V_1(x) = \frac{x'u}{\|x\|} + \frac{\sigma^2}{2\|x\|},$$

which is minimized by

$$u = -\rho x / \|x\|, \tag{43}$$

the optimal deterministic control, and

$$L^u V_1(x) = -\rho + (s - 1)\,\sigma^2 / 2\|x\|, \tag{44}$$

where s is the dimension of x. If the target set has a radius at least $\sigma^2/2\rho$, then Theorem 1 yields

$$V_1(x) - \gamma < \underline{C}(x).$$

The fact that (44) is still a function of $\|x\|$ suggests that $\underline{C}(x)$ is a function of $\|x\|$. Let us try

$$V(x) = \|x\| + a \log x'x + c, \tag{45}$$

where a and c are constants. Equation (45) is suggested by the form of (44). (It is also suggested by the observation that the "deterministic" contribution to L^uV, of $\log x'x$, $-2\rho/\|x\|$, is of the proper form to cancel part of the "stochastic" contribution of $V_1(x)$ to L^uV, which is $(s-1)\sigma^2/2\|x\|$.)

$$L^uV(x) = \frac{x'u}{\|x\|} + \frac{\sigma^2(s-1)}{2\|x\|} + \frac{ax'u}{x'x} + \frac{a\sigma^2(s-2)}{x'x}.$$

With (43),

$$L^uV(x) = -\rho - \frac{a\rho}{\|x\|} + \frac{\sigma^2(s-1)}{2\|x\|} + \frac{a\sigma^2}{x'x}(s-2).$$

Let $s = 2$ and $a = \sigma^2/2\rho$, then $L^uV(x) = -\rho$. At the target set boundary, $\partial S = \{x\colon x'x = r^2\}$, we have $V(x) = 0$. Thus, for arbitrary $r > 0$, set

$$c = -r - a\log(r^2).$$

Now, $V(x) > 0$ and $L^uV(x) = -\rho$ in $X - S$, and

$$C^u(x) = V(x) = E_x^u\int_0^{\tau_u}\rho\,d\tau = E_x^u\tau_u.$$

Also, since (43) minimizes $L^uV(x)$ over all admissible controls, by Corollary 1, (43) is the average-time-optimal control over the class of admissible controls. If $s > 2$, the procedure may be repeated. This will be developed elsewhere.

Example 6. Take the scalar case

$$dx = -x\,dt + u\,dt + \sigma\,dz$$

$$|u| \leqq 1, \quad S = \{0\},$$

$$C^u(x) = E_x^u\int_0^{\tau_u}(k + |u|)\,dt.$$

The *optimal deterministic* solution is (the deterministic version is a problem in reference 21):

$$\underline{C}_d(x) = \begin{cases} V'(x) = (k+1)\log(|x|+1), & |x| < k, \; u = -\operatorname{sign} x \\ V''(x) = (k+1)\dfrac{\log(k+1)\log|x|}{\log k}, & |x| \geqq k, \; u = 0. \end{cases} \tag{46}$$

$$\begin{aligned} L^uV'(x) &= -(k+1) - \sigma^2(k+1)/2(|x|+1)^2, \quad u = -\operatorname{sign} x \\ L^uV''(x) &= -k - \sigma^2k/x^2, \quad u = 0. \end{aligned} \tag{47}$$

At $|x| = k$, $\underline{C}_d(x)$ does not have a derivative. This is not important in the scalar case. (It can be assumed that $\sigma^2(x)$ satisfies (2) and is zero in a small neighborhood of $|x| = k$, with an insignificant change in the process.) Since $L^u\underline{C}_d(x) < -k(x,u)$ for $|x| \neq k$, Theorem 1 yields

$$C^u(x) < \underline{C}_d(x).$$

The loss for the stochastic problem is less than $\underline{C}_d(x)$, since the problem is scalar and $\underline{C}_d(x)$ is convex downward. Such an improvement is uncommon for vector problems.

By Corollary 1, if $V(x)$ and u satisfied $L^u V(x) + k + |u| = 0$ and $L^{u'} V(x) + k + |u'| \geqq 0$ for $u' \neq u$, then u is an optimal control and $V(x) = \underline{C}(x)$. Then, u must satisfy

$$\begin{aligned} u &= -\operatorname{sign} dV/dx, \quad && dV/dx > 1 \\ u &= 0, && \text{otherwise,} \end{aligned} \tag{48}$$

exactly the *form* of the deterministic optimal control. The form (48) is not admissible, but may be approximated arbitrarily closely by an admissible control. Since the problem can be well defined and solvable with a slight modification of $\sigma^2(x)$, the inadmissibility will be ignored. Since $C^u(x) < V'(x)$, $|x| < k$, it is suggested that $|d\underline{C}(x)/dx| < |dV'(x)/dx|$, $|x| < k$, and, hence, that the optimal control would be of the form

$$\begin{aligned} u &= -\operatorname{sign} x, \quad && |x| < k' < k \\ u &= 0, && |x| \geqq k'. \end{aligned}$$

The qualitative information inferred above can be substantiated by solving the exact stochastic problem (which is easy and will not be done here).

Define $S_\gamma = \{x\colon |x| \leqq \gamma\}$, $\gamma > 0$, and let X be a large set containing the origin with $\sigma^2 = 0$ outside X. Now, since $L^\circ \log(1 + |x|) < 0$ in $X - S_\gamma$ for any $\gamma > 0$, (10) yields

$$P\left[\sup_{\tau_0 \geqq t \geqq 0} \log(1 + |x_t|) \geqq \lambda\right] \leqq \log(1 + |x|)/\lambda.$$

Better bounds can be obtained if S_γ is more restricted. Let $V(x) = |x|^n$, $n \geqq 2$. Then

$$\begin{aligned} L^u V(x) &= n|x|^{n-2} A(x) \\ A(x) &= -x^2 + ux + (n-1)\sigma^2/2. \end{aligned}$$

If $A(x) < 0$ in $X - S_\gamma$, then

$$P\left[\sup_{\tau_u \geqq t \geqq 0} |x_t| \geqq \lambda\right] \leqq |x|^n/\lambda^n.$$

The smallest S_γ (such that $L^u V < 0$ in $X - S_\gamma$ and $|u| \leqq 1$) corresponds to

$$\gamma = \gamma_1 = [-1 + (1 + 2(n-1)\sigma^2)^{1/2}]/2,$$

and then we require $u = -\operatorname{sign} x$ for $\gamma_1 \leqq |x| \leqq \gamma_0$, where $\gamma_0^2 = (n-1)\sigma^2/2$.

REFERENCES

1. R. W. Bass, discussion of paper by A. Letov in *Proc. Heidelberg Conf. on Automatic Control*, ed. R. Oldenbourg, Munich, Germany (1957), pp. 209–210.
2. R. E. Kalman, S. E. Bertram, "Control System Analysis and Design via the Second Method of Liapunov," *J. Basic Eng.* (ASME), **82**, 371-393 (1960).
3. J. P. LaSalle, "Stability and Control," *J. SIAM Control*, Ser. A, 1, 1, 3–15 (1962).

4. G. Geiss, "The Analysis and Design of Nonlinear Control Systems via Liapunov's Second Method," Rpt. No. RTD-TDR-63-4076, Grumman Aircraft Corp., Bethpage, L. I. (1964).

5. N. E. Nahi, "On the Design of Optimal Systems via the Second Method of Liapunov," *IEEE Trans. on Automatic Control*, AC-9, 274-275 (1964).

6. Z. V. Rekasius, "Suboptimal Design of Intentionally Nonlinear Controllers," *IEEE Trans. on Automatic Control*, AC-9, 380-385 (1964).

7. G. W. Johnson, "Synthesis of Control Systems with Stability Constraints via the Second Method of Liapunov," *IEEE Trans. on Automatic Control*, AC-9, 270-273 (1964).

8. R. W. Bass, R. F. Weber, "On the Suboptimal Control of Autonomous Linear Systems," Hughes Aircraft Corp. Rept. (March 1965).

9. J. L. Doob, *Stochastic Processes* (New York: John Wiley and Sons, 1953).

10. E. B. Dynkin, *Markov Processes* (Berlin: Springer-Verlag, 1965) [Translation].

11. E. Wong, M. Zakai, "On the Relationship Between Ordinary and Stochastic Differential Equations," Report 64-26, Electronics Research Lab., Univ. of California, Berkeley, Cal. (1964).

12. K. Ito, "Lectures on Stochastic Processes," Tata Institute, Bombay, India, 1961.

13. E. B. Dynkin, *Foundations of the Theory of Markov Processes*, (Berlin: Springer-Verlag, 1961) [Translation].

14. H. J. Kushner, "On the Stability of Stochastic Dynamical Systems," *Proc. Nat. Acad. Sci.*, 53, 8-12 (January 1965).

15. H. J. Kushner, "On the Theory of Stochastic Stability," Report 65-1, Center for Dynamical Systems, Brown University, Providence, R. I. (1965). Also to appear in *Advances in Control Systems*, Vol. 4 (New York: Academic Press).

16. R. Z. Khas'minskii, "On the Stability of the Trajectory of Markov Processes, *Appl. Math. and Mech.* (PPM), 26, 1554-1565 (1962).

17. W. M. Wonham, "On Weak Stochastic Stability of Systems Perturbed by Noise," Report 65-4, Center for Dynamical Systems, Brown University, Providence, R. I. (1965).

18. I. G. Malkin, *Theory of Stability of Motion*, AEC Translation No. 3352, Dept. of Commerce, Washington, D. C. (1958).

19. M. Athans, P. Falb, R. T. Lacoss, "Time, Fuel, and Energy-Optimal Control of Nonlinear Norm-Invariant Systems," *IEEE Trans. on Automatic Control*, AC-8, 196-201 (1963).

20. R. E. Kalman, "Optimal Control and the Calculus of Variations," Research Institute for Advanced Study (RIAS) Report 61-3 (1961).

21. M. Athans, P. Falb, "*Optimal Control; An Introduction to the Theory and Its Applications*" (New York: McGraw-Hill, to appear in 1965).

22. H. J. Kushner, "Sufficient Conditions for Optimal Stochastic Controls," to appear in *SIAM J. Control*.

LINEAR STOCHASTIC FILTERING THEORY—REAPPRAISAL AND OUTLOOK

R. E. Kalman

Division of Engineering Mechanics, Stanford University, Stanford, Calif.

The purpose of this paper is to give a critical review of the present status of linear stochastic filtering theory, emphasizing the causes of the developments of the past five years and indicating areas where the research developments have not yet been completed.

There is a detailed assessment of the so-called Kalman-Bucy filter, from the point of view of its engineering applicability as well as in regard to its position in the mathematical theory of prediction and filtering.

The starting assumptions of the Kalman-Bucy problem are shown to be equivalent to those of the Kolmogorov-Wiener problem by explicitly constructing a Markovian realization of a second-order random process directly from the covariance function.

1. THE MOTIVES FOR THE NEW THEORY

During the past six years, the so-called Wold-Kolmogorov-Wiener filter has been superseded by the so-called Kalman-Bucy filter[1-3] in almost all practical applications of stochastic filtering theory, be it in the USA, Europe, or the USSR.

This is a pleasing phenomenon and not entirely unexpected. Along with the practical success of the new ideas has come a demand for popularized explanations. These have been often superficial, if not actually misleading. In this rather informal paper, I would like to stress the theoretical side and outline the reasoning which both Bucy and I used to evolve our version of the theory. I shall try to follow Einstein's dictum that "an explanation should be as simple as possible but no simpler." Because of limitations of space and time, I must assume of course, that the reader is familiar with the technical contents of references 1, 3, and perhaps even 6.

Reasons for revising the classical theory fall into three groups: engineering, statistical, and applied mathematical.

1. It is important to distinguish between two types of problems in system engineering: those dealing with the *external* and those with the *internal* behavior of a system. The conventional form of the classical theory calls for the solution of an integral equation, in which the unknown is the impulse response function of the optimal filter. The frequency-domain version of the theory calls

Presented at the Symposium on System Theory
Polytechnic Institute of Brooklyn, April 20, 21, 22, 1965

for the determination of the transfer function of the optimal filter. Knowing the impulse response or transfer function tells us the external behavior of the filter, or, what is roughly the same, its *performance specifications*. However, the engineer regards performance specifications as his input; he has to produce *blueprints* for systems, and so he is mainly interested in the wiring diagram of the optimal filter. This he does not get from the classical theory.

In the 1940's, "filter" was synonymous with "electric RLC network," and everyone had faith in the practicality of network synthesis procedures. Today we know that computing power is the difference between successful and unsuccessful applications of stochastic filtering, and therefore the system "wiring-diagram" is almost always desired in the form of a digital computer program. Such a program is quite similar to the equations describing classical particle mechanics. Therefore, the program specifications are conveniently given in the form of a set of first-order differential or difference equations (the so-called state variable equations), and that is precisely what the Kalman-Bucy filter does, *without* the irrelevant intermediate step of computing the input/output relations of the filter.

It is very obvious that a practical optimal filter should make use of all available data, so the filter must be able to accommodate many different inputs. This is a problem area which classical linear system theory could not treat satisfactorily. The resolution of the multivariable system structure problem using external system descriptions is a recent achievement (see reference 4 for questions relating to the frequency domain and reference 5 for the modern outlook in the time domain), which resulted from experience gained with internal (state-variable) types of system description.

In short, the principal engineering limitation of the classical theory is due to the fact that it goes only halfway toward the actual design of the system.

This discussion may have led the reader to dismiss the question of internal behavior as one of purely engineering interest. Let him remember, however, that a concrete physical system cannot function properly unless it possesses some measure of stability; and stability *cannot even be defined* without reference to the internal behavior of the system. Reference 3 and especially reference 6 contain detailed stability analyses of stochastic filters, which are not as widely known as they should be. This analysis is the most advanced theoretical contribution to state-variable stochastic filtering; it deals with matters that cannot be disregarded with impunity in practical applications.

II. The conventional view of statistics is that one should draw safe conclusions from safe assumptions. Of course, such conclusions are often too weak and do not make best use of the available information. (I am alluding to the famous debate between Bayesian and non-Bayesian statistics.) This point is of special significance in stochastic filtering.

According to the classical approach, we must start out by obtaining the covariance functions of the random processes we wish to filter. This is a sound theoretical view, since covariance functions are the appropriate statistical data for the problem. In reality, engineering management has been most reluctant to authorize the necessary expenditures for actually "measuring" the covariance functions. Hence this is seldom done. In the few cases that this is attempted, it soon becomes obvious that the covariance functions are not stationary and then the classical theory does not apply. In the new theory, the assumption of stationarity is irrelevant and not even very useful.

Any attempt to obtain the covariance functions by purely statistical means from measurement data disregards the fact that in practical cases we are usually dealing with well-defined physical systems. We should by all means make use of the "information" provided by three centuries of physics research. Information of this latter sort (easily available, for instance, in the case of satellite orbit smoothing) seems to be responsible for the practical success of Kalman-Bucy filter, for in this formulation all stochastic processes are represented via a dynamical model which is supposed to be obtained from physical rather than statistical considerations. Randomness is separated from dynamics and is represented by white-noise acting on the dynamical models. While the basic idea involved here is quite old and well known,[7] it seems to be ignored in the statistical literature. I view statistics as an experimental science. If so, then physical information should be included in statistical procedures. I don't know whether or not this has been done systematically in other fields, but it must be regarded as one of the principal ideas in stochastic filtering.

Turning to the more mathematical side of statistics, it is well known that operations on Gaussian processes may be interpreted from the point of view of least-squares, maximum likelihood, Bayesian estimation, etc. I question whether such added explanations, advanced by many in recent years, really add to the story. The Kalman-Bucy filter is in essence a *conditional probability computer*. Since it operates on Gaussian processes, it is clear that computation of the means and variances is all that is needed (see reference 6).* The conditional probability distribution displays all relevant information in the data. This is not statistics, but pure probability theory; in fact, the entrenched term "statistical filtering" is quite misleading. The function of computers is to convert data into conditional distributions. In other words, computers are useful because they transform the data into the right format. It can be shown (unpublished work in 1961) that the Kalman-Bucy filter can be derived from the requirement of maximizing the information rate (in the sense of Shannon) provided by the measurements about the unknown state variables of the signal processes. Thus for several different reasons, entirely independent of ad hoc principles such as least squares or maximum likelihood, the conditional probability computer is the natural stochastic filter. This view is also shared in the USSR. It was first emphasized there in the very important work of Stratonovich,[8] to whom we owe the vigorous new trend in nonlinear filtering theory.

A formidable obstacle to the evolution of stochastic filtering theory was the pat explanation in the engineering literature (strong in the late 1950's; fading now) that we are to look for the "best linear filter in the least-squares sense." This confuses the problem of data analysis with statistical decision making

*Although the variance equation is independent of the input data (except for the choice of data channels and sampling instants), it should be regarded as part of the filter, and usually is.

(is least squares a good error criterion?). It was only in 1958 that S. Sherman[9] pointed out that the error criterion is relatively irrelevant since almost always we are interested in the conditional mean, anyway. Sherman's paper was the decisive impetus for reference 1. Even today, most engineering texts follow the wide-sense version of filtering theory, in which the role of conditional distributions is obscure.[10] I prefer an exact solution of a restricted problem (the absolutely optimal filter for Gaussian processes) to a restricted solution of a seemingly more general problem (best linear filter for the equivalence class of second-order processes), even though in this instance the two solutions turn out to be the same. Because of the prestige of Wiener, engineering instruction tended to stick with the covariance-function (hence wide-sense) point of view, completely disregarding the fact that in many practical cases Markovian models are close at hand, while covariance functions are hard to measure.

III. An especially popular aspect of the Kalman-Bucy filter is the ease with which it can be computed. Indeed the formidable Wiener-Hopf equation is replaced with the lowly but friendly Riccati equation, familiar from the calculus of variations.

The Riccati equation opened neglected territories in system theory and it has become an important computing tool. The problem of spectral factorization can be avoided by its use; in fact, explicit solutions can be obtained to even time-varying filtering problems (see reference 6 for numerous examples) which have not yielded to the classical theory.

In spite of these successes, my present guess is that it is the applied-mathematical aspects of the theory which are most likely to change in the future. It seems that spectral methods, being more algebraic, have inherent advantages over differential equations. The formulation of nonlinear filtering in terms of (partial) differential equations appears to involve intractable analytical difficulties. It might be that algebraic methods, reminiscent of the way in which Lie groups are used to study nonlinear differential equations, will give us the first explicit, nontrivial, nonlinear filters.

2. MARKOVIAN REPRESENTATION OF SECOND-ORDER PROCESSES

Let us turn now to the technical contributions of the paper.

As seen above, the principal difference between the Wold-Kolmogorov-Wiener filter and the Kalman-Bucy filter lies in the initial specifications (covariance function vs. Markov process) of the random process to be filtered as well as in the format of the final result, the optimal filter (impulse response vs. differential equations). The relations between the latter are now well understood[11, 5] and it follows, of course, that the two theories yield equivalent results. Hence a complete parallelism between the two approaches will be established once we explain in what sense the starting assumptions are also equivalent.

In the Kalman-Bucy filter the signal process is represented via the equations

$$dx/dt = F(t)x + G(t)u(t), \tag{2.1}$$

$$y(t) = H(t)x(t), \tag{2.2}$$

where x, y, u are real n-vectors, and $u(\cdot)$ is to be interpreted (formally) as a white-noise process, with zero mean and covariance matrix

$$E\{w(t)w'(\tau)\} = \delta(t - \tau)Q(t). \qquad (' = \text{transpose}) \tag{2.3}$$

Proceeding purely formally via the properties of the δ-function, we find that the covariance matrix of the process $y(\cdot)$ is given by

$$E\{y(t)y'(\tau)\} = H(t)\left[\Phi(t,0)X(0,0)\Phi'(\tau,0) + \int_0^{\min(t,\tau)} \Phi(t,\sigma)Q(\sigma)\Phi'(\tau,\sigma)\,d\sigma\right] \times H'(\tau), \tag{2.4}$$

provided we assume that $x(0)$ has zero mean and covariance

$$E\{x(0)x'(0)\} - X(0,0). \tag{2.5}$$

(The value of

$$E[x(t)x'(\tau)] = X(t,\tau)$$

is given by the expression between the square brackets in (2.4).) $\Phi(t,\tau)$ is the transition matrix associated with the differential equation $dx/dt = F(t)x$.

We remind the reader that the mean and covariance completely characterize a Gaussian process. If we assume that $u(\cdot)$ is a Gaussian white-noise process, then $x(\cdot)$ will be also Gaussian; since the mean is identically zero, keeping track of the covariances amounts to computing probability distributions for $x(\cdot)$ and $y(\cdot)$. Instead of viewing (2.1–2) as a Gauss-Markov process, we may view $x(\cdot)$ as the equivalence class of all processes having the same covariance function $X(t,\tau)$. In this case $x(\cdot)$ is called, by abuse of language, a *second-order process*. Clearly what really matters here are the formulas, not their interpretation.

The formal steps leading to (2.4) need not worry us, because the formula itself can be established rigorously with the help of the theory of distributions. See reference 12, Chapter 3 for a very clear account.

Our problem is to reverse the above process. Given the covariance matrix

$$E\{y(t)y'(\tau)\} = \Gamma(t,\tau) \tag{2.7}$$

we wish to find a system (2.1–2) such that (2.4) holds. In analogy to similar problems in deterministic system theory, we call this the *realization* of the random process $y(\cdot)$ as a function of a Markov process. While the covariance function of $y(\cdot)$ characterizes the process only in an empirical sense, the Markovian model (2.1–2) reveals a possible physical mechanism for generating the process. In fact, the classical prediction and filtering theory may be viewed as concerned primarily with the "discovery" of a model such as (2.1–2) from the given covariance function.

The realization is *finite-dimensional* if x is an n-vector. No such assumption is made in the classical theory, but it was soon found that finite-dimensionality (equivalent to rational spectra) is essential for practical computations. We shall treat only this case.

Let us also recall[13] that any $p \times p$ matrix function Γ of two variables is a *covariance* if it is of *nonnegative definite type*, that is, given any finite sequence $t_1, \ldots, t_n$ and any n p-vectors $x_1, \ldots, x_n$ the scalar expression

$$\sum_{i,j} x_i' \Gamma(t_i, t_j) x_j \geqq 0.$$

In other words, for any choice of the t_i, the $np \times np$ matrix consisting of the blocks $\Gamma(t_i, t_j)$ is nonnegative definite.

Theorem. A covariance Γ has a finite-dimensional Markovian realization if and only if

(i) There exist two matrix functions V and W of a single variable such that

$$\Gamma(t, \tau) = V(t) W(\min\{t, \tau\}) V'(\tau) \tag{2.8}$$

(the size of W gives the dimension of the realization) where $W(t)$ is nonnegative definite for all t;

(ii) The derivative of $W(t)$ is also nonnegative definite.

This theorem closely parallels the criterion concerning the finite-dimensional realizations of time-dependent impulse-response function.[11,14,15] The proof is also similar, except for the second condition.

Proof. Sufficiency is established by setting

$$\begin{aligned} dx/dt &= u(t), \\ y(t) &= V(t) x(t), \\ \text{cov}\,\{u(t) u'(\tau)\} &= \delta(t - \tau) \dot{W}(t) \\ \text{cov}\,\{x(\theta) x'(\theta)\} &= W(0) \end{aligned}$$

It is very easy to verify that (2.4) holds as a consequence of (2.8). (Recall that the transition matrix corresponding to $F(t) \equiv 0$ is the identity.)

To prove necessity, we write

$$\begin{aligned} V(t) &= H(t) \Phi(t, 0), \\ W(t) &= \Phi(0, t) X(t, t) \Phi'(0, t), \; W(0) = X(0, 0) \end{aligned}$$

$W(t)$ is then nonnegative definite for each t. Using (2.4), it is clear that

$$\begin{aligned} E\{y(t) y'(\tau)\} &= H(t) \phi(t, 0) [W(\min\{t, \tau\})] \Phi'(\tau, 0) H'(\tau) \\ &= V(t) W(\min\{t, \tau\}) V'(\tau) \end{aligned}$$

and (2.8) is proved.

By definition of Φ,

$$dW(t)/dt = -\Phi(0, t) F(t) X(t, t) - X(t, t) F'(t) \Phi'(0, t) + \Phi(0, t)[dX(t, t)/dt] \Phi'(0, t).$$

From (2.4),

$$\begin{aligned} dX(t, t)\, dt &= \frac{d}{dt}\left[\Phi(t, 0) W(0) \Phi'(t, 0) + \int_0^t \Phi(t, \sigma) Q(\sigma) \Phi'(t, \sigma)\, d\sigma\right] \\ &= F(t) X(t, t) + X(t, t) F'(t) + Q(t). \end{aligned}$$

Hence

$$dW(t)/dt = \Phi(0, t)Q(t)\Phi'(0, t) \geqq 0,$$

which proves (ii).

Condition (2.8) implies that $\Gamma(t, \tau)$ (restricted to $t \geqq \tau$) may be realized as the impulse response of a finite-dimensional (deterministic) linear system.[11] W positive-definite corresponds to the requirement that W be the variance matrix of the state variables in the model. Requirement (ii) is needed to insure that the process $u(\cdot)$ have nonnegative variance.

Let us consider a simple example.

Example. Let $\Gamma(t, \tau) = f(\min(t, \tau))$ where f is an arbitrary nonnegative scalar function. Condition (i) is obviously satisfied with $V = 1$ and $W = f$. To prove that Γ is a covariance, let $t_1 < \ldots < t_n$ be arbitrary numbers. Then

$$[\Gamma(t_i, t_j)] = \begin{bmatrix} f(t_1) & f(t_1) & \ldots & f(t_1) \\ f(t_1) & f(t_2) & \ldots & f(t_2) \\ \cdot & \cdot & & \cdot \\ \cdot & \cdot & & \cdot \\ \cdot & \cdot & & \cdot \\ f(t_1) & f(t_2) & \ldots & f(t_n) \end{bmatrix}$$

$$[\Gamma(t_i, t_j)] = \begin{bmatrix} 1 & 1 & \ldots & 1 \\ 1 & 1 & \ldots & 1 \\ \cdot & \cdot & & \cdot \\ \cdot & \cdot & & \cdot \\ \cdot & \cdot & & \cdot \\ 1 & 1 & & 1 \end{bmatrix} \cdot f(t_1)$$

$$= \begin{bmatrix} 0 & 0 & \ldots & 0 \\ 0 & 1 & \ldots & 1 \\ \cdot & \cdot & & \cdot \\ \cdot & \cdot & & \cdot \\ \cdot & \cdot & & \cdot \\ 0 & 1 & & 1 \end{bmatrix} \cdot [f(t_2) - f(t_1)]$$

$$+ \ldots + \begin{bmatrix} 0 & 0 & \ldots & 0 \\ 0 & 0 & & 0 \\ \cdot & \cdot & & \cdot \\ \cdot & \cdot & & \cdot \\ \cdot & \cdot & & \cdot \\ 0 & 0 & & 1 \end{bmatrix} [f(t_n) - f(t_{n-1})]$$

This shows immediately that Γ is a covariance if and only if f is nondecreasing, which is the same as requirement (ii) of the theorem.

The previous theorem is more familiar in the context of stationary processes. In that case

$$\Gamma(t, \tau) = \begin{cases} \Lambda(t - \tau) & \text{if } t \geqq \tau; \\ \Lambda'(\tau - t) & \text{if } t \leqq \tau. \end{cases}$$

Here F, H should be constant matrices, and formula (2.4) simplifies to

$$\Lambda(t-\tau) = He^{F(t-\tau)}PH'$$

where $P = X(t, t) =$ constant, symmetric.

Recall Bochner's theorem: *Λ is a stationary covariance if and only if its Fourier transform is pointwise nonnegative.* This implies that the Hermitian matrix

$$H(i\omega I - F)^{-1}PH' + HP(-i\omega I - F')^{-1}H'$$

is nonnegative definite. In addition, stationarity implies that F must be a stable matrix (that is, e^{Ft} is bounded on $(0, \infty)$). Two requirements together mean that the Laplace transform of

$$\Lambda^{+}(t) = \begin{cases} \Lambda(t), & t \geqq 0\epsilon, \\ 0, & t < 0, \end{cases}$$

namely $H(sI - F)^{-1}G$,* is a *positive real matrix* (that is, Re $s \geqq 0$ implies that $\mathrm{Re}\{H(sI - F)^{-1}G + G'(-sI - F')^{-1}H'\}$ is nonnegative definite). Then we have an interesting characterization of the relation between the frequency and state-variable domain, known as the Yakubovich-Kalman-Popov Lemma.

Yakubovich-Kalman-Popov Lemma. *The following two conditions are equivalent:*

(i) The rational matrix $Z(s) = H(sI - F)^{-1}G$ is positive real;

(ii) There is a (generally nonunique) symmetric, nonnegative definite matrix Q and a uniquely corresponding positive definite symmetric matrix P such that

$$PF' + FP = -Q, \tag{2.9}$$

$$PH' = G \tag{2.10}$$

For the most general current statement of this result, for its manifold applications to linear system theory, and for its proof the reader is referred to Popov.[14]

The simplest proof is in terms of the factorization of $Z(s)$ as pointed out in reference 15. So we are led back to the conventional spectral theory! The interpretation of the result, however, is nonclassical: spectral factorization establishes the existence of Q, specifying the covariance of the white noise $u(\cdot)$. Then the stationary covariance P of the state variables of the Markovian model is established by solving (2.9). Once Q is given this solution is unique because of the stability of F and the constraint (2.10).

Thus every second-order process whose covariance possesses a proper rational spectrum has a Markovian realization. This proves that the starting assumptions for the Wold-Kolmogorov-Wiener filter and the Kalman-Bucy filter are, at least abstractly, equivalent in the finite-dimensional case.

We do not wish to create the impression that this is the final word in the filtering problem. There are several difficulties which should inspire further research:

*As is well known[11] any rational matrix $Z(s)$ with $Z(\infty) = 0$ admits a representation $Z(s) = H(sI - F)^{-1}G$, for suitable F, G, H.

(a) In general, Q (and even its rank) is nonunique. Consequently, several different Markovian models may be constructed as the realization of Λ. This is true even if the dimension of the realization is taken to be as small as possible. Deterministic realization theory shows[11] that all minimal-dimensional realizations are essentially equivalent, but in the stochastic case there exist essentially different minimal-dimensional realizations.

(b) It is not as yet known how to formulate the realization theory of stochastic processes in an intrinsic way, as is now possible for deterministic papers (see reference 5 and recent papers on algebraic automata theory). Once we can do this, the entire problem of nonlinear filtering will take on a new aspect, and of course that is presently our main research objective.

REFERENCES

1. R. E. Kalman, "A New Approach to Linear Filtering and Prediction Problems," *J. Basic. Engr.* (*Trans. ASME*), **82 D**, 34–45 (1960).
2. R. S. Bucy, Unpublished internal reports, the Johns Hopkins Applied Physics Laboratory, Silver Spring, Md.
3. R. E. Kalman and R. S. Bucy, "New Results in Linear Filtering and Prediction Theory," *J. Basic. Engr.* (*Trans. ASME*), **83 D**, 95–108 (1961).
4. R. E. Kalman, "Irreducible Realizations and the Degree of a Matrix of Rational Functions," *J. Soc. Ind. Appl. Math.*, **13**, 520–544 (1965).
5. R. E. Kalman, "Algebraic Structure of Linear Dynamical Systems. I. The Module of Σ," *Proc. Nat. Acad. Sci.* (USA), **51** (1965).
6. R. E. Kalman, "New Methods in Wiener Filtering," *Proc. First Symp. on Engineering Applications of Random Function Theory*, Purdue Univ., November, 1960 (New York: Wiley, 1963) pp. 270–388.
7. H. W. Bode and C. E. Shannon, "A Simplified Derivation of Linear Least-Squares Smoothing and Prediction Theory," *Proc. IRE*, **40**, 977–981 (1952).
8. R. L. Stratonovich, "Conditional Markov Processes," *Theor. Probab. Appl.*, **5**, 156–178 (1960).
9. S. Sherman, "Non mean square error criteria," *IRE Trans. on Information Theory*, IT-**4**, 125–126 (1958).
10. A. Papoulis, *Probability, Randon Variables, and Stochastic Processes* (New York: McGraw-Hill, 1965).
11. R. E. Kalman, "Mathematical Description of Linear Dynamical Systems," *J. Control* (SIAM), **1**, 152–192 (1963).
12. I. M. Gel′fand and N. Ya. Vilenkin, *Generalized Functions. Vol. 4: Applications to Harmonic Analysis* (New York: Academic Press, 1964).
13. M. Loève, *Probability Theory*, 3rd Edition (New York: Van Nostrand, 1963).
14. V. M. Popov, "Hyperstability and Optimality of Automatic Systems with Several Control Functions," *Rev. Roum. Sci. Tech., Electr. Energetique*, **10**, 629–690 (1964).
15. R. E. Kalman, "Lyapunov Functions for the Problem of Lur'e in Automatic Control," *Proc. Nat. Acad. Sci.* (USA), **49**, 201–205 (1963).

INFORMATION THEORY AND INFORMATION STORAGE

Norman Abramson
University of California, Berkeley, California

Information theory and its application to digital storage of information is treated. Efficient encoding and storage of the outputs of a discrete information source is discussed. This problem is then contrasted with the efficient encoding and storage of the output of a continuous source.

1. INTRODUCTION

Information theory, in the narrow sense of the term, deals with fundamental constraints which must exist on sequences of symbols used to represent messages. As such, much of the interest in applying information theory has been in communications and data transmission. Certain attempts have been made, however, to apply information theory to information processing and to information storage.[1,2,3] In this paper we explore the efficient storage of information and the limits imposed upon such storage by information theory.

Consider an information source with output $s(t)$. The output of the source, $s(t)$, will be assumed to be a sample function of a stationary random process. If we are interested in storing this sample function as a sequence of numbers $a(1)$, $a(2), \ldots$ we may have several alternatives open to us. That is, there may be a number of methods of mapping the sample function $s(t)$ into sequences $a(1)$, $a(2), \ldots$. Of these we shall be interested in a method which, while allowing us to reconstruct $s(t)$ to a sufficiently high degree of accuracy, will also provide us with a maximum economy of memory capacity. In Section 2 we use Shannon's First Theorem to provide the simplest possible nontrivial illustration of such a mapping. In Section 3 we deal with the case where $s(t)$ is a sample function of a stationary random process of a continuous parameter t.

2. DISCRETE SOURCES

Let $s(t)$, the output of our information source, consist of a sequence of statistically independent symbols $s_1, s_2, \ldots s_q$, occurring with probabilities P_i, $i = 1, 2, \ldots q$. We wish to map this sequence into a sequence of binary symbols $a(1), a(2) \ldots$. Consider first a procedure which maps each s_i separately into

Presented at the Symposium on System Theory
Polytechnic Institute of Brooklyn, April 20, 21, 22, 1965

some fixed binary sequence (code word) of length ℓ_i. Then if each sequence of source symbols is required to lead to a unique binary sequence $a(1), a(2), \ldots$ the ℓ_i must satisfy the Kraft-McMillan Inequality[4]

$$\sum_{i=1}^{q} 2^{-\ell_i} \leq 1. \tag{1}$$

Conversely, if we have a set of q integers ℓ_i satisfying (1), we can always construct an invertible mapping with code words of length $\ell_1, \ell_2, \ldots \ell_q$.[5] Now one set of ℓ_i satisfying (1) is defined by the inequalities (we shall use logarithms to the base 2 throughout this paper)

$$-\log P_i \leq \ell_i < -\log P_i + 1. \tag{2}$$

Upon multiplying (2) by P_i and summing over all i we obtain

$$H(S) \leq L_1 < H(S) + 1 \tag{3}$$

where L_1 is the average number of binary symbols used per source symbol and $H(S)$ is the entropy of the source in bits.

$$L_1 = \sum_{i=1}^{q} P_i \ell_i, \tag{4}$$

$$H(S) = -\sum_{i=1}^{q} P_i \log P_i. \tag{5}$$

Equation (3) provides an upper bound on the average amount of binary memory necessary to store each s_i. It is but a short step from this bound to an exact expression for the average number of binary digits we must use. Instead of mapping each symbol s_i separately into a binary sequence we map sequences of ns_i into binary sequences. The probabilities of the sequences of n s_i are given by $P_{i_1} P_{i_2} \ldots P_{i_n}$ and we let $\lambda_i^{(n)}$ be the length of the corresponding binary code words. Then, as in (2), we can define the lengths $\lambda_i^{(n)}$ by

$$-\log P_{i_1} P_{i_2} \ldots P_{i_n} \leq \lambda_i^{(n)} < -\log P_{i_1} P_{i_2} \ldots P_{i_n} + 1 \tag{6}$$

and upon multiplying by $P_{i_1} P_{i_2} \ldots P_{i_n}$ and summing we get

$$nH(S) \leq L_n < nH(S) + 1, \tag{7}$$

where L_n is the average number of binary symbols used for each block of n s_i symbols. Equation (7) may also be written

$$\lim_{n\to\infty} \frac{L_n}{n} = H(S) \tag{8}$$

where L_n/n is now the average number of binary digits necessary to store a single source symbol s_i. Although we have proved (8) as an upper bound to L_n/n using one method of coding, it may be shown that $H(S)$ is also a lower bound, for an arbitrary code.[6]

There are several points concerning this result which should be emphasized before we proceed, since we wish to draw a number of parallels between coding for discrete information sources and coding for continuous time sources. First we note that in order to achieve the greatest possible compression of the source output into binary symbols we must encode blocks of n source symbols at a time rather than single source symbols. This increase in code complexity is the price we pay for the economy of binary symbols we achieve. Secondly, note that the amount of compression we are able to achieve depends upon the probabilities of the source symbols in a peculiar way. Qualitatively we may say that the more the probabilities are "bunched" the more compression we can achieve; the measure of bunching we use here, however, as shown in (8), is the entropy of the source probabilities. We shall see that the entropy of the power spectral density of a stationary random process plays the same role in the case of a time continuous source. Finally, we note the nature of the sequence of binary symbols into which the source symbols are mapped. If we view these binary symbols themselves as the output of a new information source, we see that the entropy of the new source must be equal to one bit per binary digit. If this were not the case we would be able to code this new source into some other binary sequence and achieve further compression, thus violating eq. (8). But a binary information source having entropy of one bit per binary digit must consist of independent digits, each occurring with equal probability. For the coding of continuous random processes we shall see that the white bandlimited random process plays the same role as the equiprobable independent symbol discrete source. This is not surprising since, in each case, the coding procedure makes use of the redundancy in the intersymbol dependence and in the nonuniform probabilities.

3. CONTINUOUS SOURCES

An equivalent expression of Shannon's First Theorem will be more useful to us than (9) in discussing the analogous question for continuous information sources. The asymptotic equipartition property[7] (AEP) states that, for large n, almost all sequences of n source symbols occur with probability close to $2^{-nH(S)}$ and that there are $2^{nH(S)}$ such sequences.* We may state this result in a form which views the AEP simply as a property of non-negative numbers.

Let λ_i, $i = 1, 2, \ldots$ be any set of non-negative numbers satisfying

$$\sum \lambda_i = T. \tag{9}$$

Then

$$\left[\sum \frac{\lambda_i}{T}\right]^N = \frac{1}{T^N} \sum \lambda_{i_1} \lambda_{i_2} \ldots \lambda_{i_N} = 1 \tag{10}$$

and by the AEP we know that if we take N large enough we need include only $2^{NH(\lambda/T)}$ terms in the second summation above in order to make the sum greater

*Throughout this paper when 2^{nH} is not an integer we shall take 2^{nH} to mean the integer part of 2^{nH}.

than $1 - \varepsilon$, where ε is an arbitrary positive number and

$$H\left(\frac{\lambda}{T}\right) = -\sum \frac{\lambda_i}{T} \log \frac{\lambda_i}{T}. \tag{11}$$

Now we consider an information source where the output of the source is $s(t)$, a sample function of a stationary random process with autocorrelation $R(\tau)$ and spectral density $S(f)$. If the random process is bandlimited to frequencies less than W we may sample $s(t)$ at the Nyquist rate of $2W$ samples per second, store these numbers and reconstruct $s(t)$ from these samples.[8] When $S(f)$ is constant in the band $(-W, W)$ then samples taken at the Nyquist rate are uncorrelated and it seems plausible to say that $2W$ coefficients per second are necessary to reconstruct the sample functions of the process. When $S(f)$ is not flat, however, samples taken in this fashion are correlated and it seems plausible that a lower coefficient rate may be defined. A partial answer to this question has been obtained by Campbell,[9] starting from the AEP of the previous section.

Let $\varphi_i(t)$ and λ_i be the normalized eigenfunctions and eigenvalues of the integral equation

$$\int_0^T R(t-s)\varphi_i(s)\,ds = \lambda_i \varphi_i(t). \tag{12}$$

Then $s(t)$ may be expanded in $[0, T]$ in terms of these eigenfunctions[10]

$$s(t) = \sum s_i \varphi_i(t) \tag{13}$$

where

$$s_i = \int_0^T s(t)\varphi_i(t)\,dt \tag{14}$$

and

$$E[s_i s_j] = \lambda_i \delta_{ij}. \tag{15}$$

If, in addition, we normalize $s(t)$ so that

$$E[s^2(t)] = R(0) = \int S(f)\,df = 1, \tag{16}$$

we have

$$\sum \lambda_i = T. \tag{17}$$

If we approximate $s(t)$ by truncating the expansion (13) to include only μ terms

$$\hat{s}(t) = \sum_{i=1}^{\mu} s_i \varphi_i(t), \tag{18}$$

then the integral squared error of the approximation is given by

$$\frac{1}{T}\int_0^T [s(t) - \hat{s}(t)]^2 dt = 1 - \frac{1}{T}\sum_{i=1}^{\mu} \lambda_i. \tag{19}$$

In order to use these results Campbell used N different sample function $s_j(t_j)$, $j = 1, 2, \ldots N$ of the same random process to define

$$y(t_1, \ldots t_N) = s_1(t_1) \ldots s_N(t_N). \tag{20}$$

Each of the sample functions may be expanded as in (13)

$$s_j(t_j) = \sum_i s_{ij}\varphi_i(t_j) \tag{21}$$

and these expansions may be multiplied to form an expansion for $y(t_1, \ldots t_N)$. The random coefficients of this expansion are terms of the form $s_{i_1 1} \ldots s_{i_N N}$ with variances $\lambda_{i_1} \ldots \lambda_{i_N}$. If we approximate $y(t)$ by truncating this expansion to include only μ^N terms, the integral squared error of the approximation is given by

$$\frac{1}{T^N}\int_0^T \cdots \int_0^T [y(t_1, \ldots t_N) - \hat{y}(t_1, \ldots t_N)]^2 \, dt_1 \ldots dt_N$$

$$= 1 - \frac{1}{T^N} \sum_{\mu^N \text{ terms}} \lambda_{i_1} \ldots \lambda_{i_N} \tag{22}$$

where the μ^N terms included in the summation on the right correspond to the terms included in the approximation $\hat{y}(t_1, \ldots t_n)$.

A direct application of the AEP allows us to determine how large μ must be. By the AEP, if we take N large enough the right side of (22) can be made arbitrarily small as long as

$$\mu^N = 2^{NH\left(\frac{\lambda}{T}\right)} \tag{23}$$

or

$$\mu = 2^{H\left(\frac{\lambda}{T}\right)} \tag{24}$$

But

$$H\left(\frac{\lambda}{T}\right) = -\sum \frac{\lambda_i}{T} \log \frac{\lambda_i}{T}$$

$$= \log T - \frac{1}{T}\sum \lambda_i \log \lambda_i \tag{25}$$

so that

$$\frac{\mu}{T} = 2^{-\frac{1}{T}\sum \lambda_i \log \lambda_i} \tag{26}$$

Finally we use results of Grenander and Szegö dealing with the asymptotic distribution of eigenvalues of Toeplitz kernels[11] to obtain

$$Q = \lim_{T\to\infty} \frac{\mu}{T}$$

$$= 2^{-\int S(f) \log S(f)\, df} \tag{27}$$

where Q is the coefficient rate of $s(t)$, defined by Campbell.

4. DISCUSSION

The similarities between the result of Campbell (27) and that of Shannon (8) are striking. First consider the case of stationary random processes bandlimited to the interval $[-W, W]$. Under this constraint it is well known that a flat spectral density $S(f)$ maximizes the integral in (27). Hence the maximum coefficient rate of a stationary random process bandlimited to $[-W, W]$ is

$$Q = 2^{-\frac{1}{2W}\int_{-W}^{W} \log \frac{1}{2W}\, df}$$

$$= 2W \tag{28}$$

The white bandlimited random process then plays a role in the encoding of continuous sources analagous to the role of sequences of equiprobable symbols in the encoding of discrete sources. Whereas constructive coding techniques are available for discrete sources, however, no such techniques are available for continuous sources. What is lacking here are methods of mapping finite numbers of sample functions of $s(t)$ into sequences of coefficients in some manner which will allow the asymptotic realization of Campbell's coefficient rate.

Equation (28) tells us that these coefficients will be uncorrelated and identically distributed. One method obtaining a mapping of a continuous bandlimited random process into a sequence of independent identically distributed random variables is by the use of an optimum linear predictor. Let $s(t)$ be bandlimited to $[-W, W]$ and assume we know the values $s(n/2W)$, $n = 0, -1, -2, \ldots$. Then $s(1/2W)$ may be expressed as the sum of the optimum linear predictor (a known function of the previous samples) plus the prediction error, having variance given by [12]

$$[2W]\left[2^{\int_{-W}^{W} \log S(f) df}\right]. \tag{29}$$

Since the prediction error, together with the previous samples, completely specifies $s(1/2W)$, the process may be repeated to obtain $s(2/2W)$, etc. The sequence of prediction errors needed to obtain each sample constitutes a sequence of identically distributed independent random variables.

Note the differences in these two data representation techniques. In the first we require a lower coefficient rate Q, but the variance of the coefficients is increased. In the second method the coefficient rate is $2W$ per second but the variance of the coefficients is decreased. It is not hard to see that neither the coefficient rate nor the variance of the coefficients provides an adequate criterion for data compression.

In order to decrease the variance of a set of coefficients to an arbitrarily small value we need only multiply these coefficients by a constant less than one. In order to decrease the coefficient rate to an arbitrarily small value, a technique somewhat more complicated may be employed. For any given desired degree of accuracy, corresponding to the accuracy used in defining Q, we may quantize the coefficients to a necessary degree of fineness. Any pair of quantized coefficients then will have a countable set of possible values and there exists an invertible mapping which maps each pair of coefficients into a single coefficient (say, the set of rationals). This transformation provides a coefficient rate of $Q/2$, but clearly we may obtain a rate of Q/k by combining k coefficients.

Although the schemes outlined above will decrease the coefficient rate and the variance of the coefficients, they are both highly vulnerable to noise. Small variations in the new coefficients from these schemes will in general lead to large errors in the reconstructed sample functions. This defect points out the important and still unanswered question in data compression and information storage. If a fixed rate of coefficients with variance equal to one is available to represent a sample function of a stationary random process, how should these coefficients be chosen in order to minimize the effect of coefficient noise on the reconstructed sample function?

REFERENCES

1. P. Elias, "Computation in the Presence of Noise," *IBM Jounral*, 2, 4 (October 1958), pp. 346–353.
2. K. L. Jordan, "Discrete Representation of Random Signals," MIT Research Laboratory of Electronics, TR-378 (July 1961).
3. S. Winograd and J. D. Cowan, "Reliable Computation in the Presence of Noise," (Cambridge, Mass.: MIT Press, 1963).
4. N. Abramson, "Information Theory and Coding," (New York: McGraw-Hill, 1963), pp. 57–60.
5. Ibid., p. 57.
6. Ibid., p. 68.
7. B. McMillan, "The Basic Theorems of Information Theory," *Ann. Math. Statist.*, 24, 196–219.
8. A. V. Balakrishnan, "A Note on the Sampling Principle for Continuous Signals," *IRE Trans. on Information Theory*, IT-3, 143–146.
9. L. L. Campbell, "Minimum Coefficient Rate for Stationary Random Processes," *Information and Control*, 3, 360–371.
10. M. Loeve, *Probability Theory* (Princeton, N. J.: D. Van Nostrand, 1955), p. 478.
11. U. Grenander and G. Szego, *Toeplitz Forms and Their Applications*, (Univ. of Calif. Press, 1958), p. 65.
12. Ibid., p. 183.

OPTIMAL CONTROL PROBLEMS AS EXTREMAL PROBLEMS IN A BANACH SPACE *

Lucien W. Neustadt
Department of Electrical Engineering, University of Southern California
Los Angeles, Calif.

This paper presents the formulation of an extremely general variational problem in a Banach space setting. This formulation includes, as special cases, the conventional optimal control problems both with and without restricted phase coordinates. Using the concept of quasiconvexity, it is possible to derive necessary conditions for extremality in terms of the separability of two convex sets in a Banach space. The Pontryagin maximum principle, together with its extension to the problem with restricted phase coordinates, is derived from the general necessary conditions presented herein.

1. INTRODUCTION

In this paper we shall formulate a very general extremal problem, and shall present and discuss the corresponding necessary conditions for extremality.

This general extremal problem, which is formulated in Sections 2 and 3, includes, as special cases, the conventional optimal control problems, both with and without restricted phase coordinates. Further, the great generality of the problem formulation makes it possible to consider constraints on the phase trajectories of a class much wider than the usual ones wherein certain functions of the trajectory initial and final values are specified, and to allow a very broad class of "cost functionals" and admissibility criteria for the control functions.

A fundamental concept in the theory described below is that of a quasiconvex family of functions, which was first introduced by Gamkrelidze.[1] With the aid of this concept, it is possible to obtain a certain convex family of variations, and by considering these variations as elements of an appropriate Banach space, to prove a separation theorem which gives rise to the general necessary conditions for optimality. This is discussed in Section 4. In Section 5, we shall demonstrate how these conditions may be applied to various optimal control problems.

2. PROBLEM STATEMENT

Let us assume that we are given a control system whose state at any time t is described by an n-dimensional phase vector x, and let us suppose that the be-

*This research was supported in part by the Joint Services Electronics Program (U.S. Army, U.S. Navy, and U.S. Air Force) under Grant No. AF-AFOSR-496-65.

Presented at the Symposium on System Theory
Polytechnic Institute of Brooklyn, April 20, 21, 22, 1965

havior of the system is such that x is an absolutely continuous function of the time t which satisfies, for almost all t, $t_0 \leqq t \leqq t_1$ (t_0 and t_1 are assumed to be fixed), the following differential equation:

$$\dot{x}(t) = f(x(t), u(t), t). \tag{2.1}$$

Here, the n-vector valued function f is assumed to be defined on $G \times W \times I$, where G is an open set in R^n (Euclidean n-space), W is an arbitrary fixed set in R^r, $I = [t_0, t_1]$, and $u(t)$ is a measurable essentially bounded function from I to W. We shall suppose that $f(x, v, t)$ is of class C^1 with respect to $x \in G$, and measurable in $(v, t) \in W \times I$ for every fixed $x \in G$.

In general, of course, the behavior of the system, as described by the function $x(t)$ (the phase trajectory), will depend on the system's initial state, as described by $x(t_0)$, as well as on the choice of the "control" function $u(t)$. We shall be concerned with the problem of determining a control $u^*(t)$ (within a given class of admissible functions) and an initial state $x(t_0) \in G$ such that the system's behavior (i.e., the corresponding solution of (2.1), which must be defined for all $t \in I$) is, in a certain sense, extremal.

Before specifying what we mean here by an extremal, it will be necessary to introduce three sets. The first of these, which we shall denote by Ω, represents the class of admissible controls. For the moment, we shall suppose simply that Ω is a fixed class of functions from I to W, such that each member of Ω is measurable and essentially bounded.

Let $\mathcal{B}$ denote the Banach space of continuous functions x from I to R^n, normed in the conventional manner:

$$\|x\| = \max_{t \in I} |x(t)|, \tag{2.2}$$

where the vertical bars in the right-hand side of (2.2) denote the ordinary Euclidean norm in R^n. Our second set, which we shall denote by Φ, represents certain constraints imposed on the phase trajectories. Namely, we shall suppose that Φ is a fixed set of continuous (not necessarily linear) functionals $\phi(x)$ defined on an open set $N \subset \mathcal{B}$.

Our third set B, is assumed to be a fixed subset of $\mathcal{B}$. As we shall see in Section 5, B may represent the fact that a functional on the phase trajectories is being minimized, and may also represent additional constraints on the phase trajectories.

Let $Y = \{x : x \in N, \phi(x) = 0 \text{ for every } \phi \in \Phi\}$.

We are now in a position to define what we mean by an extremal. Namely, we shall say that an element $z \in N \subset \mathcal{B}$ is a Ω, Φ, B extremal if:

1) z is an absolutely continuous function whose range is contained in G,

2) $\dot{z}(t) = f(z(t), u^*(t), t)$ for almost all $t \in I$ and for some function $u^* \in \Omega$,

3) $z \in Y \cap B$, (2.3)

4) whenever x is an absolutely continuous function from I to G such that:
(a) eq. (2.1) is satisfied for almost all $t \in I$ and some $u \in \Omega$; and
(b) $x \in Y \cap B$,

then $x = z$, i.e., $x(t) \equiv z(t)$ in I.

The remainder of this paper will be devoted to presenting and discussing necessary conditions for z to be an Ω, Φ, B extremal, and to the demonstration of the fact that the solutions of a large class of optimal control problems are such extremals (by means of an appropriate choice of Ω, Φ, and B). Thus, in the sequel, we shall assume that z is a Ω, Φ, B extremal, and that (2.3) holds.

In order to obtain meaningful necessary conditions, it is necessary to make certain assumptions on the sets Ω, Φ, and B. It is to this that the next section is devoted.

3. BASIC ASSUMPTIONS

We shall assume that Ω is such that the family of functions F, defined by

$$F = \{h(x, t) : h(x, t) = f(x, u(t), t),\ u(t) \in \Omega\} \tag{3.1}$$

is quasiconvex.

Let P^ν denote the set of all vectors $\alpha = (\alpha_1, \ldots, \alpha_\nu) \in R^\nu$ such that $\alpha_i \geqq 0$ for each i and $\Sigma_{i=1}^{\nu} \alpha_i = 1$.

Then, (see reference 1) F is quasiconvex if and only if, for every compact set $X \subset G$, every finite collection $u_1, \ldots, u_m$ of elements of Ω, and every $\varepsilon > 0$, there exists a function $m(t)$, integrable over I (and possibly depending on X and the u_i, but not on ε), and functions $u_\alpha \in \Omega$, defined for every $\alpha \in P^\nu$ (and possibly depending on X, the u_i and ε), such that, if $g(x, t; \alpha) = \Sigma_{i=1}^{\nu} \alpha_i f(x, u_i(t), t) - f(x, u_\alpha(t), t)$, then the following conditions are satisfied:

1) $|f(x, u_i(t), t)| \leqq m(t)$, $|f_x(x, u_i(t), t)| \leqq m(t)$ for all $x \in X$, $t \in I$ and $i = 1, \ldots, m$;

2) $|g(x, t; \alpha)| \leqq m(t)$, $|g_x(x, t; \alpha)| \leqq m(t)$ for all $x \in X$, $t \in I$ and $\alpha \in P^\nu$;

3) $\left| \int_{\tau_1}^{\tau_2} g(x, t; \alpha)\, dt \right| < \varepsilon$ for every $x \in X$, $\alpha \in P^\nu$ and $\tau_1, \tau_2 \in I$;

4) for every sequence $\{\alpha^i\}$, with $\alpha^i \in P^\nu$ for $i = 1, 2, \ldots$, which converges to some $\overline{\alpha} \in P^\nu$, $g(x, t; \alpha^i)$ converges in measure (as a function of t on I) to $g(x, t; \overline{\alpha})$, for every $x \in X$.

In conditions 1 and 2, the vertical bars denote the ordinary Euclidean norm in R^n or R^{n^2}, and $f_x(g_x)$ denotes the Jacobian matrix derived from $f(g)$.

The assumptions we shall make on Φ are the following: Φ consists of a finite number of functionals ϕ_i ($i = 1, \ldots, m$), each of which possesses a Frechet differential at z; i.e., there exist m linear continuous functionals $\ell_1, \ldots, \ell_m$ in $\mathcal{B}^*$ (which, without loss of generality, we shall assume are linearly independent) such that

$$\frac{|\phi_i(z + x) - \ell_i(x)|}{\|x\|} \xrightarrow[\|x\| \to 0]{} 0.$$

(Note that $\phi_i(z) = 0$ for $i = 1, \ldots, m$ because $z \in Y$ by hypothesis.) We also permit the case where Φ is empty.

We shall make the following assumption on the set B: There exists a convex cone $Z \subset \mathcal{B}$, with vertex at z and containing points other than z, such that, if ρ is any ray in Z, there exists a cone Z_ρ and a number $\varepsilon > 0$ (both possibly depending on ρ) such that

1) the vertex of Z_ρ is z,

2) $Z_\rho \subset Z$,

3) Z_ρ has a non-empty interior (relative to $\mathcal{B}$),

4) ρ is an interior ray of Z_ρ,

5) there is an ε – neighborhood of z whose intersection with Z_ρ is completely contained in B.

In this case, we shall say that Z is an *internal cone* for B at z.

Let

$$\Pi = \{x : x \in \mathcal{B}, \ \ell_i(x) = 0, \ i = 1, \ldots, m\}, \tag{3.2}$$

and let

$$Z'' = \Pi \cap (Z - z) \tag{3.3}$$

where $Z - z = \{x : x = \zeta - z, \ \zeta \in Z\}$. Our final assumptions are that $Z'' \neq \Pi$, and that Z'' contains at least one point other than 0.

In Section 5, we shall describe some of the optimal control problems for which the above assumptions are valid.

4. NECESSARY CONDITIONS FOR EXTREMALITY

Before presenting the necessary conditions, it is necessary to make some definitions.

Let $\tilde{\Phi}(t)$ be the $n \times n$ matrix function which is the solution of the equation

$$\frac{d\tilde{\Phi}}{dt} = f_x(z(t), u^*(t), t)\, \tilde{\Phi}(t), \quad \tilde{\Phi}(t_0) = I \ \text{ the identity matrix.} \tag{4.1}$$

Let $[F]$ denote the convex hull of F, i.e. (see Eq. (3.1)),

$$[F] = \Big\{ h(x, t) : h(x, t) = \sum_{i=1}^{\nu} \beta_i f(x, u_i(t), t), \ \nu \text{ arbitrary}, \ (\beta_1, \ldots, \beta_\nu) \in P^\nu,$$
$$u_i \in \Omega \text{ for } i = 1, \ldots, \nu\Big\}. \tag{4.2}$$

Let L be the map from $R^n \times [F]$ to $\mathcal{B}$ defined by $L(\xi, h) = x_{\xi,h}(t)$ where

$$x_{\xi,h}(t) = \tilde{\Phi}(t)\left\{\xi + \int_{t_0}^{t} \tilde{\Phi}^{-1}(s)[h(z(s), s) - f(z(s), u^*(s), s)]\, ds\right\},$$
$$t_0 \leq t \leq t_1, \tag{4.3}$$

and let

$$K = \{L(\xi, h) : \xi \in R^n,\ h \in [F]\}. \tag{4.4}$$

Clearly, K is a convex subset of $\mathcal{B}$, and $0 \in K$.

It is then possible to prove the following basic theorem.

Theorem 4.1. If z is a Ω, Φ, B extremal, and the assumptions of Section 3 hold, then the convex sets K and Z'' (defined by (3.3), (3.2), and (4.1)–(4.4)) are separated in $\mathcal{B}$; i.e., there exists a continuous, nonzero, linear functional $\ell^* \in \mathcal{B}^*$ such that $\ell^*(x) \leqq 0$ for all $x \in K$, and $\ell^*(x) \geqq 0$ for all $x \in Z''$.

The following lemma is useful both at this point, and later in the development.

Lemma 4.1. Let R_1 and R_2 be convex sets in a Banach space $\mathcal{B}$ such that:

a) R_1 is a cone with vertex at 0 and a non-empty interior;

b) 0 is a boundary point of R_2; and

c) R_2 meets the interior of R_1.

Let $R_3 = R_1 \cap R_2$, and let $L_i = \{\ell : \ell \in \mathcal{B}^*,\ \ell(x) \leqq 0$ for all $x \in R_i\}$, $i = 1, 2, 3$. Then $L_3 = \{\ell : \ell \in \mathcal{B}^*,\ \ell = \ell_1 + \ell_2,\ \ell_i \in L_i,\ i = 1 \text{ or } 2\}$; i.e., $L_3 = L_1 + L_2$.

By virtue of Lemma 4.1, (see (3.3)) we have the following corollary to Theorem 4.1.

Corollary 4.1. If z is a Ω, Φ, B extremal and the assumptions of Section 3 hold, there exist real numbers $\alpha_1, \ldots, \alpha_m$ and a linear, continuous functional $\bar{\ell} \in \mathcal{B}^*$ such that

$$\bar{\ell}(\zeta) \geqq \bar{\ell}(z) \quad \text{for every} \quad \zeta \in Z, \tag{4.5}$$

and, if

$$\ell^* = \bar{\ell} + \sum_{i=1}^{m} \alpha_i \ell_i, \tag{4.6}$$

then $\ell^* \neq 0$ and

$$\ell^*(x) \leqq 0 \quad \text{for all} \quad x \in K. \tag{4.7}$$

This corollary is the principal result of this paper. The proofs of Theorem 4.1 and Lemma 4.1 are too lengthy to present here, and will be published elsewhere. However, we note that the proof of Theorem 4.1 is in the spirit of the proof of Theorem 2.1 in reference 1.

5. APPLICATION TO OPTIMAL CONTROL THEORY

In this section we shall describe some problems for which the assumptions set forth in Section 3 are valid, and use the separation theorem of the preceding section to obtain necessary conditions for some optimal control problems, including those with restricted phase coordinates.

Throughout the sequel we shall suppose that Ω is defined as follows: Let $U(t)$ be a function from I to the class of all subsets of W. Then let

$$\Omega = \{u : u(t) \in U(t) \text{ for almost all } t \in I,$$
$$u \text{ is measurable and essentially bounded on } I\}. \tag{5.1}$$

It is shown in reference 1 that the class F given by (3.1), where Ω is defined by (5.1), is quasiconvex. A particularly important case in control theory is the one in which $U(t) \equiv W$, and W is a closed set in R^r.

Let $\theta_i(\xi, \eta)$, $i = 1, \ldots, m$, be given differentiable functions from a neighborhood of $(z(t_0), z(t_1))$ in $R^n \times R^n$ to R^1, and suppose that the elements ϕ_i of Φ are defined as follows:

$$\phi_i(x) = \theta_i(x(t_0), x(t_1)), \quad i = 1, \ldots, m. \tag{5.2}$$

Then each ϕ_i possesses a Frechet differential ℓ_i at z, and ℓ_i is given by

$$\ell_i(x) = \theta_i' \cdot x(t_0) + \theta_i'' \cdot x(t_1), \tag{5.3}$$

where the dot denotes the ordinary scalar product for vectors in R^n, and

$$\theta_i' = \frac{\partial \theta_i(z(t_0), z(t_1))}{\partial \xi}, \quad \theta_i'' = \frac{\partial \theta_i(z(t_0), z(t_1))}{\partial \eta}.$$

Finally let θ_0 be a function with the same properties as θ_1, let ϕ_0 be the functional on $\mathcal{B}$ defined by

$$\phi_0(x) = \theta_0(x(t_0), x(t_1)) \tag{5.4}$$

and suppose that

$$B = \{z\} \cup \{x : x \in \mathcal{B}, \phi_0(x) < \phi_0(z)\}. \tag{5.5}$$

Then it is easily seen that $Z_0 = [\{0\} \cup \{x : x \in \mathcal{B}, \ell_0(x) < 0\}] + z$ is an internal cone for B at z (where ℓ_0, the Frechet differential of ϕ_0 at z, is given by (5.3) with $i = 0$).

Consequently, the sets Ω, Φ, and B defined by (5.1), (5.2), and (5.5) (together with (5.4)), respectively, satisfy the hypotheses set down in Section 3, as long as the functionals ℓ_i for $i = 0, 1, \ldots, m$ are linearly independent.

Now consider the optimal control problem that consists in finding a function $x(t) \in \mathcal{B}$ that: (a) is a solution of eq. (2.1) for some $u \in \Omega$, where Ω is given by (5.1); (b) has range in G; (c) satisfies the relations $\theta_i(x(t_0), x(t_1)) = 0$ for $i = 1, \ldots, m$; and (d) in so doing minimizes $\theta_0(x(t_0), x(t_1))$. It is evident that if z is a solution of this problem, then z is a Ω, Φ, B extremal, where Φ and B are given by (5.2) and (5.5) (with (5.4)), respectively. Thus, the necessary conditions given by Corollary 4.1 are necessary conditions also for z to be a solution of the optimal control problem.

It follows from Corollary 4.1 that (see (4.3), (4.4) and (5.3), and note that $\bar{\ell} = \alpha_0 \ell_0$ where $\alpha_0 \leqq 0$)

$$\left[\sum_{i=0}^{m} \alpha_i \theta_i' + \sum_{i=0}^{m} \alpha_i \theta_i'' \tilde{\Phi}(t_1)\right] \xi + \sum_{i=0}^{m} \alpha_i \theta_i'' \tilde{\Phi}(t_1)$$

$$\times \int_{t_0}^{t_1} \tilde{\Phi}^{-1}(s)\,[h(z(s), s) - f(z(s), u^*(s), s)]\, ds \leqq 0 \quad \text{for every } \xi \in R^n \text{ and } h \in [F]. \tag{5.6}$$

In (5.6), the θ_i' and θ_i'' are row-vectors, and ξ, h, and f column-vectors. Since (5.6) must hold for every $\xi \in R^n$ and for $h(z(s), s) = f(z(s), u^*(s), s)$, we conclude that

$$-\sum_{i=0}^{m} \alpha_i \theta_i' = \sum_{i=0}^{m} \alpha_i \theta_i'' \widetilde{\Phi}(t_1). \tag{5.7}$$

Further, (5.6) must also hold for $\xi = 0$ and for $h(z(s), s) = f(z(s), u(s), s)$, where $u \in \Omega$ is arbitrary (see (4.2)). Therefore,

$$\int_{t_0}^{t_1} \psi(s)\, f(z(s), u(s), s)\, ds \leqq \int_{t_0}^{t_1} \psi(s)\, f(z(s), u^*(s), s)\, ds \quad \text{for every } u \in \Omega, \tag{5.8}$$

where the row-vector $\psi(s)$ is given by

$$\psi(s) = \sum_{i=0}^{m} \alpha_i \theta_i'' \widetilde{\Phi}(t_1) \widetilde{\Phi}^{-1}(s), \quad t_0 \leqq s \leqq t_1. \tag{5.9}$$

It follows from (5.9), (4.1) and (5.7) that ψ is a solution of the equation

$$\dot{\psi}(t) = -\psi(t)\, f_x(z(t), u^*(t), t), \tag{5.10}$$

and that

$$\psi(t_0) = -\sum_{i=0}^{m} \alpha_i \frac{\partial \theta_i(z(t_0), z(t_1))}{\partial \xi}, \quad \psi(t_1) = \sum_{i=0}^{m} \alpha_i \frac{\partial \theta_i(z(t_0), z(t_1))}{\partial \eta}. \tag{5.11}$$

Also recall that

$$\alpha_0 \leqq 0. \tag{5.12}$$

Since $\ell^* \neq 0$, it follows that $\alpha_i \neq 0$ for some $i = 0, 1, \ldots, m$, and because of the linear independence of the ℓ_i, we can conclude that $\psi \neq 0$. The necessary conditions given by relations (5.8) and (5.10)–(5.12) have been previously derived by Gamkrelidze.[1] In reference 1 it is also shown that if f is in addition continuous in all of its arguments, and $U(t) \equiv W$, then (5.8) implies the Pontryagin maximum principle (reference 2, Ch. I, II), which here takes the form:

$$\psi(s)\, f(z(s), u^*(s), s) = \max_{v \in W} \psi(s)\, f(z(s), v, s) \quad \text{for almost all } s \in I.$$

Relations (5.11) correspond to the transversality conditions in ref. 2, pp. 45–50.

Clearly, Corollary 4.1 can also be applied to problems where the ϕ_i, $i = 0, 1, \ldots, m$, have a more general form than (5.2). It is only necessary that the ϕ_i have Frechet differentials at z. As one example, we cite the following:

$$\phi_i(x) = \theta_i(x(t_0), x(t_1), x(\tau_1), \ldots, x(\tau_s)), \quad i = 0, 1, \ldots, m,$$

where $\tau_j \in I$ for $j = 1, \ldots, s$, and $\theta_i(\xi_1, \ldots, \xi_{s+2})$, for each i, is a differentiable function from a neighborhood, in $R^{(2+s)n}$, of $(z(t_0), z(t_1), z(\tau_1), \ldots, z(\tau_s))$ to R^1.

Now let $\phi_{m+1}(x), \ldots, \phi_{m+k}(x)$ be continuous functionals defined in a neighborhood of z in $\mathcal{B}$, and let

$$\widetilde{B} = B \cap \{x : x \in \mathcal{B},\ \phi_i(x) \leqq \phi_i(z) = 0,\ i = m+1, \ldots, m+k\}. \tag{5.13}$$

If the ϕ_i, for $i = m + 1, \ldots, m + k$, possess Frechet differentials ℓ_i at z, and $Z_i = [\{0\} \cup \{x : x \in \mathcal{B}, \ell_{m+i}(x) < 0\}] + z$ for $i = 1, \ldots, k$, then it is easily verified that $\tilde{Z} = \left(\bigcap_{i=0}^{k} Z_i\right)$ is an internal cone for $\tilde{B}$ at z. Further, if $\bar{\ell}(x) \geqq \bar{\ell}(z)$ for all $x \in \tilde{Z}$, it follows immediately that

$$\bar{\ell} = \sum_{i=m+1}^{m+k} \alpha_i \ell_i + \alpha_0 \ell_0, \text{ where } \alpha_i \leqq 0 \text{ for } i = 0, m+1, \ldots, m+k. \tag{5.14}$$

Thus, if z is a Ω, Φ, $\tilde{B}$ extremal, necessary conditions can be derived as above on the basis of Corollary 4.1, together with relation (5.14).

Consider the optimal control problem that consists in finding a function $x(t) \in \mathcal{B}$ that: (i) is a solution of eq. (2.1) for some $u \in \Omega$, where Ω is given by (5.1); (ii) has range in G; (iii) satisfies the relations $\phi_i(x) = 0$ for $i = 1, \ldots, m$; (iv) satisfies the inequalities $\phi_i(x) \leqq 0$ for $i = m + 1, \ldots, m + k$; and (v) in so doing minimizes $\phi_0(x)$. Clearly if z is a solution of this problem, then z is a Ω, Φ, $\tilde{B}$ extremal (where $\tilde{B}$ is given by (5.13) and (5.5), and $\Phi = \{\phi_1, \ldots, \phi_m\}$). If the ϕ_i, $i = 0, 1, \ldots, m + k$, possess Frechet differentials ℓ_1 at z which are linearly independent, then z satisfies the necessary conditions of corollary 4.1 (but, since B has been replaced by $\tilde{B}$, Z must be replaced by $\tilde{Z}$ in (4.5)), and, by virtue of (5.14), (4.6) takes the form

$$\ell^* = \sum_{i=0}^{m+k} \alpha_i \ell_i, \ \alpha_0 \leqq 0, \ \alpha_{m+i} \leqq \text{ for } i = 1, \ldots, k. \tag{5.15}$$

It is interesting to note that, except for the sign of certain α_i, the form of (5.15) is unchanged if the roles of any two of the ϕ_i are interchanged in the optimal control problem statement. Thus, there exists a duality between two problems that differ only in that the minimized and constraint functionals have been interchanged.

Finally, let us consider the problem where $\tilde{B}$ is again given by (5.13), but where some of the ϕ_i for $i > m$ *do not* possess Frechet differentials at z. For example, let

$$\phi_{m+i}(x) = \max_{t \in I} g_i(x(t), t), \quad i = 1, \ldots, k, \tag{5.16}$$

where $g_1, \ldots, g_k$ are given fixed functions from R^{n+1} to R^1 which we shall assume to be continuous, and in class C^1 with respect to x. Then, if the optimal control problem is as described in the preceding paragraph, and the ϕ_i, for $i > m$, are given by (5.16), it follows that the constraints (iv) are equivalent to the inequalities

$$g_i(x(t), t) \leqq 0 \quad \text{for all } t \in I \text{ and } i = 1, \ldots, k,$$

so that we have a problem with restricted phase coordinates. In order to be able to apply Corollary 4.1 and obtain necessary conditions for z to be a solution of this problem, it is necessary to determine an internal cone for $\tilde{B}$.

Let $B_i = \{x : x \in \mathcal{B}, \phi_{m+i}(x) \leqq 0\}$, $i = 1, \ldots, k$, so that $\widetilde{B} = \bigcap_{i=1}^{k} B_i \cap B$. It is not difficult to show that the convex cone Z'_i, defined by

$$Z'_i = z + [\{x : x \in \mathcal{B}, [\text{grad } g_i(z(t), t)] \cdot x(t) < 0 \text{ for all } t \in I_i\} \cup \{0\}], \quad (5.17)$$

where

$$I_i = \{t : t \in I, g_i(z(t), t) = 0\},$$

is an internal cone for B_i at z (for $i = 1, \ldots, k$), and that (if we set $Z'_0 = Z_0$)

$$\hat{Z} = \bigcap_{i=0}^{k} Z'_i$$

is an internal cone for $\widetilde{B}$ at z (so long as $\hat{Z}$ contains points other than z). Further, it follows from Lemma 4.1 that, if $\ell(x) \geqq \ell(z)$ for every $x \in \hat{Z}$, then

$$\bar{\ell} = \alpha_0 \ell_0 + \sum_{i=m+1}^{m+k} \alpha_i \ell_i, \text{ where } \alpha_0 \leqq 0$$

and

$$\ell_{m+i}(x) \geqq \ell_{m+i}(z) \text{ for every } x \in Z'_i \text{ and } i = 1, \ldots, k. \quad (5.18)$$

According to Corollary 4.1, if z is a solution of the optimal control problem with restricted phase coordinates described in the preceding paragraph, then there exist real numbers $\alpha_0, \alpha_1, \ldots, \alpha_{m+k}$, and linear continuous functionals $\ell_{m+1}, \ldots, \ell_{m+k}$ satisfying relations (5.18), such that if $\ell^* = \Sigma_{i=0}^{m+k} \alpha_i \ell_i$, then $\ell^* \neq 0$ and $\ell^*(x) \leqq 0$ for every $x \in K$ (see (4.3) and (4.4)).

If $\ell_{m+1} \in \mathcal{B}^*$ satisfies (5.18) (and (5.17)), then it follows directly from standard representation theorems that

$$\ell_{m+i}(x) = \int_{t_0}^{t_1} [x(t) \cdot \text{grad } g_i(z(t), t)] \, d\lambda(t),$$

where $\lambda(t)$ is a non-increasing, scalar-valued function which is constant on every subinterval of I that does not meet I_i.

We can now derive, in a fashion similar to the derivation of conditions (5.8) and (5.10)–(5.12), necessary conditions for the optimal control problem with restricted phase coordinates, and, assuming that the g_i are in class C^2 with respect to x, arrive at results which are very similar to those presented in reference 2, Chapter VI, and references 3 and 4, under hypotheses stronger than those made here.

Let us also remark that Corollary 4.1 can, in a very similar manner, be applied to the problem where ϕ_0 is of the form (5.16) (and therefore does not generally possess a Frechet differential). In this case again, there are duality theorems with respect to an interchange of the "minimized" functional ϕ_0 (or constraint function g_0) and a constraint functional ϕ_{m+i} (or constraint function g_i).

In this paper we have been concerned exclusively with fixed-time problems. However, by means of minor modifications of the arguments and definitions described above, variable-time problems can also be considered.

ACKNOWLEDGMENT

The author is indebted to Dr. R. V. Gamkrelidze for many stimulating conversations and for his suggestions and remarks which motivated and initiated the author's research into the problem described in this paper.

REFERENCES

1. R. V. Gamkrelidze, "On Some Extremal Problems in the Theory of Differential Equations with Applications to the Theory of Optimal Control," *J. SIAM,* Ser. A: Control, 3(1965).
2. L. S. Pontryagin, V. G. Boltyanskii, R. V. Gamkrelidze, and E. F. Mishchenko, "The Mathematical Theory of Optimal Processes" [Translation from Russian] (New York: John Wiley, 1962).
3. J. Warga, "Minimizing Variational Curves Restricted to a Preassigned Set," *Trans. Amer. Math. Soc.*, 112, 432-455 (1964).
4. J. Warga, "Unilateral Variational Problems with Several Inequalities," *Michigan Math J.*, to appear.

OPTIMUM DEMODULATION OF SIGNALS THROUGH RANDOMLY FADING MEDIA*

Mischa Schwartz
Department of Electrical Engineering
Polytechnic Institute of Brooklyn, Brooklyn, N.Y.

Using an abstract vector space approach, optimum demodulators are obtained for the case of analog-type signals transmitted through random fading media. Additive Gaussian noise is assumed. The channels considered are non-time-dispersive. The demodulator implementations are shown to be of the phase-locked loop type previously derived by Youla for deterministic channels, with adaptively varying gain controls introduced to account for channel amplitude variations. Examples considered include slow fading with random amplitude variations, slow fading with amplitude and phase variations, and rapid fading with amplitude variations.

I. INTRODUCTION

We consider in this paper the problem of optimally demodulating an analogue-type signal transmitted through a randomly fading channel. Additive Gaussian noise is assumed as well. The results obtained here are for the case of a non-time-dispersive channel only, so that the effects of the channel may be treated as multiplicative noise. As our optimization criterion we choose the maximum a posteriori estimate. This work thus extends the well-known results of D. C. Youla[1] to include the effect of the random channel.**

Specifically, we consider a transmitted cw signal $s[t, a(t)]$ which has been modulated by the information-bearing signal $a(t)$. As examples we have $s[t, a(t)] = a(t) \cos \omega_0 t$ (double-sideband AM), $\cos [\omega_0 t + a(t)]$ (PM-phase modulation), and $\cos [\omega_0 t + \int a(t) dt]$ (FM). For simplicity's sake, we shall refer only to PM-type signals in discussing optimum realizations of demodulators, but extensions to other types of signals are readily obtained. The modulating signal $a(t)$ will be assumed to be a nonstationary Gaussian variable with correlation function $R_a(t, y)$ given.

*The research described herein was supported by the National Science Foundation, Washington, D.C., under NSF Grant No. GP-2059.

**After the work leading to the present paper was completed, the author became aware of parallel work carried out by Dr. H. Van Trees of MIT, and reported on at the 1964 Wescon Conference, Los Angeles, Calif. Although his optimum demodulators are identical in some cases to those obtained here, the approaches used differ to some extent; the concepts of abstract vector spaces are utilized here in solving the problem, while Van Trees has applied the technique of Karhunen-Loeve expansions. Some results obtained, particularly those in Part III, complement those obtained by Van Trees.

Presented at the Symposium on System Theory
Polytechnic Institute of Brooklyn, April 20, 21, 22, 1965

The received signal $v(t)$ is then assumed to be of the form

$$v(t) = A(t)\, s[t, a(t)] + n(t), \quad 0 \leq t \leq T, \tag{1}$$

if the channel may be assumed to introduce amplitude variations only, or of the more general form

$$v(t) = x(t)\, s_1[t, a(t)] + y(t)\, s_2[t, a(t)] + n(t), \quad 0 \leq t \leq T, \tag{2}$$

where phase effects must be taken into account as well. $A(t)$, $x(t)$, and $y(t)$ are assumed to be random variables with known probability distributions. The additive noise $n(t)$ is assumed Gaussian with correlation function $R_n(t, y)$ specified.

From the known waveshape $v(t)$, measured over an arbitrary interval T, we attempt to continuously estimate, as best as possible, the modulating signal $a(t)$.

In Part II of this paper we summarize the necessary concepts of abstract vector spaces applicable to this problem, considering as an example Youla's case of a nonfading channel. In Part III we consider a slowly varying channel model with the amplitudes A in eq. (1), or x and y in eq. (2) constant over the interval T and describable by their first order probability density functions. In Part IV we consider the case of a time-varying channel representable by eq. (1), with Gaussian statistics only.

We shall find that in all cases the implementation of the optimum demodulators corresponds to Youla's phase-locked loop implementation with the addition of an adaptive amplifier, or form of automatic-gain-control (agc) circuit. This gain control is obtained by cross-correlating the received signal with the estimated modulated signal $s[t, a(t)]$. As has been pointed out by Van Trees (see footnote on preceding page), this is directly analogous to estimator correlators encountered in other estimation problems.

II. SUMMARY OF ABSTRACT VECTOR SPACE CONCEPTS.[2] APPLICATION TO MAXIMUM A POSTERIORI ESTIMATION IN NONFADING CASE

By a vector space S is meant a set of elements (vectors), a, b, c, etc., satisfying the following properties:

1. $a + b = b + a = c$, with c another vector in space S,
2. $a + (b + c) = (a + b) + c$,
3. $x(a + b) = xa + xb$, x a scalar,
4. $x(ya) = (xy)a$, x and y scalars.
5. A zero (null) vector is defined such that for every a, $0\, a = 0$.

In particular, the vectors we shall be considering will be the space of all real-valued functions $a(t)$ Lebesgue integrable over the interval $(0, T)$.† The scalars will all be real numbers in this paper.

†The definitions are easily extendable to complex vectors and scalars, but we shall consider real quantities only in this paper.

We also define a *scalar* or *inner* product (a, b) with the following properties:

1. $(a, b) = (b, a)$,†
2. $(xa + yb, c) = x(a, c) + y(b, c)$,
3. $(a, a) > 0$ (if a is not the zero vector).

The inner product is a *scalar* function of the vector a and b, and is the extension to abstract spaces of the projection of a on b in Euclidean 3-dimensional spaces. In our case of functions $a(t)$ and $b(t)$ defined over the interval $(0, T)$, the inner product will be a real number

$$(a, b) = \int_0^T a(t)\, b(t)\, dt. \tag{3}‡$$

The final concept of abstract vector spaces necessary for the discussion is that of the operator R which transforms one vector a into another vector $b = Ra$ in the same space. A linear operator or transformation is one for which $R(xa + yb) = xRa + yRb$. For our purposes we shall be interested in the linear operator

$$Ra = \int_0^T R(t, y)\, a(y)\, dy = b(t). \tag{4}$$

An inverse operator R^{-1} can be shown to exist if and only if $Ra = 0$ implies $a = 0$. Then $R(R^{-1} a) = a$ and $R^{-1}(Ra) = a$. With both R and R^{-1} defined, we also have $RR^{-1} = I = R^{-1}R$, with I, the identity operator, defined by $Ia = a$ for every vector a. We shall assume the existence of an inverse operator throughout this paper.

Consider now a function $n(t)$, $0 \leq t < T$, derived from a (possibly nonstationary) Gaussian process. Its autocorrelation function $R_n(t, y)$ is assumed given. We then show in Appendix A that the probability density function of the vector n is given by

$$p(n) - Ke^{-1/2\,(n - a,\, R_n^{-1}[n - a])}, \tag{5}$$

with K a constant, the vector a the expected value of n, and R_n^{-1} the inverse operator corresponding to $R_n(t, y)$. Thus, letting a vector $g = R_n^{-1}[n - a]$, and assuming the existence of the inverse operator,

$$n(t) - a(t) = \int_0^T R_n(t, y)\, g(y)\, dy. \tag{6}$$

Alternately, the time function $g(t)$ is given by

$$g(t) = \int_0^T R_n^{-1}(t, y)\, [n(y) - a(y)]\, dy. \tag{7}$$

†For complex vectors this is defined as $(a, b) = \overline{(b, a)}$, with the bar overhead representing complex conjugate.

‡For complex $a(t)$, $b(t)$, $(a, b) = \int_0^T a(t)\, \overline{b(t)}\, dt$.

We now apply this to the maximum a posteriori estimation of an analogue signal $a(t)$, after reception in the presence of additive Gaussian noise $n(t)$. The received signal, $v(t)$, is given by

$$v(t) = s[t, a(t)] + n(t), \quad 0 \leq t \leq T, \tag{8}$$

with s[ ], as noted previously, the modulated signal. (This is the case solved by D. C. Youla, when the effects of the channel are either deterministic or may be ignored). By an optimum demodulator we then mean one satisfying the equation

$$\frac{\partial}{\partial a} p(a/v) = 0. \tag{9}$$

The a posteriori density function $p(a/v)$ represents the probability of having transmitted vector a, given vector v received. Expressing $p(a/v)$ in terms of a priori density functions we get

$$\frac{\partial}{\partial a} p(a)\, p(v/a) = 0. \tag{10}$$

Alternately, and more simply, because of the monotonic properties of the logarithm, the maximum a posteriori estimate of $a(t)$ is obtained by solving the equation

$$\frac{\partial}{\partial a} \ln p(a)\, p(v/a) = 0. \tag{10a}$$

From eqs. (5) and (8), with $n(t)$ Gaussian as assumed,

$$\frac{\partial}{\partial a} \ln p(v/a) = -\frac{1}{2} \frac{\partial}{\partial a} (v - s,\ R_n^{-1} [v - s]). \tag{11}$$

The indicated differentiation of a scalar with respect to a vector is the vector space equivalent of the gradient in geometrical vector spaces, and, as shown in Appendix B, gives rise to the following vector:

$$\frac{\partial}{\partial a} (v - s,\ R_n^{-1} [v - s]) = -2 \frac{\partial s}{\partial a} R_n^{-1} [v - s]. \tag{12}$$

If we now assume $a(t)$ is a (possibly nonstationary) Gaussian variable with correlation function $R_a(t, y)$ and zero average value, we also have,

$$\begin{aligned} \frac{\partial}{\partial a} \ln p(a) &= -\frac{1}{2} \frac{\partial}{\partial a} (a,\ R_a^{-1}\, a) \\ &= -R_a^{-1}\, a. \end{aligned} \tag{13}$$

(The indicated differentiation is a special case of that shown in eq. (12)).

Combining eqs. (10a), (11), (12), and (13), we get finally as the optimum estimate of a,

$$R_a^{-1}\, a^* = \frac{\partial s}{\partial a^*} R_n^{-1} [v - s]. \tag{14}$$

Here a^* represents the *estimate* of a. Carrying out the inverse transformation we get

$$a^* = R_a \left[\frac{\partial s}{\partial a^*} g\right], \tag{15}$$

where the vector g is given by

$$g = R_n^{-1} [v - s] \tag{16}$$

or

$$[v - s] = R_n \, g. \tag{16a}$$

These vector equations can now be written, using eq. (4), in the desired integral forms:

$$a^*(t) = \int_0^T R_a(t, y) \frac{\partial s[(y, a^*)]}{\partial a^*} g(y)\, dy \tag{17}$$

where $g(y)$ is given by the equation

$$v(t) - s(t) = \int_0^T R_n(t, y)\, g(y)\, dy. \tag{18}$$

These are the equations obtained previously by D. C. Youla.[1]

In the special case of additive *white* Gaussian noise, $R_n(t, y) = (n_0/2)\,\delta(t - y)$, with $n_0/2$ the two-sided spectral density, and we get the much simpler equation for $a^*(t)$,

$$a^*(t) = \frac{2}{n_0} \int_0^T R_a(t, y) \frac{\partial s}{\partial a^*} [v - s]\, dy. \tag{19}$$

If $s(t)$ represents a high-frequency angle-modulated carrier, the term $(\partial s/\partial a^*)\, s$ consists of frequency terms centered at twice the carrier frequency and integrates to zero after multiplication by the essentially low frequency quantity $R_a(t, y)$. For this case,

$$a^*(t) \doteq \frac{2}{n_0} \int_0^T R_a(t, y) \frac{\partial s(y, a^*)}{\partial a^*} v(y)\, dy. \tag{20}$$

The circuit of Fig. 1 represents the nonphysically realizable implementation of eq. (20). As noted by Youla[1] this circuit is very similar to that of the phase-locked loop, particularly if we allow $T \longrightarrow \infty$.

III. SLOWLY VARYING FADING CHANNEL: NON-TIME-DISPERSIVE

As the first example of the effect of transmission through a random-type channel we consider eq. (1) with $A(t)$ assumed constant over the interval of estimation $(0, T)$. We assume the probability density function $p(A)$ given. This then cor-

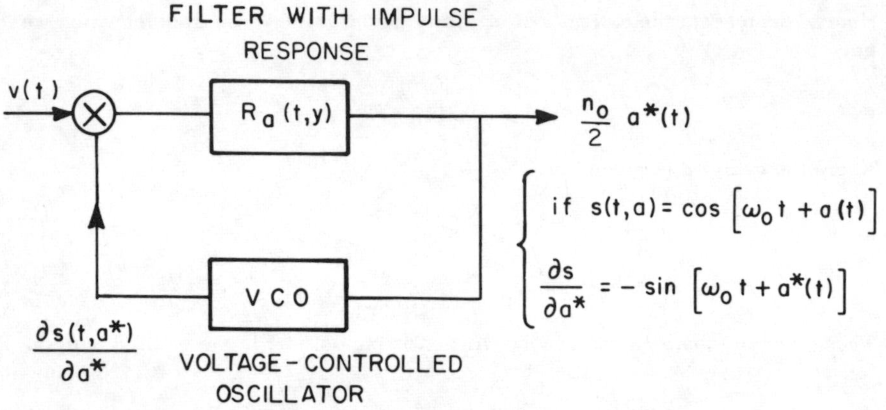

Fig. 1. Optimum demodulator, additive white noise.

responds to the case of a slowly fading channel with statistical variations in the amplitude of the received signal only.

We again have as the equation for the maximum a posteriori estimate

$$\frac{\partial}{\partial a} \ln p(a)\, p(v/a) = 0. \tag{10a}$$

Since both $a(t)$ and A are statistical variables, however, we have

$$p(v/a) = \int p(A)\, p(v/a, A)\, dA, \tag{21}$$

with

$$p(v/a, A) = k\, e^{-1/2\,(v - A s,\ R_n^{-1}[v - A s])} \tag{22}$$

Then

$$\frac{\partial}{\partial a} \ln p(v/a) = \int p(A) \frac{\partial}{\partial a} p(v/a, A)\, dA/p(v/a)$$

$$= -\frac{\partial s}{\partial a} R_n^{-1} (\overline{A}\, v - \overline{A^2} s), \tag{23}$$

after introducing eq. (22) and performing the indicated differentiation. The quantities $\overline{A}$ and $\overline{A^2}$ are scalars given respectively by

$$\overline{A} \equiv \int A\, p(A)\, p(v/a, A)\, dA/p(v/a) \tag{24}$$

and

$$\overline{A^2} \equiv \int A^2\, p(A)\, p(v/a, A)\, dA/p(v/a). \tag{25}$$

$\overline{A}$ thus represents, as indicated by its symbol, an *average gain* to be used in the demodulator. This is apparent by comparison with eq. (12) for the case of constant amplitude. (The amplitude there was assumed incorporated in the terms s and $\partial s/\partial a$).

Proceeding as previously, it is apparent that the final result for the maximum a posteriori estimate is given by the vector equations

$$a^* = R_a \frac{\partial s}{\partial a^*} h \tag{26}$$

with

$$h = R_n^{-1} [\overline{A}\, v - \overline{A^2}\, s] \tag{27}$$

or by the equivalent integral equations

$$a^*(t) = \int_0^T R_a(t, y) \frac{\partial s(y, a^*)}{\partial a^*} h(y)\, dy \tag{28}$$

with

$$\overline{A}\, v(t) - \overline{A^2}\, s(t) = \int_0^T R_n(t, y)\, h(y)\, dy. \tag{29}$$

In the special case of additive white noise of two-sided spectral density $n_0/2$, we get, corresponding to eq. (19),

$$a^*(t) = \frac{2}{n_0} \int_0^T R_a(t, y) \frac{\partial s}{\partial a^*} [\overline{A}\, v(y) - \overline{A^2}\, s(y)]\, dy. \tag{30}$$

In particular, if the second term inside the brackets may again be neglected ($s(t)$ a high frequency sinusoid), we get the optimum demodulator of Fig. 2. Note that

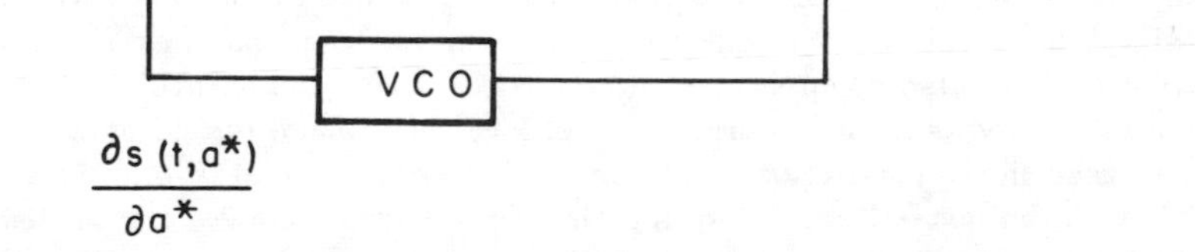

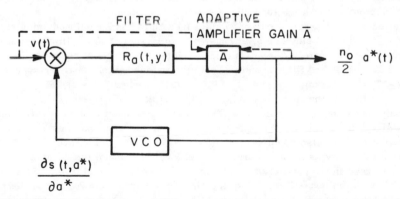

Fig. 2. Optimum demodulator, slowly varying fading channel, additive white noise.

this is identical to that of Fig. 1 except for the addition of an amplifier of gain $\overline{A}$. Instead of an amplifier, a multiplier multiplying $\overline{A}$ and v or $\overline{A}$ and $v(\partial s/\partial a^*)$ could be used.

We shall consider two examples for the evaluation of $\overline{A}$ and $\overline{A^2}$: Gaussian-distributed amplitude and the Rayleigh-distributed case. We shall then consider both amplitude and phase variations.

A. Gaussian-Distributed Amplitude

$$p(A) = \frac{e^{-(A-m)^2/2\sigma_A^2}}{\sqrt{2\pi\,\sigma_A^2}} \tag{31}$$

The amplitude A thus has an average value of m and variance σ_A^2. Then using eqs. (22) and (31) in eqs. (24) and (25) we obtain†

$$\overline{A} = \frac{Q}{P}, \quad \overline{A^2} = \frac{Q^2}{P^2} + \frac{1}{2P} \tag{32}$$

where Q and P are given, respectively, by

$$Q = \frac{\int_0^T s(t, a^*)\, v(t)\, dt}{n_0} + \frac{m}{2\,\sigma_A^2} \tag{33}$$

and

$$P = \int_0^T \frac{s^2\, dt}{n_0} + \frac{1}{2\,\sigma_A^2}. \tag{34}$$

These expressions lend themselves to a rather interesting interpretation if we now make the reasonable assumption that the energy in the signal $s(t, a^*)$ is a constant independent of $a(t)$ and the time of integration T. This is specifically true for the case of an angle-modulated carrier at center frequency ω_0 if $\omega_0 T \gg 2\pi$. Under this assumption P is a constant and $\overline{A} \propto Q$. As is apparent from eq. (33), the gain $\overline{A}$ has a constant value proportional to the *average* value m of the incoming signal amplitude plus a variable component given by the cross-correlation of the incoming received signal $v(t)$ with the *estimated* modulated signal $s(t, a^*)$. As noted previously, this may be interpreted as an amplitude estimator correlator. Alternately, the cross-correlation operation may of course be interpreted as a matched filter operation, with the matched filter impulse response $s(t - T, a^*)$ changing continuously with the estimated output $a^*(t)$.

We note from the form of eq. (33) that the variable component of the gain $\overline{A}$ is adjusted every T seconds only. This is of course due to the assumption that the signal amplitude A, although statistically varying, remains constant over the interval T. It is also apparent that there must be a time delay involved in the actual estimation of $a(t)$: the amplifier setting, once found, for example, can only be used in the estimation of $a(t)$ in the following interval $(0, T)$. This is tied in with the nonrealizability of the circuits of Figs. 1 and 2. The implementations shown suggest physically realizable circuits that can be compared with the optimum devices.

The relative effect of the constant and variable parts of the gain depend upon the relative amount of multiplicative and additive noise. For example if $\sigma_A^2 \longrightarrow 0$ (multiplicative "noise" disappears, A is constant at the value m), it is apparent that $Q/P \longrightarrow m$, and $\overline{A} \longrightarrow m$, $\overline{A^2} \longrightarrow m^2$. A quantitative measure for the rela-

†These results were also obtained by D. C. Youla in the unpublished report cited in reference 1.

tive effect of the two noises is obtained by defining a parameter α equal to the ratio of additive to multiplicative noise:

$$\alpha \equiv \frac{n_0}{2\,\sigma_A^2\,T} \tag{35}$$

Then

$$\overline{A} = \frac{Q}{P} = \frac{m\alpha + \frac{1}{T}\int_0^T sv\,dt}{\alpha + \frac{1}{T}\int_0^T s^2\,dt}. \tag{36}$$

For simplicity's sake, assume $s(t, a)$ to be an angle-modulated carrier (e.g., $\cos[\omega_0 t + a(t)]$). Then, as noted previously, P is a constant. Specifically,

$$\frac{1}{T}\int_0^T s^2\,dt \doteq 1/2,$$

and

$$\overline{A} = \frac{Q}{P} \doteq \frac{m\alpha}{\alpha + \frac{1}{2}} + \frac{1}{\left(\alpha + \frac{1}{2}\right)T}\int_0^T sv\,dt. \tag{37}$$

Two extreme cases are of interest:

(1) $\alpha \gg 1$ (additive noise dominates)

Then

$$\overline{A} = \frac{Q}{P} \doteq m + \frac{1}{\alpha T}\int_0^T sv\,dt, \tag{38}$$

with the second, variable, term normally small compared with the first.

(2) $\alpha \ll 1$ (multiplicative noise dominates)

$$\overline{A} = \frac{Q}{P} \doteq \frac{2}{T}\int_0^T sv\,dt. \tag{39}$$

If the estimated function $a^*(t)$ is reasonably close to the actual $a(t)$, $\overline{A}$ is very nearly just A, the variable amplitude. The amplifier gain of Fig. 2 thus "follows" the statistically variable amplitude. For example, with $s(t, a^*) = \cos[\omega_0 t + a^*(t)]$, and $v(t) \doteq A\cos[\omega_0 t + a(t)]$ (additive noise is assumed negligible here),

$$\overline{A} \doteq A\,\frac{1}{T}\int_0^T \cos(a - a^*)\,dt.$$

If $a - a^* \ll \pi/2$, then $\overline{A} \doteq A$.

In Fig. 3 we show the estimator correlator implementation of the adaptive amplifier of Fig. 2 as obtained from eq. (37). Note the similarity in the systems of

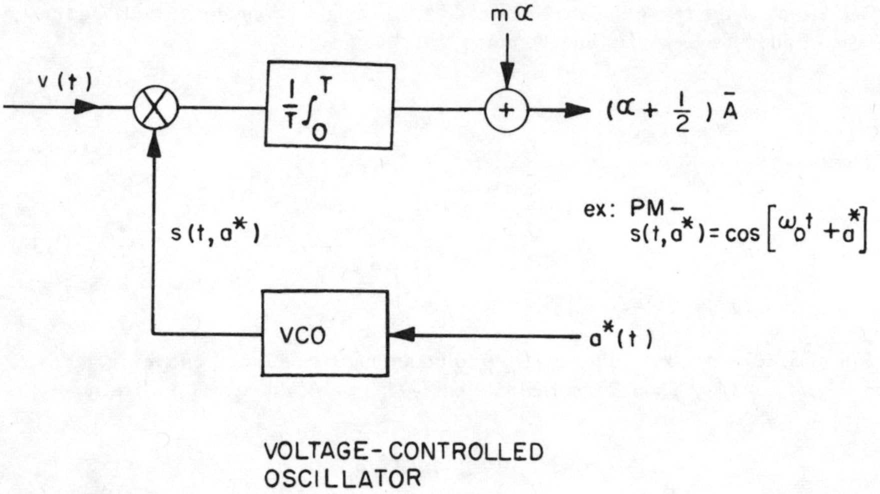

Fig. 3. Adaptive gain control, amplifier of Fig. 2. (Gaussian or Rayleigh amplitude distributions; latter for high multiplicative to additive noise ratio only).

Figs. 2 and 3. Both $a^*(t)$ and $\bar{A}$ are obtained by estimator-correlator techniques. Van Trees has pointed out that the simultaneous maximum a posteriori estimation of two or more time functions $a_1(t)$, $a_2(t)$, ... leads to estimator correlators for each.

B. Rayleigh-Distributed Amplitude

Here

$$p(A) = \frac{A\,e^{-A^2/2\sigma^2}}{\sigma^2}. \tag{40}$$

Carrying out the appropriate integration of eq. (24), as in the Gaussian case, we obtain the following rather complex-looking result:

$$\bar{A} = \frac{Q'}{P'}\left\{1 + \frac{1}{2\beta^2 + \dfrac{2\beta}{\sqrt{\pi}}\dfrac{e^{-\beta^2}}{(1+\operatorname{erf}\beta)}}\right\} \tag{41}$$

β is a dimensionless parameter given by

$$\beta \equiv \frac{Q'}{\sqrt{P'}} \tag{42}$$

with

$$Q' \equiv \frac{1}{n_0}\int_0^T s(t, a^*)\,v(t)\,dt, \tag{43}$$

$$P' \equiv \frac{1}{2\,\sigma^2} + \frac{1}{n_0} \int_0^T s^2\,dt, \tag{44}$$

and

$$\operatorname{erf} x \equiv \frac{2}{\sqrt{\pi}} \int_0^x e^{-x^2}\,dx \tag{45}$$

Note the similarity of Q' and P' with Q and P (eqs. (33) and (34)) in the Gaussian case.

Although eq. (41) looks quite cumbersome it is easily interpreted in the limiting cases $|\beta| > 1$ and $\beta < 1$. For the first case we obtain

$$\overline{A} \doteq \frac{Q'}{P'} = \frac{\dfrac{1}{T}\displaystyle\int_0^T s(t, a^*)\, v(t)\,dt}{\alpha + \dfrac{1}{T}\displaystyle\int_0^T \sigma^2(t, a^*)\,dt}, \quad |\beta| > 1. \tag{46}$$

Here, as in the Gaussian case, we have defined the parameter α as essentially the ratio of additive to multiplicative noise:

$$\alpha \equiv \frac{n_0}{2\,\sigma^2 T}. \tag{47}$$

If we again assume $s(t, a^*)$ to be a high-frequency sinusoid, with $\omega_0 T \gg 1$, the expression for the variable gain simplifies still further to

$$\overline{A} \doteq \left(\frac{1}{\alpha + \dfrac{1}{2}}\right) \frac{1}{T} \int_0^T s(t, a^*)\, v(t)\,dt, \quad |\beta| > 1. \tag{48}$$

Note that this is identical to eq. (37) for the Gaussian case if we let $m = 0$ there. Figure 3 thus applies to the Rayleigh-distributed amplitude if we set $m = 0$ and assume $|\beta| > 1$.

We shall now show that $\beta > 1$ corresponds to the case where the multiplicative noise dominates. Note from eqs. (42) and (43) that β is a statistical quantity dependent on both the additive and multiplicative noise. Its effective value $E(\beta)$ and variance σ_β^2 are readily found, however, under the simplifying assumptions that $a - a^* \ll \pi/2$ (i.e., the estimate is close to the true value of $a(t)$), and that $s(t, a^*)$ is uncorrelated with the additive noise $n(t)$ and the multiplicative noise A (this latter assumption may be justified in terms of the relative "bandwidths" of $a(t)$, $n(t)$, and A). They are given, respectively, by

$$E(\beta) = \frac{\sqrt{\pi}}{2} \frac{1}{\sqrt{2\alpha\,(1 + 2\alpha)}} \tag{49}$$

and

$$\sigma_\beta^2 = \frac{\left(2 - \dfrac{\pi}{2} + 2\alpha\right)}{4\alpha\,(2\alpha + 1)}. \tag{50}$$

In particular, we have the following extreme cases:

(1) $\alpha << 0.2$ (multiplicative noise dominates)

$$\sigma_\beta^2 \doteq \frac{0.1}{\alpha} >> 0.5, \quad E(\beta) \doteq \frac{0.6}{\sqrt{\alpha}} > 1, \quad \frac{E(\beta)}{\sigma_\beta} \doteq 2 \tag{51}$$

(2) $\alpha >> 1$ (additive noise dominates)

$$\sigma_\beta^2 \doteq \frac{1}{4\alpha} << 0.25, \quad E(\beta) \doteq \frac{0.4}{\alpha} << 0.4, \quad \frac{E(\beta)}{\sigma_\beta} \doteq \frac{0.8}{\sqrt{\alpha}} << 1 \tag{52}$$

The case of $\beta > 1$ thus corresponds to small α or large multiplicative noise compared with the additive noise.

For the other limiting case of $\beta < 1$, corresponding to small multiplicative noise compared with the additive noise, eq. (41) for the gain is readily shown to be approximated by the constant value

$$\overline{A} \doteq \frac{1}{2}\sqrt{\frac{\pi}{P'}} = \sqrt{\frac{\pi}{2}}\,\sigma, \tag{53}$$

just the average value of the assumed Rayleigh-distributed variable. In this case, then, the amplifier of Fig. 2 has a constant gain.

C. Both Amplitude and Phase Variations

Real channels introduce not only amplitude variations but phase variations as well. As an example, if the transmitted signal is $\cos[\omega_0 t + a(t)]$, the received signal is often found to be of the form $A \cos[\omega_0 t + a(t) + \theta]$, with A and θ random variables with statistics dependent on the channel. Most commonly, measurements indicate that A has a Rayleigh distribution or a Rayleigh distribution with a specular component (the so-called Ricean distribution).

It is of course well known that the Rayleigh amplitude distribution may be realized by adding two quadrature carrier terms, each with uncorrelated Gaussian amplitudes. Thus, we may write the two equivalent expressions

$$\begin{aligned} v(t) &= A \cos[\omega_0 t + a(t) + \theta] + n(t) \\ &= x \cos[\omega_0 t + a(t)] + y \sin[\omega_0 t + a(t)] + n(t). \end{aligned} \tag{54}$$

We assume x and y to be uncorrelated Gaussian variables with the same variance σ^2 (this is not necessary for the analysis that follows, however), and expected values respectively given by $E(x) = m_1$, and $E(y) = m_2$.

If $m_1 = m_2 = 0$, we get the Rayleigh distribution for the amplitude A and a uniform phase distribution. For either m_1 or $m_2 = 0$ we get the Ricean distribution in amplitude with a rather complex distribution in phase.[3]

The decomposition of the randomly phased signal into the two Gaussian-distributed quadrature terms of eq. (54) enables us to apply the maximum a posteriori analysis quite readily. In particular, if the two quadrature terms may be assumed orthogonal over the estimation interval T, the optimum estimator is found to be that obtained by estimating each of the quadrature terms separately and superposing the results.

For ease in performing the analysis and to obtain somewhat more general results, we consider the received signal plus noise $v(t)$ to be given by

$$v(t) = x s_1 [t, a(t)] + y s_2 [t, a(t)] + n(t), \quad 0 \leq t \leq T, \tag{55}$$

(the intelligence $a(t)$ is assumed to modulate *two* signals simultaneously). Assuming $n(t)$ to be white noise of spectral density $n_0/2$ again for simplicity, it is found in rather straightforward fashion that the best estimate of $a(t)$ in the maximum a posteriori sense is given by

$$\frac{n_0}{2} a^*(t) = \int_0^T R_a(t, z)\, v(z) \left[\frac{\partial s_1}{\partial a^*} M_1 + \frac{\partial s_2}{\partial a^*} M_2\right] dz - \int_0^T R_a(t, z) \int_{-\infty}^{\infty} \times \int_{-\infty}^{\infty} \frac{\partial}{\partial a^*} (x s_1 + y s_2) \left[\frac{(x s_1 + y s_2) p(x, y) p(v/a, x, y)}{p(v/a)}\right] dx dy dz. \tag{56}$$

Here

$$M_1 \equiv \int\int x p(x, y) p(v/a, x, y) dx dy / p(v/a). \tag{57}$$

M_2 is the same parameter with x replaced by y. Note that M_1 and M_2 are analogous to the $\bar{A}$ defined previously (eq. (24)) in the single signal case.

Actually carrying out the indicated integration of eq. (57), we get an expression similar to those of eqs. (32)–(34):

$$M_j = \frac{Q_j'}{P_j'} = \frac{Q_j - \dfrac{Q_i}{P_i n_0} \displaystyle\int_0^T s_1(t) s_2(t) dt}{P_j - \dfrac{1}{n_0 P_i} \left[\displaystyle\int_0^T s_1(t) s_2(t) dt\right]^2} \quad \begin{cases} j = 1, 2 \\ i = 2, 1 \end{cases}. \tag{58}$$

Here, as previously,

$$Q_j = \frac{m_j}{2\sigma^2} + \frac{1}{n_0} \int_0^T s_j(t) v(t) dt \tag{59}$$

$$j = 1, 2$$

$$P_j = \frac{1}{2\sigma^2} + \frac{1}{n_0} \int_0^T s_j^2 dt \tag{60}$$

(The explicit dependence of $s_1(t)$ and $s_2(t)$ upon $a^*(t)$ is not shown to simplify the printing).

Note that in general the estimation involves a cross-correlation between $s_1(t)$ and $s_2(t)$ as well as between $\partial s_1/\partial a$, s_2, $\partial s_2/\partial a$, and s_1. If we assume s_1 and s_2 to be orthogonal, high-frequency sinewaves (as in eq. (54)), the second integral in eq. (56) as well as the cross-product terms in eq. (58) vanish, and we are left with the much simpler looking expressions

$$\frac{n_0 a^*(t)}{2} = \int_0^T R_a(t, z) v(z) \left[\frac{\partial s_1}{\partial a^*} M_1 + \frac{\partial s_2}{\partial a^*} M_2\right] dz \tag{61}$$

with

$$\left(\alpha + \frac{1}{2}\right) M_j = m_j\, \alpha + \frac{1}{T} \int_0^T s_j(t, a^*)\, v(t)\, dt, \quad j = 1, 2. \tag{62}$$

Note again that this is identical with eq. (37).

The estimate is thus obtained by cross-correlating with each quadrature term separately and superposing the result: the implementation suggested is shown in Fig. 4 for the special case of a high-frequency phase-modulated carrier.

One voltage-controlled oscillator (VCO) with 90° phase shift networks may be used in place of the different VCO's shown.

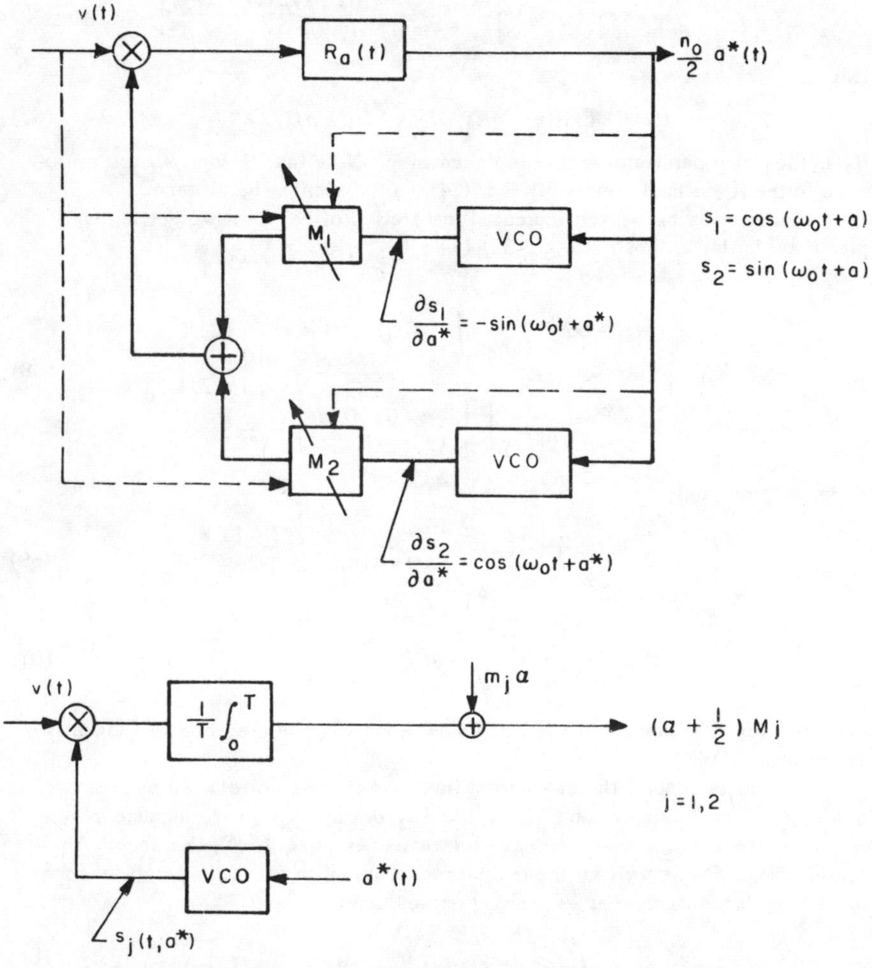

Fig. 4. Optimum demodulator, slowly fading channel with Gaussian quadrature components.

IV. FADING CHANNEL WITH TIME-VARYING AMPLITUDE

We now assume the amplitude variation introduced by the channel to be rapid enough to be noticeable within the estimation interval T. An analysis similar to that of the previous section then again leads to an optimum estimator of the phase-locked loop type. The adaptive amplifier that appears has a *continuously varying gain,* however. The gain in this case is found by *continuously* estimating the signal amplitude and is realized by an amplitude estimator correlator in the case of small multiplicative noise.

For simplicity's sake, we restrict ourselves here to the case of a single signal with multiplicative Gaussian amplitude variations only. It is apparent that this may be extended to include the effect of phase variations as well by adding an orthogonal signal term as in the previous section.

We then have the problem of estimating $a(t)$, with the received signal plus noise given by

$$v(t) = A(t)s[t, a(t)] + n(t), \quad 0 \leq t \leq T. \tag{63}$$

Here $A(t)$, $a(t)$ and $n(t)$ are all Gaussian vectors with correlation functions $R_A(t, y)$, $R_a(t, y)$, $R_n(t, y)$ respectively. (This contrasts with the previous section in which A was a scalar). Setting up the equation for the maximum a posteriori estimate we find, as previously,

$$R_a^{-1}\, a = -\frac{1}{p(v/a)} \frac{\partial p(v/a)}{\partial a}. \tag{64}$$

Here, however,

$$p(v/a) = \int \dots \int p(A)p(v/a, A)dA \tag{65}$$

with $dA \equiv dA_1 dA_2 \dots$, and A_j the projection of A on an appropriate set of orthogonal basis functions (see Appendix A): $A_j = (A, \phi_j)$. In particular we now have, because of the vector character of A,

$$p(A) = k_1 e^{-1/2\,(A,\, R_A^{-1} A)}. \tag{66}$$

Also, as previously,

$$p(v/a, A) = k_2 e^{-1/2\,(v - As,\, R_n^{-1}[v - As])}, \tag{67}$$

but with $[As]$ considered a vector. It is then readily shown that

$$\frac{\partial p(v/a, A)}{\partial a} = -\,p(v/a, A)\, A \frac{\partial s}{\partial a} R_n^{-1}\,(v - AS); \tag{68}$$

(i.e., $\partial[As]/\partial a = A(\partial s/\partial a)$, if A is independent of a).

Combining the equations above, and assuming additive white noise of spectral density $n_0/2$ for simplicity, we obtain the following vector equation for the optimum estimate of a:

$$a^* = \frac{2}{n_0} R_a \frac{\partial s}{\partial a^*} [mv - ns], \tag{69}$$

m and n are both vectors, comparable, respectively, to $\overline{A}$ and $\overline{A^2}$ in the previous section, given by

$$m \equiv \int \ldots \int A\, p(A)\, p(v/a, A)\, dA/p(v/a) \tag{70}$$

and

$$n \equiv \int \ldots \int A^2\, p(A)\, p(v/a, A)\, dA/p(v/a). \tag{71}$$

We shall again drop the second term involving ns on the assumption that it gives rise ultimately to negligible second harmonic terms.

The integral equation equivalent of the vector equation is then given by

$$a^*(t) = \frac{2}{n_0} \int_0^T R_a(t, y)\, \frac{\partial s(y, a^*)}{\partial a^*}\, m(y)\, v(y)\, dy. \tag{72}$$

The gain factor $m(t)$ is thus continuously changing with time, as is to be expected because of the assumption of a time-varying signal amplitude due to channel fluctuations.

One possible implementation suggested by eq. (72) is shown in Fig. 5. Note that the adaptive amplifier $m(t)$ could just as well be placed directly in the $v(t)$

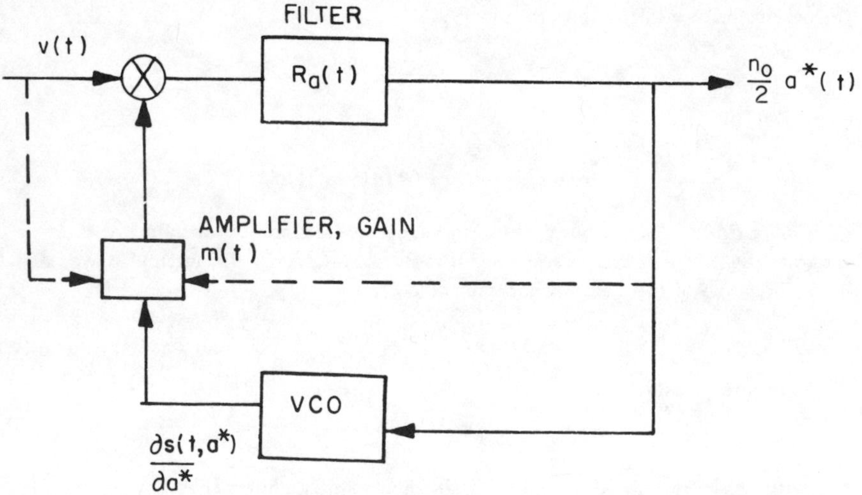

Fig. 5. Optimum demodulator, fading channel.

lead or following the multiplier shown. Alternately, instead of using an amplifier, an alternate implementation suggested by eq. (72) would be to form the desired quantity $m(t)$ from the measured values of $v(t)$ and $a^*(t)$ (this is discussed further below), multiply this by $v(t)\,[\partial s(t)/\partial a^*]$, and pass the resultant time function through a filter of impulse response $R_a(t)$. Such an implementation is shown in Fig. 6.

The evaluation of the vector m and hence the implementation of $m(t)$ is readily carried out by noting that the quadratic forms in the exponent of $p(A)$ and

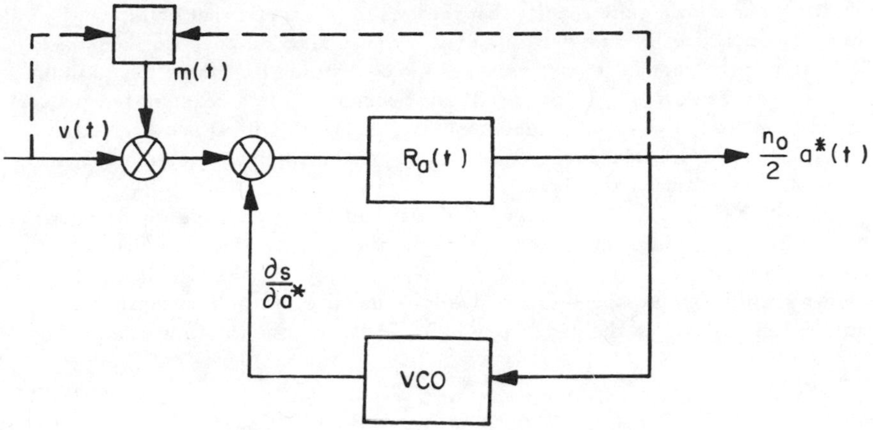

Fig. 6. Another possible implementation.

$p(v/a, A)$ may be combined into the equivalent quadratic form $(A - m_0, G[A - m_0])$.† Here m_0 is a resultant vector and G an operator. But the desired vector m is then just the average value of a resultant Gaussian distribution and is given precisely by the vector m_0.[4]

Consider then the sum $(A, R_A^{-1} A)$ plus $(2/n_0)(v - As, v - As)$ obtained from eqs. (66) and (67) with $R_n^{-1} [\ ] = (2/n_0) [\ ]$. Expanding the inner products, dropping the term $(2/n_0)(v, v)$ common to both numerator and denominator of eq. (70), and using the inner product identities, $(v, As) = (As, v) = (A, sv)$, $(As, As) = (A, As^2)$ and $(A, Gm) = (m, GA)$ with G an operator, we eventually find the desired vector $m = m_0$ to be given by

$$Gm = \frac{2}{n_0} sv \tag{73}$$

where the operator G is defined by

$$GA \equiv R_A^{-1} A + \frac{2}{n_0} s^2 A. \tag{74}$$

The formal solution for m, again assuming the appropriate inverses to exist, is given by

$$m = \frac{2}{n_0} R_A [sv - s^2 m]$$

or

$$m(t) = \frac{2}{n_0} \int_0^T R_A(t, y) [s(y) v(y) - s^2(y) m(y)] \, dy. \tag{75}$$

†This is of course the same as completing the square with simple quadratics.

It may be shown quite readily that this result is exactly that obtained when a variable amplitude is to be estimated using the maximum a posteriori approach. Note that if the channel is now assumed slowly varying over the T second interval, we may write $R_A(t, y) = \sigma_A^2$, $m(t)$ (and hence $m(y)$) is a constant independent of time and we get exactly as previously $m = \overline{A} = Q/P$, with Q and P given by eqs. (33) and (34). (The average value m of the Gaussian distribution appearing in eq. (33) is assumed zero here.)

Equation (75) is readily implemented, particularly in the case where $s(t, a)$ is a high-frequency sinusoid. For simplicity's sake, we consider two limiting cases, however: $R_A^{-1} A >> (2/n_0)\, s^2 A$ and $R_A^{-1} A << (2/n_0) s^2 A$. It may be shown that these correspond respectively to the case of small multiplicative noise (both relative to the additive noise). Thus, assume the first case. Then we also have

$$A >> \frac{2}{n_0} R_A\, s^2 A \tag{76}$$

or, in integral form,

$$A(t) >> \frac{2}{n_0} \int_0^T R_A(t, y) s^2(y, a^*)\, A(y)\, dy. \tag{77}$$

But $|s(y, a)| \leq 1$ if $s(y) = \cos(\omega_0 y + a)$, for example, and $R_A(t, y) \leq R_A(t, t) = E(A^2)$. It is then readily shown that

$$E(A^2) << \frac{n_0}{2T}, \tag{78}$$

just the condition for small multiplicative noise. The other limiting case corresponds of course to the opposite condition.

For the case of small multiplicative noise,

$$m(t) \doteq \frac{2}{n_0} \int_0^T R_A(t, y) s(y, a^*) v(y)\, dy. \tag{79}$$

The implementation suggested by this equation is shown in Fig. 7. Note the symmetry apparent between this equation and that of eq. (72) involving the estimate of $a^*(t)$. This is also apparent from a comparison of Figs. 5 and 7. Both $a^*(t)$ and $m(t)$ thus involve the use of estimator correlators, and the symmetry of the result indicates that, were the problem to be that of estimating amplitude with the phase randomly distributed due to the channel, the same results would be obtained.

For the case of large multiplicative noise $[E(A^2) >> n_0/2T]$, we find very simply that

$$s(t, a^*) m(t) = v(t). \tag{80}$$

The quantity $m(t)$ is thus adjusted to drive $s(t, a^*)m$ to the incoming $v(t)$. As a check, with negligible additive noise, $v(t) = A(t)\, s(t, a)$. Then if $a^*(t)$ is close to $a(t)$, $m(t) \doteq A(t)$, and the gain control follows the channel amplitude variations.

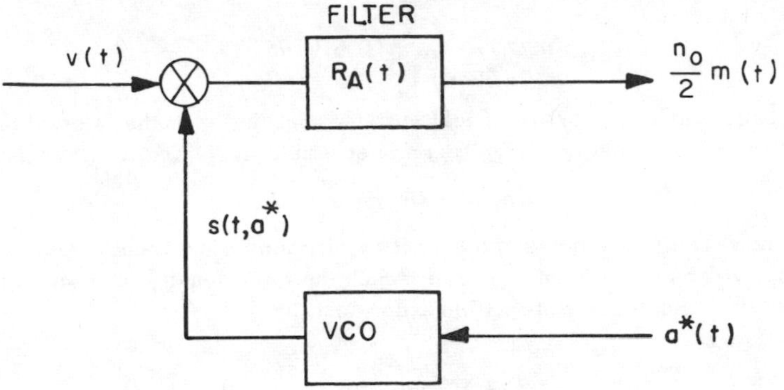

Fig. 7. Variable gain factor, small multiplicative noise.

APPENDIX A

We show here that the probability density function of a Gaussian vector $n(t)$, $0 \leq t \leq T$, with correlation function $R_n(t, y)$ and zero average value $[E(n) = 0]$ may be written in the form

$$p(n) = k e^{-1/2\,(n,\, R_n^{-1} n)}, \tag{A1}$$

with the inner product interpreted as in Section II.

To do this we expand both n and the vector $g = R_n^{-1} n$ in the orthonormal expansions

$$n = \sum_j (n, \phi_j)\phi_j = \sum_j n_j \phi_j$$

and

$$g = \sum_j (g, \phi_j)\phi_j = \sum_j g_j \phi_j \tag{A2}$$

with

$$(\phi_i, \phi_j) = 0, \quad i \neq j, = 1, \quad i = j. \tag{A3}$$

(The representation of a vector in terms of an orthornormal basis set appropriate to the particular vector space is discussed in the references cited in reference 2). Both n_j and g_j are the scalars defined by the respective inner products. Using the orthonormal property (eq. (A3)) of the ϕ_j's we then find

$$(n, g) = \left(\sum_j n_j \phi_j, \sum_i g_i \phi_i\right) = \sum_j n_j g_j. \tag{A4}$$

Now consider the scalar n_j's. These are Gaussian variables. Since $E(n) = 0$, $E(n_j) = 0$ also. In addition,

$$E[n_i n_j] \equiv R_{ij} = E[(n, \phi_i)(n, \phi_j)]. \tag{A5}$$

But

$$(n, \phi_i) = \int_0^T n(t)\,\phi_i(t)\,dt \tag{A6}$$

in our particular vector space of real variables defined over the interval (0, T). Interchanging the order of integration and ensemble averaging, we then have

$$E[n_i n_j] = (R_n \phi_i, \phi_j) = R_{ij}. \tag{A7}$$

Since the vector n is representable by its projections n_j on the ϕ_j vector set, the probability density function $p(n)$ of n is just the joint density function of the n_j coefficients, and is given, to within a constant, by

$$p(n) = k\,e^{-1/2 \sum_i \sum_j n_i D_{ij} n_j} = k\,e^{-1/2 \sum_i n_i g_i} \tag{A8†}$$

Here the D_{ij}'s are the coefficients of the matrix obtained by inverting the matrix with elements R_{ij}:

$$D_m = R_m^{-1}, \quad \text{with } D_m \text{ and } R_m \text{ matrices.}$$

The g_i coefficients shown in eq. (A8) are defined by

$$g_i \equiv \sum_j D_{ij}\, n_j \tag{A9}$$

and may be considered the projections of some vector g on the orthonormal set ϕ_j:

$$\left.\begin{aligned} g &= \sum_j g_j \phi_j \\ g_j &= (g, \phi_j) \end{aligned}\right\} \tag{A10}$$

From eq. (A4), we may therefore write $p(n)$ in the form

$$p(n) = k\,e^{-1/2\,(n,\,g)}. \tag{A11}$$

But now consider the vector g: It is easy to show that this vector corresponds to a linear transformation of n, $g = Dn$.
For, with

$$n = \sum_j n_j \phi_j, \quad n_j = (n, \phi_j), \tag{A12}$$

the linear transformation Dn is given by

$$Dn = \sum_j n_j\, D\phi_j. \tag{A13}$$

†This is of course the same procedure followed in the usual Karhunen-Loeve expansion but there is no need to choose the set of ϕ_j such that the n_j's are uncorrelated.

But the vector $D\phi_j$ may itself be expanded in the same orthonormal set,

$$D\phi_j = \sum_i D_{ij}\phi_i, \quad D_{ij} = (D\phi_j, \phi_i) = (D\phi_i, \phi_j) \tag{A14}$$

Combining eqs. (A13) and (A14), we have

$$Dn = \sum_i \sum_j D_{ij} n_j \phi_i = \sum_i g_i \phi_i \tag{A15}$$

with

$$g_i = \sum_j D_{ij} n_j \tag{A16}$$

as in eq. (A9).

The probability density function $p(n)$ may thus be further written as

$$p(n) = k e^{-1/2\,(n,\,Dn)} \tag{A17}$$

Comparing eqs. (A14) and (A7), it is apparent that the R_{ij} coefficients of eq. (A7) must correspond to an operator R_n. Hence we must have

$$g = Dn - R_n^{-1} n$$

and eq. (A1) is obtained.

More generally, if $E(n) = s$, we can show

$$p(n) = k e^{-1/2\,(n-s,\, R_n^{-1}[n-s])}. \tag{A18}$$

APPENDIX B

We consider here the significance of the derivative of a scalar with respect to a vector encountered several times in the paper. Specifically consider the scalar x defined by an inner product:

$$x = (g, Dg) = (g, h) \tag{B1}$$

with $g = g(a)$, both a and g vectors. We then inquire as to the meaning and evaluation of $\partial x/\partial a$.

Expanding the vectors g, Dg, and h into their respective orthonormal basis sets (see Appendix A), we have

$$x = (g, Dg) = \sum_i g_i h_i \tag{B2}$$

$$h_i = \sum_j D_{ij}\, g_j \tag{B3}$$

Here $g_i = g_i(a_i)$, with g_i the projection of vector a on ϕ_i.

We then have

$$\frac{\partial x}{\partial a_k} = \sum_i g_i \frac{\partial h_i}{\partial a_k} + h_k \frac{\partial g_k}{\partial a_k}. \tag{B4}$$

But

$$\frac{\partial h_i}{\partial a_k} = D_{ik} \frac{\partial g_k}{\partial a_k}, \tag{B5}$$

from eq. (B3). Combining eqs. (B4) and (B5), and using (B3), we then have

$$\frac{\partial x}{\partial a_k} = 2 h_k \frac{\partial g_k}{\partial a_k} \tag{B6}$$

We then define $\partial x/\partial a$ to be a vector whose projections on the ϕ_j's are given precisely by eq. (B6). This gives us

$$\frac{\partial x}{\partial a} = 2h \frac{\partial g}{\partial a} = 2Dg \frac{\partial g}{\partial a} = 2 \frac{\partial g}{\partial a} Dg. \tag{B7}$$

As an example, let $g = v - s$, $s = s(a)$, $D = R_a^{-1}$ as in Section II. Then

$$\frac{\partial}{\partial a} (v - s, R_a^{-1} [v - s]) = -2 \frac{\partial s}{\partial a} R_n^{-1} [v - s], \tag{B8}$$

as in eq. (12).

REFERENCES

1. D. C. Youla, "The Use of the Method of Maximum Likelihood in Estimating Continuous-Modulated Intelligence which has been Corrupted by Noise," *IRE Trans. on Information Theory*, PGIT-3, 90–106 (March 1954). (A first approach to the problem considered here was also made by Youla in an unpublished report, D. C. Youla, "The Application of Maximum-Likelihood Techniques to Several Problems in Communication Theory," Report No. R-524-56, Polytechnic Institute of Brooklyn (October 1956)).
2. See, e.g., B. Friedman, *Principles and Techniques of Applied Mathematics* (New York: John Wiley, 1956), or J. Indritz, *Methods in Analysis* (New York: Macmillan, 1963).
3. M. Schwartz, *Information Transmission, Modulation, and Noise* (New York: McGraw-Hill, 1959), p. 411.
4. See, e.g., W. B. Davenport and W. L. Root, *Random Signals and Noise* (New York: McGraw-Hill, 1958), p. 152.

LINEAR MEAN SQUARE FILTERING AND ESTIMATION WHEN PROCESS STATISTICS ARE UNDEFINED

Donald E. Johansen
Applied Research Laboratory, Sylvania Electronic Systems, Waltham, Mass.

Presently available techniques for separating signal from random noise require extensive information on the detailed nature of signal waveform. It is customary, for example, to assume that signal structure is either deterministic and characterized by a finite number of unknown parameters, or that it obeys known statistical behavior.

In many applications such information is nonexistent or unavailable. This paper considers a *minimax* formulation of such problems, in which the noise is assumed to obey statistical laws, but target statistics do not exist. The object is to find that filter design which *minimizes* the *maximum* value of estimation error taken over all admissible signal waveforms, $x(t)$. A complete solution is obtained for a simple problem in which measurement noise is white, and the second derivative of $x(t)$ is bounded to a specified level at all points in time. Such problems arise naturally in the radar tracking of an evasive vehicle under the control of an intelligent adversary. They also arise in the problem of trajectory estimation on a missile test range, since a priori statistics for a malfunctioning missile cannot by nature be obtained.

A numerical technique is used to solve for the minimax position and velocity estimators when measurements are available over finite intervals of time. Solutions are obtained for both the filtering (real-time) and smoothing (non-real-time) case. Sensitivity of the resulting designs are investigated with respect to errors or uncertainty in design parameters. Solution to the infinite observation time problem is obtained by passage to the limit $T \longrightarrow \infty$. It is shown that the impulse response function for the minimax filter, when measurements are available over the infinite or semi-infinite interval, has a finite time history.

1. INTRODUCTION

Available engineering methods for separating signal from noise require considerable a priori information concerning signal waveforms. Customary methods of design require the assumption that the signal to be estimated is either random with known statistics, or that it is "deterministic" and known to within a finite number of parameters. Methods of designing filters for estimating random signals have been developed by Wiener and Kolmogoroff.[1] An example of the estimation of "deterministic" processes is provided by techniques of polynomial smoothing.[2] Various generalizations and combinations of these approaches are also possible. A particularly elegant and useful solution to the combined problem has been presented by Kalman.[3]

The assumption that the signal is deterministic (except for a finite number of parameters) is valid for targets with low maneuverability, such as satellites or

Presented at the Symposium on System Theory
Polytechnic Institute of Brooklyn, April 20, 21, 22, 1965

ballistic missiles. Such an assumption is not valid for targets maneuvering rapidly when observation times of interest are relatively long. The assumption that motion is a random process is valid for maneuvering targets provided that suitable statistical measures of target motion can be obtained.

In many applications, statistics for target motion are either nonexistent or unavailable. An example of a case in which statistics do not exist is provided by the problem of radar tracking of an evasive vehicle under the control of an intelligent adversary. In such situations it is not reasonable to assume that target motion is deterministic or that it is drawn from a random process. A frequently more realistic assumption is that the vehicle pilot uses his knowledge of estimator design to pick that motion, consistent with constraints on vehicle dynamics, to maximize estimation error.

A somewhat different situation arises on a missile test range. It is in the nature of a test situation that one is looking for and must expect to find phenomena that have not previously been experienced. It follows that even though an underlying statistical process may be imagined to exist, one is *not* able to run the necessary experiments to find out what these statistics might be. A satisfactory model for such situations is to design the filter on the assumption that the target undergoes the worst case maneuver consistent with dynamical constraints. A more detailed discussion of these applications will be found in reference 4.

This paper considers a minimax formulation of the estimation problem in which the object is to find that filter design which *minimizes* the *maximum* value of estimation error taken over all admissible signal waveform $x(t)$. A complete solution is obtained for a simple but important special case, in which measurement noise is white and target acceleration is bounded in absolute value at all points in time. The paper applies a numerical technique for design of the filter when measurements are available over finite intervals of time. Solutions are given for estimation of both position and velocity for both the real time and nonreal time case. Sensitivity of the design is investigated with respect to errors in choice of design parameters. The numerical results obtained in this paper suggest possibilities for an analytic solution for the case in which measurements are available into the infinite pass. This analytic solution, together with comparisons with other approaches to the filter problem, will be found in reference 4.

The appropriateness of the minimax formulation for certain problems in estimation theory has been pointed out by a number of authors.[5,6] Computable solutions, however, have been hard to obtain. Solutions for several simplified minimax problems have been obtained by Yovits,[7] Carlton,[8] and Zahl.[9] This paper solves a problem which is often more realistic than any of these previously solved cases.

2. STATEMENT OF THE PROBLEM

We assume the availability of linear measurements of the signal $x(t)$ corrupted by additive noise $w(t)$:

$$z(t) = x(t) + w(t). \tag{1}$$

Our objective is to design a filter, defined by its impulse response function $h(t)$, which operates on past observations $z(t)$ on the interval $(-T, 0)$, to determine the best linear estimate of $x(t)$ at the present time: $t = 0$,

$$\hat{x}(0) = \int_0^T h(t)\, z(-t)\, dt. \tag{2}$$

The loss function used for design of $h(t)$ is the quadratic performance index

$$\phi^2 = \mathcal{E}_w \{[\hat{x}(0) - x(0)]^2\}, \tag{3}$$

where the expected value is taken over the statistics for the noise.

The solution developed in this paper is for a special case: First it is assumed that the corrupting signal $w(t)$ is white-noise with spectral density* Q:

$$\begin{aligned} \mathcal{E}\{w(t)\, w(t')\} &= Q\, \delta(t - t') \\ \mathcal{E}\{w(t)\} &= 0 \\ \mathcal{E}\{x(t)\, w(t')\} &= 0 \end{aligned} \tag{4}$$

Substituting the estimate (2) for $\hat{x}(0)$ in (3), using the relationship (1), and carrying out the expected value over the noise statistics (4), yields

$$\phi^2\{h, x\} = \left[\int_0^T h(\tau)\, x(-\tau)\, d\tau - x(0) \right]^2 + Q \int_0^T [h(\tau)]^2\, d\tau. \tag{5}$$

Note that the performance index (5) is a *functional* on both the filter impulse response function $h(t)$, and the target maneuver $x(t)$. Because of the expected value operation, the performance index is independent of the noise signal $w(t)$.

There are a number of assumptions that one might like to make concerning target motion. The one used in this paper is that target acceleration is bounded in absolute magnitude according to**

$$|\ddot{x}(t)| \leq \alpha; \quad \text{for all } -\infty \leq t \leq \infty, \tag{6}$$

where α is a known constant. Other assumptions, such as simultaneously bounding both acceleration and rate of change of acceleration, or assuming acceleration to be the sum of a random and a bounded deterministic part, might also be considered. Such problems all fit into the general philosophy followed here and are the logical next step in the development of the theory.

The bounded acceleration constraint (6) is chosen for solution in this paper since: i) it is a good first approximation to the two physical problems discussed previously; ii) it represents the simplest nontrivial problem that can be solved in closed form; and iii) it provides a good vehicle for understanding the complexities of the minimax approach.

In the problem solved in this paper it will be assumed that the target chooses its maneuver consistent with the constraint (6) to maximize estimation error. Given a filter design $h(t)$ performance (maximum mean square error) is

*The symbol $\delta(t)$ is the Dirac delta function.

**The dot notation denotes a time derivative: $(\dot{\ }) = d/dt(\ )$; $(\ddot{\ }) = d^2/dt^2(\ )$.

evaluated as

$$\phi^2\{h\} = \max_{|\ddot{x}| \leq \alpha} \phi^2\{h, x\}. \tag{7}$$

The design problem therefore is to minimize (7). It is required to find the optimal filter $h^*(t)$ and the "least favorable" target maneuver $x^*(t)$ which solves the functional equation

$$\phi^2\{h^*, x^*\} = \min_h \max_{|\ddot{x}| \leq \alpha} \phi^2\{h, x\}, \tag{8}$$

where $\phi^2\{h, x\}$ is the expression for the performance index given by (5).

A sketch illustrating the meaning of the minimax problem (8) is shown in Fig. 1. The tabulated values are evaluations of $\phi^2\{h, x\}$ for different choices of maneuver $x(t)$ and filter $h(t)$. The case illustrated is for a simplified problem in which nature is able to choose from among four possible target maneuvers: $x_1(t)$, $x_2(t)$, $x_3(t)$, and $x_4(t)$; and the designer is able to choose from among three possible filters: $h_1(t)$, $h_2(t)$, and $h_3(t)$.

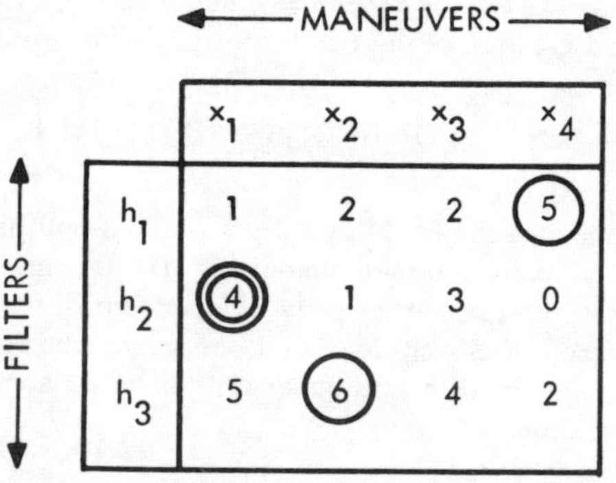

Fig. 1. Interpretation of the minimax problem. Tabulation of performance index $\phi^2\{h, x\}$ for different filters h_i and maneuvers x_j.

The largest value of ϕ^2 obtainable for each filter h_i is circled. The double-circled quantity is the required smallest of the three circled quantities. The answer to the minimax problem illustrated in Fig. 1 is to use the filter $h = h_2$; and for nature to use the "least favorable" maneuver $x = x_1$. The resulting mean square error is $\phi^2 = 4$.

At this point, it is useful to compare the minimax problem (1)–(8) solved in this paper with the somewhat different problems solved by Yovits,[7] Carlton,[8] and Zahl:[9] Yovits[7] and Carlton[8] assume that the process $x(t)$ is characterized statistically by a spectral distribution, but that the engineer does not happen to know what this spectral distribution is. Their minimax formulation gives nature the choice of spectrum, whereas we give her the choice of specific trajectory. Their approach retains the basic statistical description of the trajectory used in the more familiar estimation methods. The approach adopted in the present paper assumes that a statistical description of the target trajectory makes no sense at all.

Zahl[9] states a very general version of the minimax problem solved here, but has only obtained solutions for a special case. Zahl's solutions are restricted to the case in which the target is constrained to follow a polynomial path. His formulation differs from the usual polynomial smoothing techniques in that he considers bounds on the amplitude, velocity, and acceleration of the path. Whereas Zahl considers polynomial trajectories, the solution presented in the present paper considers *arbitrary* target trajectories $x(t)$, subject only to the constraint on acceleration implied by eq. (6). Trajectories are not required to have known functional form, or even that they be analytic. The solution to the problem (1)–(8), in fact, turns out to be only piecewise analytic.

3. THE MODIFIED MINIMAX PROBLEM

The first step in solution of the minimax estimation problem (5), (8) is to reformulate it in the following equivalent form:

$$\phi^2\{h^*, x^*\} = \min_{h \in H} \max_{|\ddot{x}| \leq \alpha} \phi^2\{h, x\}, \tag{9}$$

where $\phi^2\{h, x\}$ is the modified performance index

$$\phi^2\{h, x\} = \left[\int_0^T \rho(\tau)\, \ddot{x}(-\tau)\, d\tau\right]^2 + Q\int_0^T [h(\tau)]^2\, d\tau, \tag{10}$$

$$\rho(t) = \int_t^T (\tau - t)\, h(\tau)\, d\tau, \tag{11}$$

and H is the set

$$H = \left\{ h(t) \,\middle|\, \begin{matrix} \int_0^T \tau h(\tau)\, d\tau = 0 \\ \int_0^T h(\tau)\, d\tau = 1 \end{matrix} \right\}. \tag{12}$$

The function $\rho(t)$ plays a central role in all subsequent developments and will be referred to as the "characteristic function."

To prove the equivalence of equations (5)–(8) with (9)–(12), observe the identity

$$\int_0^T h(\tau)\, x(-\tau)\, d\tau = \int_0^T \rho(\tau)\, \ddot{x}(-\tau)\, d\tau - \rho(0)\, \dot{x}(0) - \dot{\rho}(0)\, x(0), \tag{13}$$

which may be verified by using (11) and integrating twice by parts. Substituting eq. (13) into (5) yields

$$\phi^2\{h, x\} = \left\{\int_0^T \rho(\tau)\,\ddot{x}(-\tau)\,d\tau - \rho(0)\,\dot{x}(0) - [\dot{\rho}(0) + 1]\,x(0)\right\}^2 + Q\int_0^T [h(\tau)]^2\,d\tau. \quad (14)$$

Equation (8) clearly implies

$$\phi^2\{h^*, x^*\} \geq \phi^2\{h^*, x\}; \quad \text{for all } x(t) \text{ such that } |\ddot{x}| \leq \alpha. \quad (15)$$

Using (14) this becomes

$$\left.\begin{aligned} &\left\{\int_0^T \rho^*(\tau)\,\ddot{x}^*(-\tau)\,d\tau - \rho^*(0)\,\dot{x}^*(0) - [\dot{\rho}^*(0) + 1]\,x^*(0)\right\}^2 \\ &\quad \geq \left\{\int_0^T \rho^*(\tau)\,\ddot{x}(-\tau)\,d\tau - \rho^*(0)\,\dot{x}(0) - [\dot{\rho}^*(0) + 1]\,x(0)\right\}^2 \\ &\text{for all } x(0),\ \dot{x}(0), \text{ and } \ddot{x}(t) \text{ such that } |\ddot{x}| \leq \alpha. \end{aligned}\right\} \quad (16)$$

The only way the inequality (16) can hold is for the coefficients of $x(0)$ and $\dot{x}(0)$ to vanish

$$\rho^*(0) = 0, \qquad \dot{\rho}^*(0) = -1 \quad (17)$$

which implies the constraint $h^* \epsilon H$. Since $h^* \epsilon H$, it is permissible to restrict the choice of h in performing the minimization of (8) according to the modified minimax problem (9). In making this restriction, furthermore, the coefficients of $\dot{x}(0)$ and $x(0)$ in (14) automatically vanish. Hence (5) may be replaced by the modified performance index (10).

The constraints (12) may be given direct physical interpretation: The first constraint requires that the filter be insensitive to translations in target velocity, while the second specifies that it react in direct proportion to translations of position.

4. DERIVATION OF THE EULER-LAGRANGE EQUATIONS FOR THE OPTIMAL FILTER

The statement of the modified minimax problem given by eqs. (9)–(10) implies that the minimization and maximization operators should be applied in a specific order.† As in most minimax problems, the solution is considerably simplified if

†This is a result of the assumption that nature is able to choose the target maneuver with complete a priori knowledge of the filter impulse response function, whereas the filter designer makes his choice in complete ignorance. This situation is somewhat different from that considered in the usual context of problems of differential games.[10] It will shortly be shown, however, that the "min-max" operators in (9)–(10) in fact commute. The result is that, although the formulations of (9)–(10) and the corresponding problem of differential games are superficially different, the solutions (and method of solution) will be identical.

it can be shown that a saddle point exists and that the "min" and "max" operators commute.

The definition that the point (h^*, x^*) be a saddle point is that

$$\phi^2\{h^*, x^*\} = \max_{|\ddot{x}| \leq \alpha} \phi^2\{h^*, x\} \tag{18}$$

$$= \min_{h \in H} \phi^2\{h, x^*\}. \tag{19}$$

According to the "saddle point" theorem,[11] eqs. (18)–(19) are sufficient conditions that (h^*, x^*) solve the minimax problem (9)–(10).

In the event that a saddle point exists, the problem (9)–(10) can be replaced by the equivalent pair of problems (18)–(19) in the calculus of variations. Our method of solution will be first to set up and then solve a pair of sufficient conditions on x^* and h^* for solution of the problems (18) and (19).

Maximization Over Target Maneuver

Let us substitute the performance index (10) into eq. (18). The resulting maximization problem is similar to that encountered in the well-known "bang-bang" control problem:[12] The second term in (10), and the function $\rho(t)$ appearing in the first term, depend only upon the filter $h(t)$ and hence are held constant throughout the maximization. Only the function $\ddot{x}(t)$ may vary. The integral in brackets in (10) assumes its largest possible value when $\ddot{x}(t)$ lies on the constraint boundary according to the relation†

$$\ddot{x}^*(-t) = \pm\alpha \operatorname{sgn}\{\rho(t)\}; \quad 0 \leq t \leq T. \tag{20}$$

Equation (20) is the desired necessary and sufficient condition relating the optimal target maneuver $x^*(t)$ to the filter design $h(t)$. The choice of $\pm$ sign in (20) is arbitrary, but once chosen must remain the same at all points on the interval $0 \leq t \leq T$.

Minimization Over Filter Design

Let us next consider the problem (19) where it is required to minimize $\phi^2\{h, x^*\}$ with respect to the filter design $h(t)$. Substitution of (11) into (10) shows that $\phi^2\{h, x\}$ is non-negative definite and therefore a convex functional of $h(t)$. The constraints (12), furthermore, are linear. Restriction of a convex functional by linear constraints does not alter the convexity of the problems. If there is more than one stationary point to such problems they must be connected and equal. It follows that the usual necessary conditions for a local extremal to the

†The "sgn" function is defined as

$$\operatorname{sgn}\{y\} = \begin{cases} 1; & y > 0 \\ -1; & y < 0 \end{cases}$$

The value of this function at $y = 0$ is left unspecified by the maximization problem (18). For the moment its value will be left open. The correct value of $\operatorname{sgn}\{0\}$ will be established later as a condition for solving the minimization problem (19).

problem (19), provided by the calculus of variations, correspond to an absolute minimum.

Let us introduce the new variables:

$$\nu(t) = \frac{1}{\alpha}\int_t^T \rho(\tau)\, \ddot{x}^*(-\tau)\, d\tau, \qquad \rho(t) = \int_t^T (\tau - t)\, h(\tau)\, d\tau,$$

$$\mu(t) = \int_t^T h(\tau)\, d\tau, \tag{21}$$

where for completeness eq. (11), defining the characteristic function, has also been included. Let us in addition use the subscript "0" notation to denote evaluation at $t = 0$:

$$\nu_0 = \nu(0); \quad \rho_0 = \rho(0); \quad \mu_0 = \mu(0). \tag{22}$$

Differentiating and using the property $h \in H$, it is not difficult to show that ν, μ, and ρ satisfy the differential equations plus boundary conditions

$$\begin{aligned} \dot{\nu} &= -\frac{1}{\alpha}\rho\ddot{x}^*; && \nu(T) = 0, \\ \dot{\rho} &= -\mu; && \rho_0 = 0; \ \rho(T) = 0, \\ \dot{\mu} &= -h; && \mu_0 = 1; \ \mu(T) = 0. \end{aligned} \tag{23}$$

Substituting (21)–(22) into (10) and evaluating at $x = x^*$ yields

$$\phi^2\{h, x^*\} = \alpha^2\nu_0^2 + Q\int_0^T [h(\tau)]^2\, d\tau. \tag{24}$$

The problem (23)–(24) is in the form of the standard Mayer-Bolza problem[13] in the calculus of variations. In this form it may be interpreted as that of minimizing eq. (24) subject to the set of equations (23) as constraints. The usual method of finding the local extrema of such problems is to adjoin eq. (23) to (24) with Lagrange multipliers

$$\phi^2 = \alpha^2\nu_0^2 + \gamma_\rho[\rho_0] + \gamma_\mu[\mu_0 - 1] + \int_0^T \left[Qh^2 + \left(\dot{\nu} + \frac{1}{\alpha}\rho\ddot{x}^*\right)\lambda_\nu + (\dot{\rho} + \mu)\lambda_\rho + (\dot{\mu} + h)\lambda_\mu\right] d\tau. \tag{25}$$

Integrating by parts, forming the first variation with respect to ν, ρ, μ, h, ν_0, ρ_0, and μ_0, setting to zero, and rearranging terms, yields

$$0 \equiv \delta\phi^2 = \int_0^T \left[-\dot{\lambda}_\nu\delta\nu - \left(\dot{\lambda}_\rho - \frac{1}{\alpha}\ddot{x}^*\lambda_\nu\right)\delta\rho - (\dot{\lambda}_\mu - \lambda_\rho)\,\delta\mu + (2Qh + \lambda_\mu)\,\delta h\right] d\tau$$
$$+ (2\alpha^2\nu_0 - \lambda_\nu(0))\,\delta\nu_0 + (\gamma_\rho - \lambda_\rho(0))\,\delta\rho_0 + (\gamma_\mu - \lambda_\mu(0))\,\delta\mu_0. \tag{26}$$

The equality in (26) must hold for all variations $\delta\nu$, $\delta\rho$, $\delta\mu$, δh, $\delta\nu_0$, $\delta\rho_0$, and $\delta\mu_0$. It follows that the coefficients of these quantities must vanish, and there results

$$\begin{aligned}
&\dot{\lambda}_\nu = 0 \quad &(a)\qquad 2\alpha^2\nu_0 &= \lambda_\nu(0) \quad (e)\\
&\dot{\lambda}_\rho = \frac{1}{\alpha}\ddot{x}^*\lambda_\nu \quad &(b)\qquad \gamma_\rho &= \lambda_\rho(0) \quad (f)\\
&\dot{\lambda}_\mu = \lambda_\rho \quad &(c)\qquad \gamma_\mu &= \lambda_\mu(0) \quad (g).\\
&2hQ = -\lambda_\mu \quad &(d)\qquad &
\end{aligned} \tag{27}$$

According to equations (27 a, e),

$$\lambda_\nu(t) = 2\alpha^2\nu_0. \tag{28}$$

Defining the new variable

$$\lambda = \frac{\lambda_\rho}{2Q}, \tag{29}$$

and eliminating λ_ρ, λ_μ, and λ_ν among eq. (27 b–d) yields the two differential equations

$$\dot{h} = -\lambda, \quad \dot{\lambda} = \frac{\alpha}{Q}\nu_0\ddot{x}^*. \tag{30}$$

The last two of eqs. (27) will not be required.

Equations (23) and (30) are the Euler-Lagrange equations for the minimization problem (19). Since the minimized functional is convex, it follows that these equations are sufficient as well as necessary conditions for solution.

The Combined Euler-Lagrange Equations

Equations (20) and (23), (30) are the individual sufficient conditions for the two calculus of variations problems (18) and (19). Substituting† (20) for $\ddot{x}^*$ into (23) and (30), and using the ( )* notation to emphasize that the solution to these equations is the required optimum, yields the combined set of sufficient conditions for solution of the minimax problem (9)–(10):

$$\begin{aligned}
\dot{\nu}^* &= -|\rho^*|; & & \nu^*(T) = 0,\\
\dot{\rho}^* &= -\mu^*; & \rho_0^* = \rho^*(0) = 0;\ & \rho^*(T) = 0,\\
\dot{\mu}^* &= -h^*; & \mu_0^* = \mu^*(0) = 1;\ & \mu^*(T) = 0,\\
\dot{h}^* &= -\lambda^*, & &\\
\dot{\lambda}^* &= \frac{\alpha^2}{Q}\nu_0^*\,\mathrm{sgn}\,(\rho^*). & &
\end{aligned} \tag{31}$$

Using these equations, it is now possible to simplify the form of the performance index. Integrating the integral appearing on the right-hand side of (24) twice by parts, simplifying using (31), and then substituting back into (24), yields the performance for the optimal filter

$$\phi^2 = Qh^*(0) \tag{32}$$

where $h^*(0)$ denotes the evaluation of the optimal impulse response function at $t = 0$.

†The plus sign is arbitrarily chosen in eq. (20).

5. NORMALIZATION OF THE EULER-LAGRANGE EQUATIONS

The five differential equations and five boundary conditions (31) define a two-point boundary value problem for the optimal filter. To solve these equations, it is convenient to introduce a change in amplitude and time scale

$$\nu^*,\ \rho^*,\ \mu^*,\ h^*,\ \lambda^*,\ T,\ t \Longrightarrow \tilde{\nu},\ \tilde{\rho},\ \tilde{\mu},\ \tilde{h},\ \tilde{\lambda},\ \tilde{T},\ \tau, \tag{33}$$

according to the definitions

$$\begin{aligned}
\nu^*(t) &= \frac{\alpha^2\nu_0^*}{Q}\,\Delta^5\,\tilde{\nu}(\tau), && \text{(a)}\\
\rho^*(t) &= \varepsilon\,\frac{\alpha^2\nu_0^*}{Q}\,\Delta^4\,\tilde{\rho}(\tau), && \text{(b)}\\
\mu^*(t) &= \varepsilon\,\frac{\alpha^2\nu_0^*}{Q}\,\Delta^3\,\tilde{\mu}(\tau), && \text{(c)}\\
h^*(t) &= \varepsilon\,\frac{\alpha^2\nu_0^*}{Q}\,\Delta^2\,\tilde{h}(\tau), && \text{(d)}\\
\lambda^*(t) &= \varepsilon\,\frac{\alpha^2\nu_0^*}{Q}\,\Delta\,\tilde{\lambda}(\tau), && \text{(e)}\\
\tilde{T} &= \frac{T}{\Delta} + \tau_0,
\end{aligned} \tag{34}$$

where the new time variable is rescaled and shifted according to

$$\tau = \frac{t}{\Delta} + \tau_0. \tag{35}$$

The parameters defining the change of variable are Δ, τ_0, and ε. Of these, τ_0 is allowed to assume any real value, but Δ is restricted to be positive, and ε will be limited to ± 1:

$$\Delta > 0, \quad \varepsilon^2 = 1. \tag{36}$$

Values will be chosen for these parameters in the next section.

In addition to (34)–(36) the convention will be adopted that a subscript "0" on a normalized quantity denotes evaluation at $\tau = \tau_0$:

$$\begin{aligned}
\tilde{\nu}_0 &= \tilde{\nu}(\tau_0), \quad \tilde{\rho}_0 = \tilde{\rho}(\tau_0),\\
\tilde{\mu}_0 = \tilde{\mu}(\tau_0), \quad \tilde{h}_0 &= \tilde{h}(\tau_0), \quad \tilde{\lambda}_0 = \tilde{\lambda}(\tau_0).
\end{aligned} \tag{37}$$

Using (34)–(36) and the non-negative properties of Q and ν_0^*, the Euler-Lagrange equations (31) transform into:

$$\begin{aligned}
&\dot{\tilde{\nu}} = -|\tilde{\rho}|; && && \tilde{\nu}(\tilde{T}) = 0,\\
&\dot{\tilde{\rho}} = -\tilde{\mu}; && \tilde{\rho}(\tau_0) = 0; && \tilde{\rho}(\tilde{T}) = 0,\\
&\dot{\tilde{\mu}} = -\tilde{h}; && \tilde{\mu}(\tau_0) = \frac{1}{\varepsilon\Delta^3}\,\frac{Q}{\alpha^2\nu_0^*}; && \tilde{\mu}(\tilde{T}) = 0,\\
&\dot{\tilde{h}} = -\tilde{\lambda},\\
&\dot{\tilde{\lambda}} = \operatorname{sgn}(\tilde{\rho}).
\end{aligned} \tag{38}$$

Setting: (i) $t = 0$ in (34a), and (ii) using the boundary condition for $\tilde{\mu}(\tau_0)$ appearing in (38) yields the important relationships

$$\Delta = \left(\frac{\alpha^2}{Q}\tilde{\nu}_0\right)^{-1/5},$$
$$\nu_0^* = \frac{1}{\varepsilon\Delta^3}\,\frac{Q}{\alpha^2\tilde{\mu}(\tau_0)} = \frac{\tilde{\nu}_0^{3/5}}{\varepsilon\tilde{\mu}_0}\left(\frac{Q}{\alpha^2}\right)^{2/5}, \tag{39}$$

Substituting (35) and (39) into (34d) and (34f), and then substituting into (32) it is now straightforward to evaluate the optimal filter and its resulting performance

$$h^*(t) = \left(\frac{\alpha^2}{Q}\right)^{1/5}\frac{\tilde{\nu}_0^{1/5}}{\tilde{\mu}_0}\,\tilde{h}\left[\left(\frac{\alpha^2}{Q}\tilde{\nu}_0\right)^{1/5} t + \tau_0\right],$$
$$T = \left(\frac{\alpha^2}{Q}\tilde{\nu}_0\right)^{-1/5}(\tilde{T} - \tau_0), \tag{40}$$
$$\phi^2 = (\alpha^2 Q^4)^{1/5}\,\frac{\tilde{\nu}_0^{1/5}}{\tilde{\mu}_0}\,\tilde{h}(\tau_0).$$

The advantage of the normalization (34) is that the coefficient $\alpha^2\nu_0^*/Q$ (which depends on the *unknown* quantity ν_0^*) is removed from the differential equation portion of (31) and incorporated into the boundary conditions on $\tilde{\mu}$ (see eq. (38)). The result is that the differential equations for the normalized problem (38) are *piecewise linear* between zeros of $\tilde{\rho}$. In the following section, the nonlinearity of the boundary conditions in (38) will be removed by introduction of an appropriate parameterization. This will make it possible to obtain a complete (parameterized) solution for the normalized problem (38). Using (40), it will then be possible to evaluate the optimal $h^*(t)$, T, and ϕ^2 in terms of the parameterization.

6. SOLUTION FOR FINITE NUMBER OF ZEROS

The characteristic function $\rho(t)$ which solves the unnormalized problem (31) can be expected to have one or more zeros on the interval $t = (0, T)$. Let us temporarily restrict ourselves to the case in which the number of such zeros is finite. The zeros on the interval $(0, T)$ will be denoted by the notation T_k:

$$\rho^*(T_k) = 0; \quad k = 0, 1, 2, \ldots, N,$$
$$\rho^*(t) \neq 0; \quad t \neq T_k, \tag{41}$$

where

$$0 = T_0 < T_1 \leq T_2 \leq \ldots < T_N = T. \tag{42}$$

and N is the total number of such zeros. It is agreed that multiple zeros, if they exist, are counted in proportion to their multiplicity, except for the multiple zero at $T_N = T$, which is counted only once. Note that the point $t = 0$ cannot be a multiple zero by virtue of the boundary condition $\dot{\rho}_0^* = -\mu_0^* = -1$ in (31).

It is convenient to choose the following values for the parameters defining the transformation (34):

$$\Delta = T_N - T_{N-1}, \quad \tau_0 = -\frac{T_N}{T_N - T_{N-1}}, \tag{43}$$

and

$$\varepsilon = (-)^N. \tag{44}$$

The first two of these choices, (43), is made so that (i) [see eq. (34f)]:

$$\widetilde{T} = 0, \tag{45}$$

and (ii) the last oscillation of the characteristic function $\rho^*(t)$ is transformed into the unit interval $\tau = (-1, 0)$ [see eqs. (41), (34b), and (35)]:

$$\widetilde{\rho}(-1) = 0 = \widetilde{\rho}(0), \quad \widetilde{\rho}(\tau) \neq 0; \quad -1 < \tau < 0. \tag{46}$$

To see the implication of the choice (44), it is observed from the boundary conditions (17) that

$$\dot{\rho}_0^* = -\mu_0^* = -1, \tag{47}$$

and hence that the unnormalized characteristic function $\rho^*(t)$ is negative on its first oscillation

$$\rho^*(t) < 0; \quad 0 < t < T_1. \tag{48}$$

On the Nth oscillation, it must therefore have the sign

$$\text{sgn}\,[\rho^*(t)] = (-)^N; \quad T_{N-1} < t < T_N. \tag{49}$$

Recalling that the interval $t = (T_{N-1}, T_N)$ transforms into the interval $\tau = (-1, 0)$, it follows, by eqs. (34b), (44), and (49), and the fact that $\alpha^2 \nu_0^* \Delta^4 / Q$ is positive, that

$$\widetilde{\rho}(\tau) > 0; \quad -1 < \tau < 0. \tag{50}$$

Returning to the differential equations (38) for the normalized problem and using the property (45), it is seen that:

i) $\widetilde{\rho}(\tau)$ is piecewise a fourth-order polynomial. The only discontinuities in $\widetilde{\rho}(\tau)$ are at its zeros: $\widetilde{\rho}(\tau) = 0$.

ii) $\widetilde{\rho}(\tau)$, $\dot{\widetilde{\rho}}(\tau)$, $\ddot{\widetilde{\rho}}(\tau)$, and $\dddot{\widetilde{\rho}}(\tau)$ are continuous across these discontinuities.

iii) The fourth derivative of $\widetilde{\rho}(\tau)$ has unit magnitude and the negative of the sign of $\widetilde{\rho}(\tau)$:

$$\frac{d^4}{d\tau^4}\widetilde{\rho}(\tau) = -\text{sgn}\,[\widetilde{\rho}(\tau)].$$

iv) $\widetilde{\rho}(0) = 0$, $\dot{\widetilde{\rho}}(0) = 0$.

(51)

In addition, the properties (50) and (51iii) imply that

$$\frac{d^4}{d\tau^4}\,\tilde{\rho}(\tau) = -1; \quad -1 < \tau < 0. \tag{52}$$

The properties (46), (50), (51), and (52) completely define the form of the normalized characteristic function. The most general form this function can possibly have on the interval $\tau = (-1, 0)$ is

$$\tilde{\rho}(\tau) = \frac{1}{24}\,\tau^2(1+\tau)(\zeta - \tau); \quad -1 \leq \tau \leq 0, \tag{53}$$

where the parameter ζ is constrained to be non-negative

$$\zeta \geq 0. \tag{54}$$

All solutions to the minimax estimation problem having a finite number of zeros must normalize to the form (53)–(54). It follows that the two quantities ζ and N completely parameterize our choice of solution: Each solution of the minimax estimation problem having a finite number of zeros must correspond to a specific choice of the values $[\zeta, N]$. It is possible, therefore, to investigate all such solutions by merely scanning the various combinations of pairs $[\zeta, N]$. The procedure for finding the solution for a particular choice of $[\zeta, N]$ is:

(55)

i) Use (53) to compute $\tilde{\rho}(\tau)$ on the interval $(-1, 0)$.

ii) Extrapolate $\tilde{\rho}(\tau)$ back a total of $N - 1$ additional zero crossings (in the direction of negative τ) using the properties (51i–iii). Determine the location of the final zero crossing $\tau = \tau_0$.

iii) Evaluate the quantities

$$\tilde{\nu}_0 = \int_{\tau_0}^{\tilde{T}} |\tilde{\rho}(\tau')|\, d\tau',$$

$$\tilde{\mu}_0 = -\dot{\tilde{\rho}}(\tau_0),$$

$$\tilde{h}(\tau) = \ddot{\tilde{\rho}}(\tau); \quad \tau_0 \leq \tau \leq 0.$$

iv) Compute the optimal filter and its performance (40), using the results (55iii).

7. NUMERICAL SOLUTION FOR POSITION FILTERING PROBLEM

Solution for $T < T_{max}$

A digital computer has been used to implement the procedure (55) for computing solutions to the minimax estimation problem. Results are shown in Tables 1 and 2 and in Figs. 2 through 4.

Tabulations of the rms performance, ϕ, and the observation time, T, against the parameters $[\zeta, N]$ are shown in Tables 1 and 2. It is evident from these tabu-

TABLE 1. PERFORMANCE OF FINITE TIME POSITION FILTER

Parameter ζ	Number of Zeros of Characteristic Function N	Observation Time $\left(\frac{\alpha^2}{Q}\right)^{1/5} T$	Maximum RMS Error $\frac{\phi}{\left(\alpha Q^2\right)^{1/5}}$
∞	1	0	∞
10^4	1	0.4918960	2.8517024
10^2	1	1.2341243	1.8047742
10	1	1.9356076	1.4698530
1	1	2.8252345	1.3303250
0	1	3.4375439	1.3211481
∞	2	3.4375439	1.3211481
10^4	2	3.4376585	1.3211481
10^2	2	3.4490698	1.3211480
10	2	3.5429574	1.3211361
1	2	3.8469184	1.3210518
0	2	4.0338534	1.3210417
∞	3	4.0338534	1.3210417
10^4	3	4.0338812	1.3210417
10^2	3	4.0366324	1.3210417
10	3	4.0590967	1.3210417
1	3	4.1328155	1.3210416
0	3	4.1782930	1.3210416
∞	4	4.1782930	1.3210416
10^4	4	4.1782997	1.3210416
10^2	4	4.1789658	1.3210416
10	4	4.1844036	1.3210416
1	4	4.2022530	1.3210416
0	4	4.2132649	1.3210416

TABLE 2. PERFORMANCE OF FINITE TIME POSITION FILTER

Parameter ζ	Number of Zeros of Characteristic Function N	Observation Time $\left(\frac{\alpha^2}{Q}\right)^{1/5} T$	Maximum RMS Error $\frac{\phi}{\left(\alpha Q^2\right)^{1/5}}$
	1	3.4375439	1.3211481
	2	4.0338534	1.3210417
	3	4.1782930	1.3210416
	4	4.2132649	1.3210416
	5	4.2217324	1.3210416
	6	4.2237826	
	7	4.2242790	
	8	4.2243991	
0	9	4.2244282	
	10	4.2244353	
	11	4.2244370	
	12	4.2244374	1.3210416
	13	4.2244375	
	14	4.2244375	
	15	4.2244375	
	16	4.2244375	
	17		
	18	4.2244375	
	19		
	20		

lations that there is a one-to-one correspondence between the parameters $[\zeta, N]$, on the one hand, and the observation time T on the other. The tabulations also show a limit point at the maximum observation time

$$T_{\max} = \lim_{N\to\infty} T_N = 4.2244375 \left(\frac{Q}{\alpha^2}\right)^{1/5}, \tag{56}$$

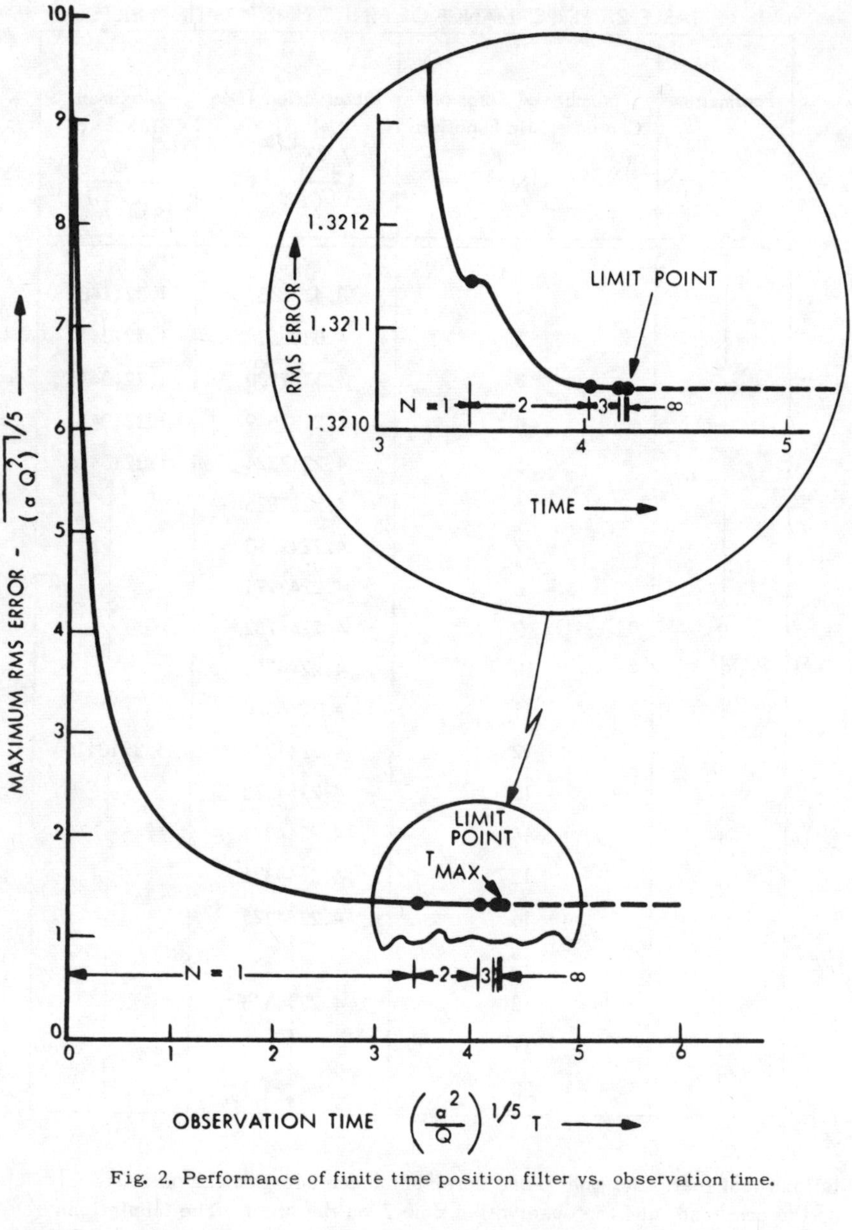

Fig. 2. Performance of finite time position filter vs. observation time.

corresponding to an infinite number ($N = \infty$) of oscillations of the characteristic function. A graph of the rms performance index ϕ versus observation time T is shown in Fig. 2.

The solution for the performance index as a function of T, shown in Fig. 2, is clearly continuous as ζ varies from zero to infinity for each value of N. It is shown in Appendix A that the filters corresponding to the two end points of the parameterization, $[0, N] \Longleftrightarrow [\infty, N+1]$, are identical. It follows that the curve of Fig. 2 is defined and continuous everywhere on the interval $0 \leq T < T_{max}$. Since eqs. (31) are sufficient conditions for a minimax solution the parameterization $[\zeta, N]$ completely defines the solution for all observation times less than $T = T_{max}$.

Sketches for the optimal impulse response function are shown in Figs. 3a–f for the cases shown in Table 3.

TABLE 3. LEGEND FOR FIGURE 3

Figure No.	N	ζ	Observation Time T
3a	1	3	$2.40\ (Q/\alpha^2)^{1/5}$
3b	1	0.3	$3.17\ (Q/\alpha^2)^{1/5}$
3c	1	0	$3.44\ (Q/\alpha^2)^{1/5}$
3d	2	1	$3.85\ (Q/\alpha^2)^{1/5}$
3e	2	0	$4.03\ (Q/\alpha^2)^{1/5}$
3f	∞	-	$T \geq T_{max} = 4.22\ (Q/\alpha^2)^{1/5}$

Also shown in Fig. 3 is the "least favorable" target acceleration, $\ddot{x}^*(-t)$, defined by eq. (20), corresponding to the target's best strategy against the optimal filter. It is observed that for $T - T_{max}$ both the optimal filter and the least favorable target maneuver are "chatter solutions," with limit points at $t = T_{max}$. It is also noted that the value of the target maneuver is important to the problem only within the region $(-T, 0)$ where observations are actually made.

Solution for $T \geq T_{max}$

The numerical solutions obtained using the parameterization $[\zeta, N]$ provide results only for observation times less than T_{max}. By the terms of the development, the parameterization $[\zeta, N]$ is exhaustive and must include all solutions having a finite number of zeros. It follows that for $T \geq T_{max}$ the characteristic function cannot have a finite number of zeros.

A clue to what the solution for $T \geq T_{max}$ should be is obtained by inspection of the numerical results for $T < T_{max}$. It is found† that the third and fourth deriv-

†For brevity the raw numerical data supporting this statement is not included.

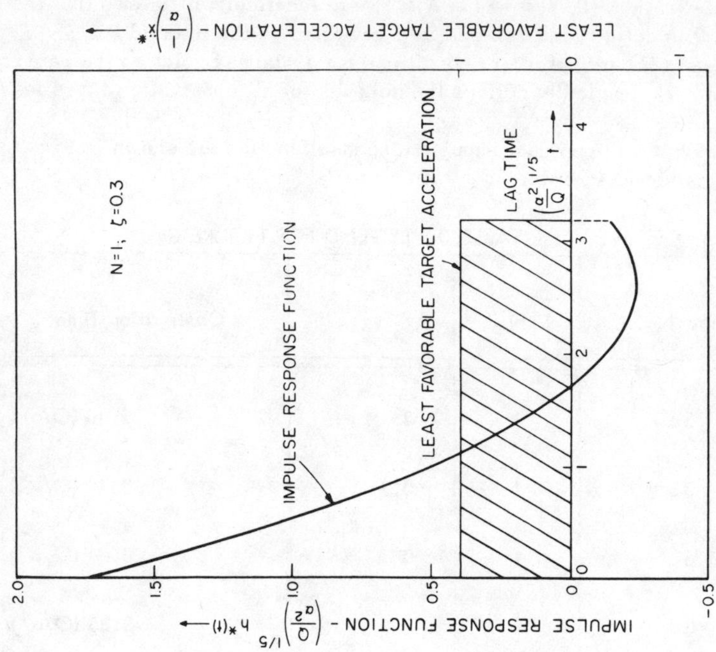

Fig. 3b. Impulse response function for finite observation time.

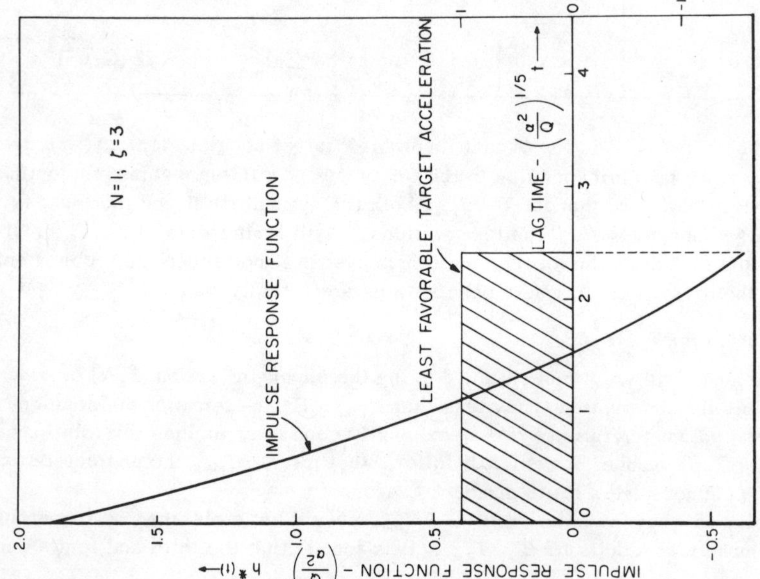

Fig. 3a. Impulse response function for finite observation time.

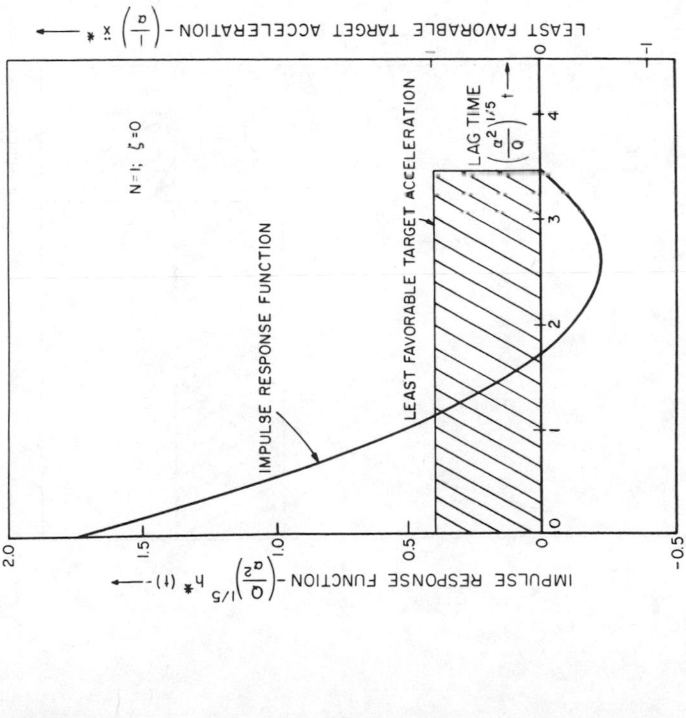

Fig. 3c. Impulse response function for finite observation time.

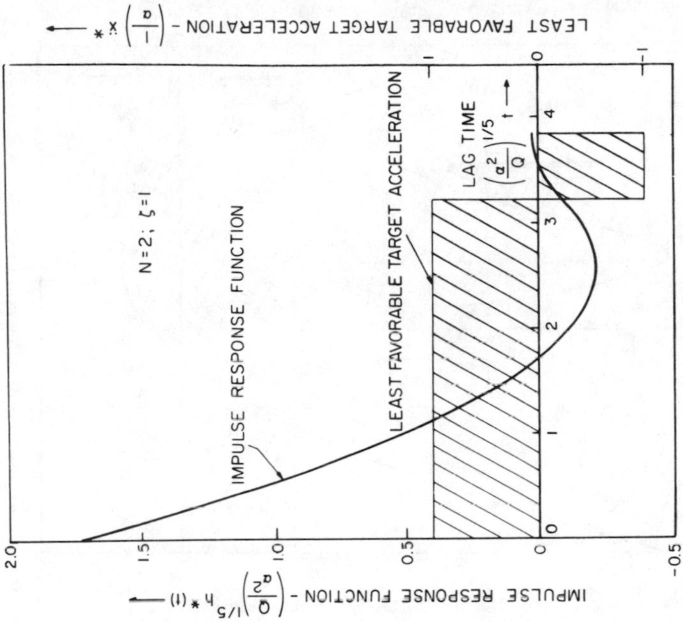

Fig. 3d. Impulse response function for finite observation time.

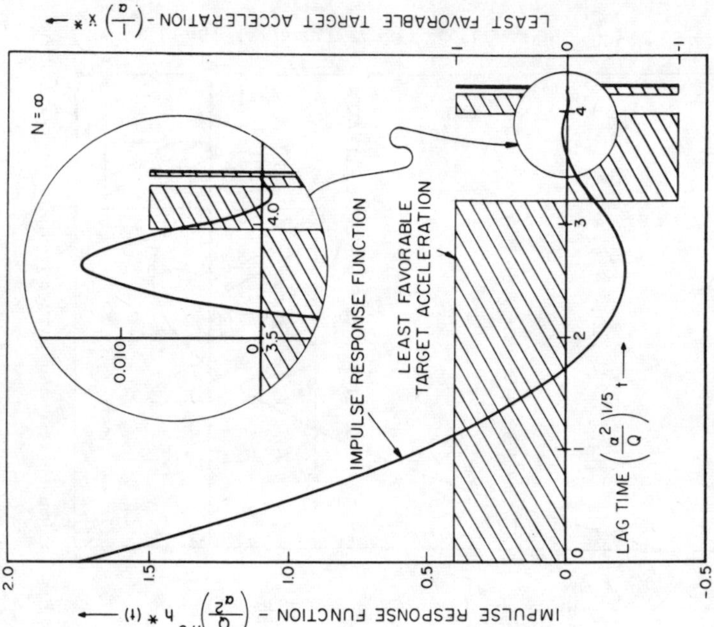

Fig. 3f. Impulse response function for limiting observation time $T \longrightarrow T_{max}$.

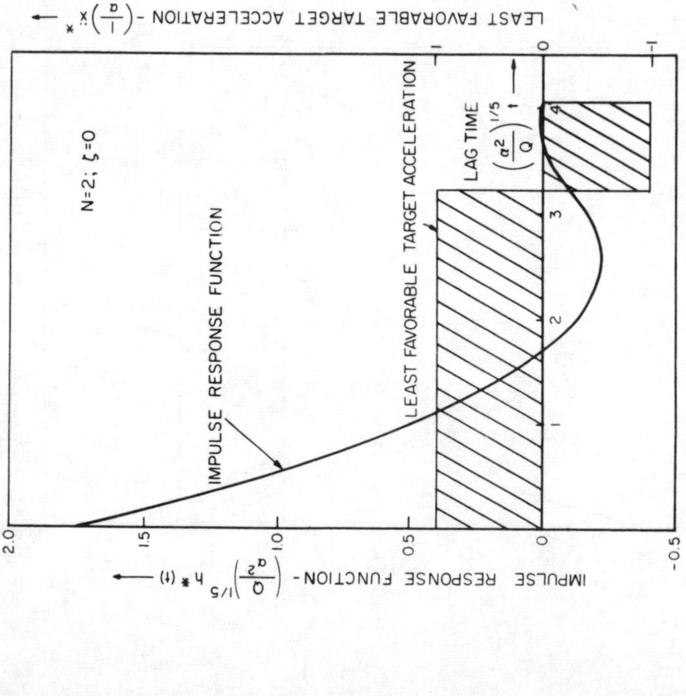

Fig. 3e. Impulse response function for finite observation time.

atives of $\rho^*(t)$, evaluated at $t = T$, approach zero as T approaches $T_{\max}$. Combining these limits with the boundary conditions in (31), results in

$$\begin{aligned} \rho^*(T_{\max}) &= 0, \\ \dot{\rho}^*(T_{\max}) &= 0, \\ \ddot{\rho}^*(T_{\max}) &= 0, \\ \dddot{\rho}^*(T_{\max}) &= 0. \end{aligned} \tag{57}$$

The properties (57) together with (31) imply that a legitimate solution to the Euler-Lagrange equations for $T \geq T_{\max}$ can be obtained by using the limiting solution for $T = T_{\max}$ on the interval $(0, T_{\max})$ and setting $h^*(t)$ to zero on the remaining interval:

$$h^*(t) = \begin{cases} h^*_{T_{\max}}(t); & 0 \leq t < T_{\max} \\ 0 \quad ; & T_{\max} \leq t \leq T, \end{cases} \tag{58}$$

where $h^*_{T_{\max}}(t)$ is the limiting solution for observation times $T = T_{\max}$, as shown in Fig. 3f. It is easily verified [using (11)] that the characteristic function for the solution (58) is zero on the interval $T_{\max} \leq t \leq T$, and matches the limiting solution, $\rho^*_{T_{\max}}$, on the interval $0 \leq t < T_{\max}$. The performance of this filter is identical to that for $T = T_{\max}$

$$\phi = \phi_{T_{\max}} = 1.3210\,(\alpha Q^2)^{1/5}, \tag{59}$$

as shown by the dashed "extension" in Fig. 2. Since the Euler-Lagrange equations are a sufficiency condition, it follows that (58) is the optimal solution for $T \geq T_{\max}$.

Analytic Solution for T $\geq$ T$_{max}$

A sketch of the characteristic function for problems involving large observation times, $T \geq T_{\max}$, is shown in Fig. 4. This function is oscillatory with zeros occurring at the points

$$t\left(\frac{\alpha^2}{Q}\right)^{1/5} = 3.202,\ 3.977,\ 4.164,\ 4.210,\ \ldots. \tag{60}$$

Note that the scale of the graph is such that the oscillations occurring after the first can only be seen on an expanded scale.

Inspection of Fig. 4 reveals a very interesting feature: Although the scales are different, the second oscillation of the characteristic function has the same general *shape* as the first. The third and all later oscillations also have the same shape. It would appear that successive oscillations of $\rho(t)$ are related to one another by an inversion of sign and rescaling of both time and amplitude. This suggests that an assumption of "damped periodicity" might be introduced for the characteristic function as a basis for *analytic solution* of problems with large observation times. The details of such an analysis are carried out in reference 4, and an analytic solution for the case $T \geq T_{\max}$ is explicitly obtained. This analytic solution is completely consistent with the numerical solution (Fig. 3f) displayed here.

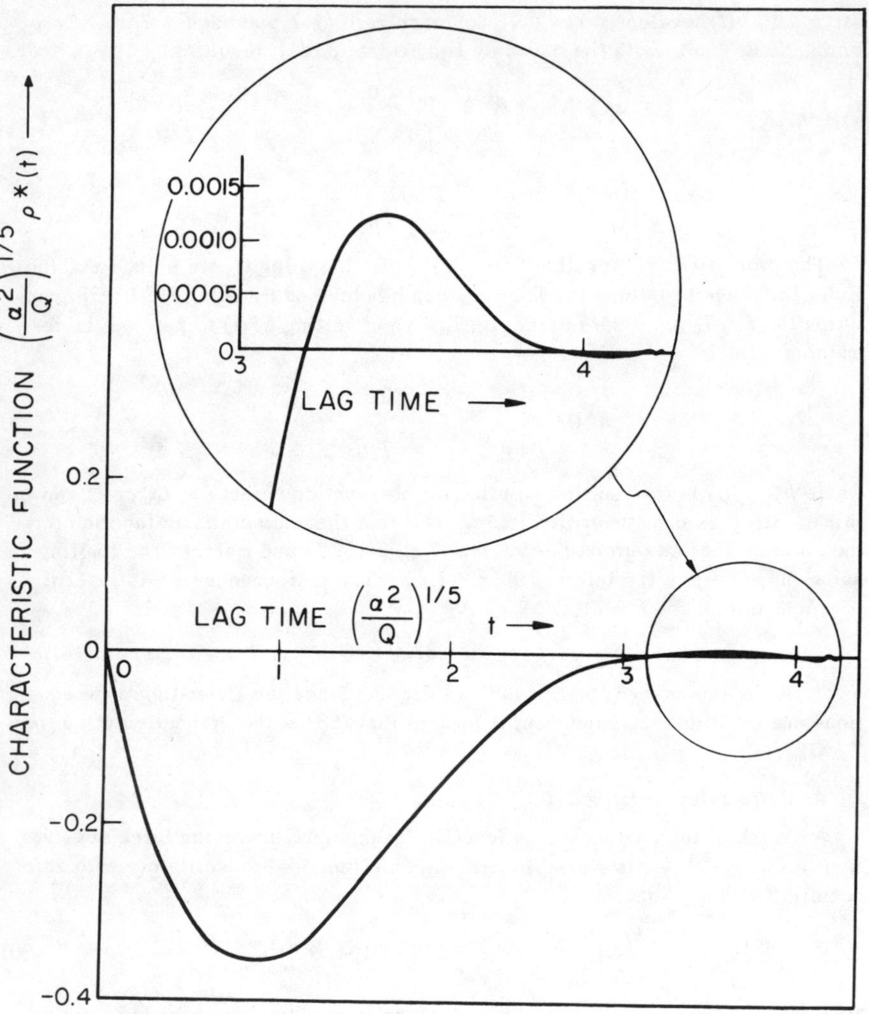

Fig. 4. Characteristic function for observation time $T = T_{max}$.

Discussion

It is clear from the results presented in these pages that increasing the available observation time beyond the first oscillation at $T = 3.44\ (Q/\alpha^2)^{1/5}$ introduces a discontinuity in the solution and, therefore, considerably complicates the filter design. Furthermore, from Table 2 (or Fig. 2), it is observed that the improvement in performance realized by such an increase is negligible; the "relative" improvement in rms error effected by using the true optimum filter rather than truncating the observations at $T = T_1$ is

$$\frac{\Delta\phi}{\phi} = \frac{1.32115 - 1.32104}{1.32115} \sim 10^{-4}. \tag{61}$$

The ratio (61) suggests that an excellent "suboptimal" filter design can be obtained for the case of long observation times without a "chatter" solution by arbitrarily truncating the observations at $T = 3.44\,(Q/\alpha^2)^{1/5}$. The performance of such a solution will be within 0.01 per cent of the true optimum! The development of this and other "suboptimal" filter designs more useful for practical design is discussed in reference 14.

8. EXTENSIONS—POSITION SMOOTHING AND THE ESTIMATION OF VELOCITY

A. Position Smoothing

In the position smoothing problem, it is assumed that observations are available on both sides of the point to be estimated. Let us restrict ourselves to the symmetric problem in which measurements are available on the interval $(-T, T)$. Again anticipating that the filter will be time-invariant, the estimate and performance indices become

$$\hat{x}(0) = \int_{-T}^{T} h(\tau) z(-\tau)\, d\tau, \tag{2A}$$

$$\phi^2\{h, x\} = \left[\int_{-T}^{T} h(\tau) x(-\tau)\, d\tau - x(0)\right]^2 + Q \int_{-T}^{T} [h(\tau)]^2\, d\tau. \tag{5A}$$

The modified minimax problem [eqs. (9)–(12)] is developed as before, with the following change in definition for the characteristic function:

$$\rho(t) = \begin{cases} \displaystyle\int_{t}^{T} (\tau - t) h(\tau)\, d\tau; & 0 < t \le T \\ \displaystyle\int_{-T}^{t} (t - \tau) h(\tau)\, d\tau; & -T \le t < 0. \end{cases} \tag{11A}$$

The integration by parts yields

$$\int_{-T}^{T} h(\tau) x(-\tau)\, d\tau = \int_{-T}^{T} \rho(\tau) \ddot{x}(-\tau)\, d\tau + [\dot{\rho}(0^-) - \dot{\rho}(0^+)]\, x(0) + [\rho(0^-) - \rho(0^+)]\, \dot{x}(0), \tag{13A}$$

so that eqs. (12) and (10) become

$$H = \left\{ h(t) \left| \begin{array}{l} \displaystyle\int_{-T}^{T} \tau h(\tau)\, d\tau = 0 \\ \displaystyle\int_{-T}^{T} h(\tau)\, d\tau = 1 \end{array} \right. \right\}, \tag{12A}$$

$$\phi^2\{h, x\} = \left[\int_{-T}^{T} \rho(\tau) \ddot{x}(-\tau)\, d\tau\right]^2 + Q \int_{-T}^{T} [h(\tau)]^2\, d\tau. \tag{10A}$$

The maximization over target maneuver [eqs. (18) and (20)] is unchanged except for the change of limits:

$$\ddot{x}^*(-t) = \pm\alpha \ \mathrm{sgn}\{\rho(t)\}; \quad -T \leq t \leq T. \tag{20A}$$

It is shown in Appendix B that the optimal filter for the problem (10A) must be symmetric

$$h^*(t) = h^*(-t). \tag{62}$$

This implies that $h^*(t)$ can be represented in terms of a second function $h'(t)$ according to

$$h^*(t) = \begin{cases} \frac{1}{2}\, h'(t); & 0 < t \leq T, \\ \frac{1}{2}\, h'(-t); & -T \leq t < 0. \end{cases} \tag{63}$$

From (62), (11A), and (20A), it follows that $\ddot{x}^*(t)$ is also symmetric. Substituting (63) into (10A) and using (11A) yields

$$\phi^2\{h^*, x^*\} = \left[\int_0^T \rho'(\tau)\,\ddot{x}^*(-\tau)\,d\tau\right]^2 + \frac{1}{2}\,Q\int_0^T [h'(\tau)]^2\,d\tau \tag{10A$'$}$$

where

$$\rho'(t) = \int_t^T (\tau - t)\,h'(\tau)\,d\tau. \tag{64}$$

Upon substituting (63) into the constraint equations (12A) it is discovered that the first of the two constraints is *automatically satisfied.* Hence, eq. (12) simplifies to

$$H = \left\{h'(t) \,\middle|\, \int_0^T h'(\tau)\,d\tau = 1\right\}. \tag{12A$'$}$$

The problem (18)–(19), (10A′), and (12A′) is identical to the position filtering problem (18–19), (10), and (12) considered earlier, except for: i) the absence of the first constraint in (12); and ii) the change of parameter $Q \Longrightarrow \frac{1}{2}\,Q$. The solution of this new problem is carried through identically to that of Section 4 as far as eq. (22). The boundary condition on $\rho(0)$ in (23) is missing. Accordingly in (26) the term $\gamma_\rho \delta \rho_0$ will also be missing. The result is that Equation (27f) is replaced by $\lambda_\rho(0) = 0$. Carrying through subsequent derivations it is found that the constraint on $\rho^*(0)$ in (31) is missing, and in its place one must use the new constraint

$$\rho^*(0) = 0 \Longrightarrow \lambda^*(0) = 0. \tag{65}$$

Similarly, the constraint on $\tilde{\rho}(\tau_0)$ in the normalized equations (38) is replaced by the constraint on $\tilde{\lambda}$,

$$\tilde{\rho}(\tau_0) = 0 \Longrightarrow \tilde{\lambda}(\tau_0) = 0. \tag{38A}$$

Replacing Q by $1/2\ Q$, and dividing the expression for $h^*(t)$ in (40) by 2 in accordance with (63), yields

$$h^*(t) = h^*(-t) = \frac{1}{2}\left(\frac{2\alpha^2}{Q}\right)^{1/5} \frac{\tilde{\nu}_0^{1/5}}{\tilde{\mu}_0}\, \tilde{h}\left[\left(\frac{2\alpha^2}{Q}\,\tilde{\nu}_0\right)^{1/5} t + \tau_0\right]$$

$$T = \left(\frac{2\alpha^2}{Q}\,\tilde{\nu}_0\right)^{-1/5} (\tilde{T} - \tau_0)$$

$$\phi^2 = \left(\frac{\alpha^2 Q^4}{2^4}\right)^{1/5} \frac{\tilde{\nu}_0^{1/5}}{\tilde{\mu}_0}\, \tilde{h}(\tau_0) \qquad (40A)$$

The effect of the modified boundary condition (38A) is to alter the stopping condition indicated in step (ii) of (55). The point τ_0 is no longer interpreted as a zero of $\tilde{\rho}(\tau)$, but instead as a zero of $\tilde{\lambda}(\tau)$. The rule then is to extrapolate back a total of $(N-1)$ additional zeros of $\tilde{\lambda}(t)$, using the rules for extrapolation of the characteristic function $\tilde{\rho}(t)$ given in (51).

Numerical results for the infinite time position smoothing problem $T \longrightarrow \infty$ have been obtained using the numerical approach of Section 7. The impulse response function of the optimal filter for $T \longrightarrow \infty$ is shown in Fig. 5. The performance of this filter is

$$\phi = 0.6572\,(\alpha Q^2)^{1/5}, \qquad (66)$$

and the maximum observation time is

$$T_{\max} = \pm 3.291 \left(\frac{Q}{\alpha^2}\right)^{1/5} \qquad (67)$$

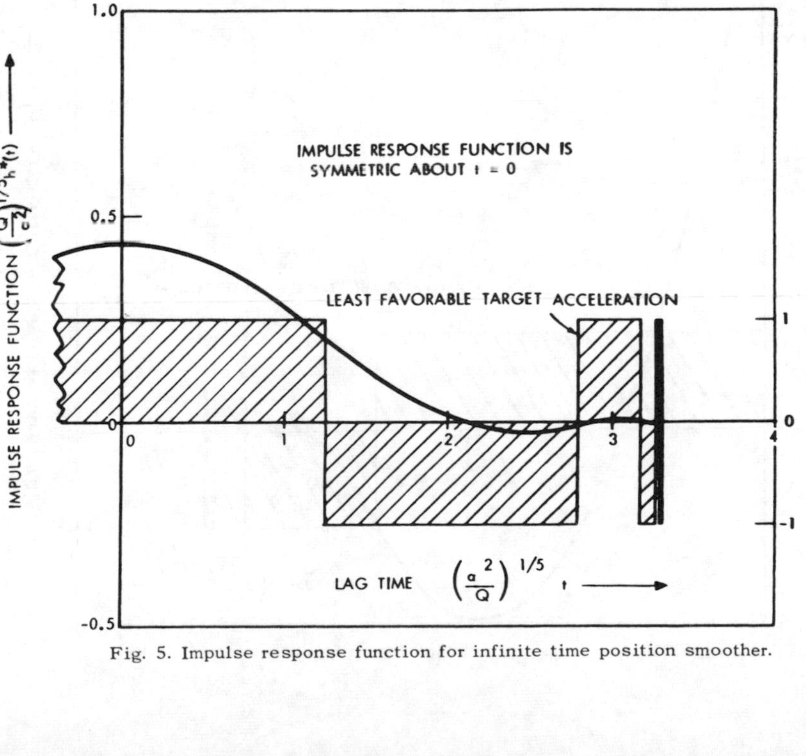

Fig. 5. Impulse response function for infinite time position smoother.

B. Velocity Filtering

The pertinent modifications of Sections 2 and 3 are

$$\hat{\dot{x}}(0) = \int_0^T h(\tau) z(-\tau)\, d\tau, \tag{2B}$$

$$\begin{aligned} \phi^2\{h, x\} &= \mathcal{E}_w\{[\hat{\dot{x}}(0) - \dot{x}(0)]^2\} \\ &= \left[\int_0^T h(\tau) x(-\tau)\, d\tau - \dot{x}(0)\right]^2 + Q\int_0^T [h(\tau)]^2\, d\tau, \end{aligned} \tag{5B}$$

$$H = \left\{ h(t) \,\middle|\, \begin{array}{l} \displaystyle\int_0^T \tau h(\tau)\, d\tau = -1 \\ \displaystyle\int_0^T h(\tau)\, d\tau = 0 \end{array} \right\}, \tag{12B}$$

with the definition for $\rho(\tau)$ left unchanged.

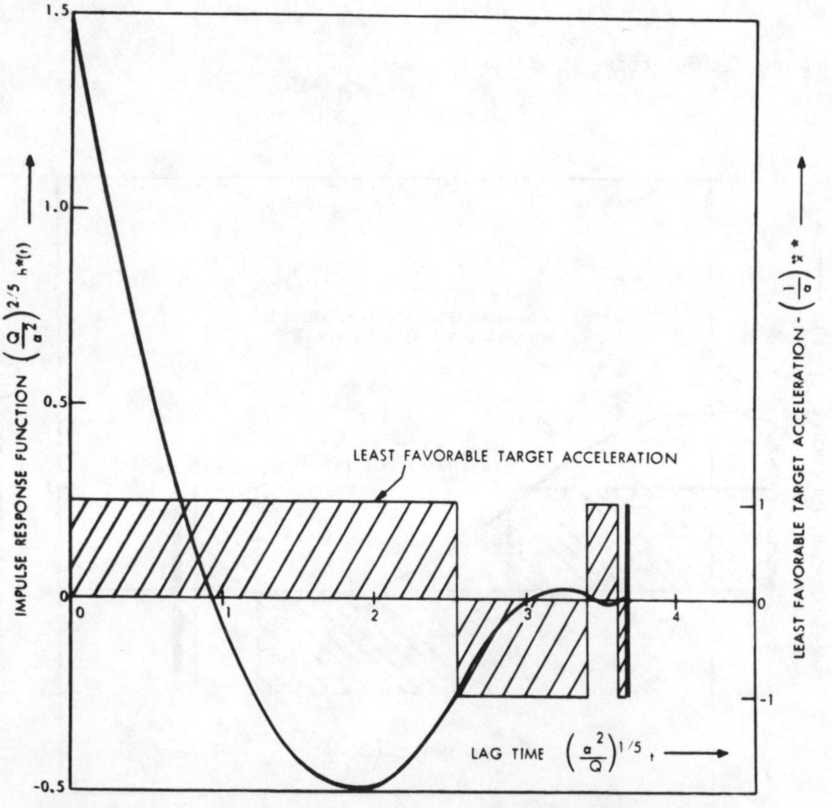

Fig. 6. Impulse response function for infinite time velocity filter.

The maximization over target maneuver yields the same result (20) obtained before.

In the minimization over filter design, the constraints on ρ_0^* and μ_0^* in (31) are replaced by

$$\left.\begin{array}{l}\rho_0^* = 0\\ \mu_0^* = 1\end{array}\right\} \Longrightarrow \left\{\begin{array}{l}\rho_0^* = -1\\ \mu_0^* = 0\end{array}\right. \tag{31B}$$

and in (38) by

$$\left.\begin{array}{l}\tilde{\rho}(\tau_0) = 0\\[2ex] \tilde{\mu}(\tau_0) = \dfrac{Q}{\varepsilon\Delta^3\alpha^2\nu_0^*}\end{array}\right\} \Longrightarrow \left\{\begin{array}{l}\tilde{\rho}(\tau_0) = -\dfrac{Q}{\varepsilon\Delta^4\alpha^2\nu_0^*}\\[2ex] \tilde{\mu}(\tau_0) = 0\end{array}\right. \tag{38B}$$

Integration of the integral on the right-hand side of (24) by parts this time yields

$$\phi^2 = Q\lambda^*(0). \tag{32B}$$

Similarly eqs. (39) and (40) become

$$\left.\begin{array}{l}\Delta = \left(\dfrac{\alpha^2}{Q}\tilde{\nu}_0\right)^{-1/5},\\[2ex] \nu_0^* = -\dfrac{\tilde{\nu}_0^{4/5}}{\varepsilon\tilde{\rho}_0}\left(\dfrac{Q}{\alpha^2}\right)^{1/5},\end{array}\right\} \tag{39B}$$

$$\left.\begin{array}{l}h^*(t) = -\left(\dfrac{\alpha^2}{Q}\right)^{2/5}\dfrac{\tilde{\nu}_0^{2/5}}{\tilde{\rho}_0}h\left[\left(\dfrac{\alpha^2}{Q}\tilde{\nu}_0\right)^{1/5}t + \tau_0\right],\\[2ex] T = \left(\dfrac{\alpha^2}{Q}\tilde{\nu}_0\right)^{-1/5}(\tilde{T} - \tau_0).\\[2ex] \phi^2 = (\alpha^3 Q)^{2/5}\dfrac{\tilde{\nu}_0^{3/5}}{(-\tilde{\rho}_0)}\tilde{\lambda}(\tau_0).\end{array}\right\} \tag{40B}$$

This time the value τ_0 corresponds to a zero of $\tilde{\mu}(\tau)$ in accordance with (38B). Solutions have been obtained for the infinite time velocity filtering problem $T \longrightarrow \infty$ using the numerical approach of Section 7. The impulse response function is sketched in Fig. 6. The performance is

$$\phi = 1.458\,(\alpha^3 Q)^{1/5}, \tag{68}$$

while the maximum observation time is

$$T_{\max} = 3.688\left(\frac{Q}{\alpha^2}\right)^{1/5} \tag{69}$$

C. Velocity Smoothing

Equations (2B), (5B), (12B), and (20) remain unchanged except for replacement of the lower limit of integration by "$-T$." The characteristic function $\rho(t)$ is the "two sided" function defined by eq. (11A).

Using an argument similar to that given in Appendix B for the position smoothing problem, it is found that the optimal filter for the velocity smoothing problem is anti-symmetric:

$$h^*(t) = \begin{cases} \frac{1}{2} h'(t); & 0 < t \leq T \\ -\frac{1}{2} h'(-t); & -T \leq t < 0. \end{cases} \tag{70}$$

The performance index (10) then becomes

$$\phi^2\{h^*, x^*\} = \left[\int_0^T \rho'(\tau)\ddot{x}^*(-\tau)d\tau\right]^2 + \frac{1}{2}Q \int_0^T [h'(\tau)]^2 d\tau. \tag{10C}$$

The second of the two constraints on $h(t)$ automatically disappears, and (12B) becomes

$$H = \left\{h'(t) \,\middle|\, \int_0^T \tau h'(\tau)d\tau = -1\right\}. \tag{12C}$$

Equations (10C), (12C), (19), and (20) are identical to those for the velocity smoothing problem, except for: i) the absence of the second constraint in (12B); and ii) the change of parameter $Q \Longrightarrow \frac{1}{2}Q$. Because of i), the boundary conditions in (31B) and (38B) become

$$\left.\begin{matrix} \rho_0^* = -1 \\ \mu_0^* = 0 \end{matrix}\right\} \Longrightarrow \left\{\begin{matrix} \rho_0^* = -1 \\ h_0^* = 0, \end{matrix}\right. \tag{31C}$$

$$\left.\begin{matrix} \tilde{\rho}(\tau_0) = -\dfrac{Q}{\varepsilon\Delta^4\alpha^2\nu_0^*} \\ \tilde{\mu}(\tau_0) = 0 \end{matrix}\right\} \Longrightarrow \left\{\begin{matrix} \tilde{\rho}(\tau_0) = -\dfrac{Q}{\varepsilon\Delta^4\alpha^2\nu_0^*} \\ \tilde{h}(\tau_0) = 0 \end{matrix}\right. \tag{38C}$$

Similarly, the filter equations and performance index are obtained by replacing Q by $1/2\ Q$ in (40B) and dividing $h^*(t)$ by 2 according to (70):

$$h^*(t) = -h^*(-t) = -\frac{1}{2}\left(\frac{2\alpha^2}{Q}\right)^{2/5} \frac{\tilde{\nu}_0^{2/5}}{\tilde{\rho}_0} \tilde{h}\left[\left(\frac{2\alpha^2}{Q}\tilde{\nu}_0\right)^{1/5} t + \tau_0\right],$$

$$T = \left(\frac{2\alpha^2}{Q}\tilde{\nu}_0\right)^{-1/5} (\tilde{T} - \tau_0), \tag{40C}$$

$$\phi^2 = \left(\frac{\alpha^3 Q}{2}\right)^{2/5} \frac{\tilde{\nu}_0^{3/5}}{(-\tilde{\rho}_0)} \tilde{\lambda}(\tau_0).$$

The stopping value τ_0 is obtained as a zero of $\tilde{h}(\tau)$. The solution for the optimal filter, based on the numerical solution of Section 7 for $T \longrightarrow \infty$, is sketched in Fig. 7. The performance is

$$\phi = 0.8089\,(\alpha^3 Q)^{1/5}, \tag{71}$$

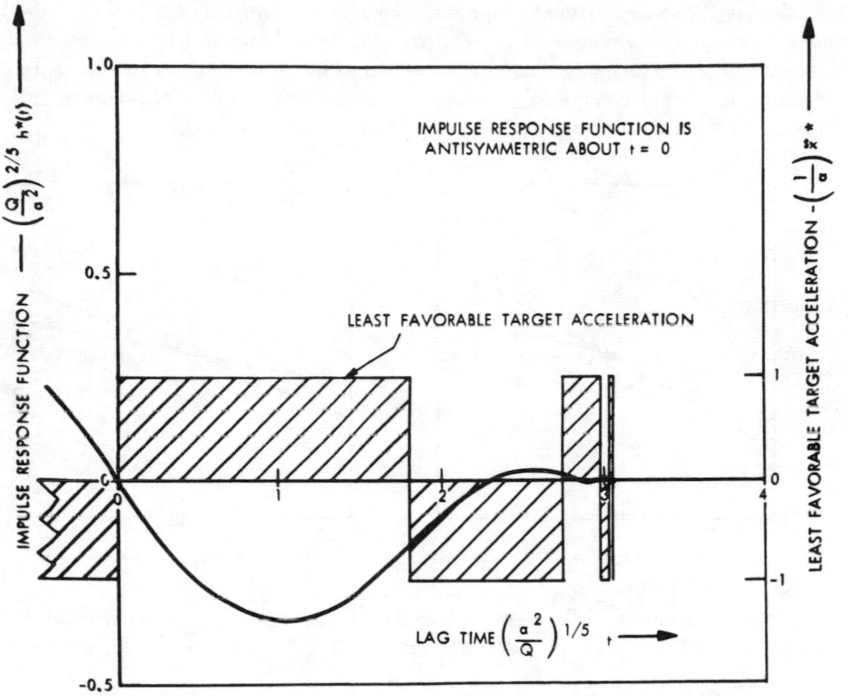

Fig. 7. Impulse response function for infinite time velocity smoother.

while the maximum observation time is

$$T_{\max} = \pm 3.049 \left(\frac{Q}{\alpha^2}\right)^{1/5}. \tag{72}$$

9. SENSITIVITY OF MINIMAX FILTER TO CHANGES—OR ERRORS—IN KNOWLEDGE OF DESIGN PARAMETERS

Effect of Changes in α and Q

Let us specialize to the infinite time case $T \longrightarrow \infty$ and define the sensitivity ratio

$$\frac{\phi}{\phi_0} = \frac{\text{rms error for acceleration bound } \alpha \text{ and noise } Q}{\text{rms error for acceleration bound } \alpha_0 \text{ and noise } Q_0}. \tag{73}$$

Values for this ratio are computed using the third of eqs. (40) in Section 5, and of eqs. (40A, B. C) in Section 8:

$$\left.\begin{aligned} \frac{\phi}{\phi_0} &= \left(\frac{\alpha}{\alpha_0}\right)^{1/5} \left(\frac{Q}{Q_0}\right)^{2/5}; \quad \text{position filtering or smoothing,} \\ \frac{\phi}{\phi_0} &= \left(\frac{\alpha}{\alpha_0}\right)^{3/5} \left(\frac{Q}{Q_0}\right)^{1/5}; \quad \text{velocity filtering or smoothing.} \end{aligned}\right\} \tag{74}$$

Sketches of these sensitivity ratios with respect to changes in α (with fixed Q) and with respect to changes in Q (with fixed α) are shown in Fig. 8. The most sensitive of these ratios is that for the effect of changes in α on the estimate of velocity: A tenfold change in α is seen to produce only a fourfold change in ϕ. These ratios are fairly insensitive to changes in either α or Q.

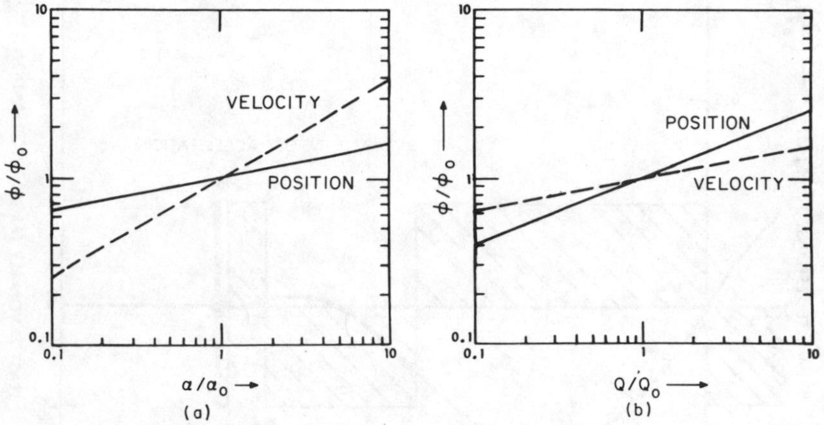

Fig. 8. Sensitivity of rms error to changes in α and Q. (a) Sensitivity of α. (b) Sensitivity to Q.

Effect of Errors in Knowledge of α

The acceleration bound α must be specified by the designer. In most applications its value will be chosen subjectively. The errors resulting from incorrect choice of the bound are therefore of interest.

Let us again specialize to the case of infinite observation times $T \longrightarrow \infty$, and define

$$\phi(\alpha;\alpha_0) = \text{Realized rms error when estimator is designed using wrong acceleration bound } \alpha_0\text{, when true bound is } \alpha. \tag{75}$$

Consider the ratios:

$$\frac{\phi(\alpha;\alpha_0)}{\phi(\alpha_0;\alpha_0)} = \frac{\text{actual rms performance}}{\text{rms performance computed on basis of wrong acceleration bound}},$$
$$\frac{\phi(\alpha;\alpha_0)}{\phi(\alpha;\alpha)} = \frac{\text{actual rms performance}}{\text{rms performance obtainable if true acceleration bound } \alpha \text{ were known}}. \tag{76}$$

The first of these ratios describes how the actual estimation error compares with the computed error determined on the basis of the wrong acceleration bound α_0. The second ratio describes how the actual estimation error compares with what the error would have been if the true bound α were known.

Expressions for computing the ratios (76) will now be derived: Let us denote the optimal value of $\rho(t)$ computed on the basis of an arbitrary acceleration bound

α^* by the notation $\rho^*(t)$. As a result of the work of Section 5, it is known that the solution for all other values of the acceleration bound α_0 may be computed as a renormalization of $\rho^*(t)$, having the general form

$$\rho(t) = \frac{1}{b}\,\rho^*(\xi t). \tag{77}$$

The coefficient b is readily evaluated: According to eqs. (31), (65), (31B), and (31C), *both* $\rho(t)$ and $\rho^*(t)$ in (77) must satisfy the boundary conditions shown in Table 4. A simple analysis shows that b and ξ are related by

$$b = \begin{cases} \xi; & \text{position filtering and smoothing,} \\ 1; & \text{velocity filtering and smoothing.} \end{cases} \tag{78}$$

TABLE 4. BOUNDARY CONDITIONS ON $\rho(t)$

	BOUNDARY CONDITIONS	
Position Filtering:	$\dot{\rho}(0) = -1$	$\rho(0) = 0$
Position Smoothing:	$\dot{\rho}(0) = -1$	$\dddot{\rho}(0) = 0$
Velocity Filtering:	$\rho(0) = -1$	$\dot{\rho}(0) = 0$
Velocity Smoothing:	$\rho(0) = -1$	$\ddot{\rho}(0) = 0$

Defining

$$k = \begin{cases} 1; & \text{position filtering and smoothing} \\ 0; & \text{velocity filtering and smoothing,} \end{cases} \tag{79}$$

the characteristic function (77) may be written as

$$\rho(t) = \frac{1}{\xi^k}\,\rho^*(\xi t). \tag{80}$$

Clearly [see eq. (31)], the corresponding $h(t)$ must have the form

$$h(t) = \xi^{2-k}\,h^*(\xi t). \tag{81}$$

The performance index resulting from an arbitrary filter design $h(t)$, when the acceleration bound is α, and the noise power density is Q may be obtained by carrying out the maximization implied by eq. (7). The result of this maximization is given by eq. (20). Substituting this expression into (10) yields the performance evaluation†

†Equation (82) is the performance expression for the real-time estimation case. The analogous result for non-real-time estimation is obtained by changing the limits of integration to $(-\infty, \infty)$, in this and all subsequent derivations.

$$\phi^2\{h\} = \alpha^2 \left[\int_0^\infty |\rho(t)|\,dt\right]^2 + Q\int_0^\infty [h(t)]^2 dt, \tag{82}$$

for the case of infinite observation times: $T \longrightarrow \infty$.

To evaluate the parameter ξ, let us substitute (80–81) into (82), replace α by α_0, and change the variable of integration as follows:

$$\phi^2\{h\} = \frac{\alpha_0^2}{\xi^{2k+2}}\left[\int_0^\infty |\rho^*(\tau)|\,d\tau\right]^2 + Q\,\xi^{3-2k}\int_0^\infty [h^*(\tau)]^2 d\tau. \tag{83}$$

This expression must clearly be a minimum with respect to variation of ξ:

$$0 = \frac{\partial\phi^2}{\partial\xi} = -(2+2k)\frac{\alpha_0^2}{\xi^{2k+3}}\left[\int_0^\infty |\rho^*(\tau)|\,d\tau\right]^2 + (3-2k)\,Q\,\xi^{2-2k}\int_0^\infty [h^*(\tau)]^2 d\tau. \tag{84}$$

By definition $\rho^*(t)$ is the optimal solution corresponding to the bound α^*. In the event that $\alpha_0 = \alpha^*$, the solution to (83) must correspond to $\xi = 1$. It follows from (84) that

$$\int_0^\infty [h^*(\tau)]^2 d\tau = \left(\frac{2+2k}{3-2k}\right)\frac{(\alpha^*)^2}{Q}\left[\int_0^\infty |\rho^*(\tau)|\,d\tau\right]^2. \tag{85}$$

Substituting this back into (84) and solving for ξ, results in:

$$\xi = \left(\frac{\alpha_0}{\alpha^*}\right)^{2/5}. \tag{86}$$

Let us now compute the quantity defined in (75). Substituting (80)–(81), (85), and (86) into (82) and evaluating, yields

$$\phi^2\{\alpha;\alpha_0\} = \left[\alpha^2 + \left(\frac{2+2k}{3-2k}\right)\alpha_0^2\right]\left(\frac{\alpha^*}{\alpha_0}\right)^{(4k+4)/5}\left[\int_0^\infty |\rho^*(\tau)|\,d\tau\right]^2. \tag{87}$$

The ratios (76) now become:

$$\frac{\phi(\alpha;\alpha_0)}{\phi(\alpha_0;\alpha_0)} = \begin{cases} \sqrt{\dfrac{1}{5}\left[4 + \left(\dfrac{\alpha}{\alpha_0}\right)^2\right]}; & \text{position filtering and smoothing} \\ \sqrt{\dfrac{1}{5}\left[2 + 3\left(\dfrac{\alpha}{\alpha_0}\right)^2\right]}; & \text{velocity filtering and smoothing} \end{cases} \tag{88}$$

$$\frac{\phi(\alpha;\alpha_0)}{\phi(\alpha,\alpha)} = \begin{cases} \left(\dfrac{\alpha_0}{\alpha}\right)^{1/5}\sqrt{\dfrac{1}{5}\left[4 + \left(\dfrac{\alpha}{\alpha_0}\right)^2\right]}; & \text{position filtering and smoothing} \\ \left(\dfrac{\alpha_0}{\alpha}\right)^{3/5}\sqrt{\dfrac{1}{5}\left[2 + 3\left(\dfrac{\alpha}{\alpha_0}\right)^2\right]}; & \text{velocity filtering and smoothing} \end{cases} \tag{89}$$

Sketches of these ratios are shown in Fig. 9. The curves for the ratio $\phi(\alpha;\alpha_0)/\phi(\alpha;\alpha)$ show a very broad minimum. Performance of the minimax estimator is relatively insensitive to errors as large as 100–200 per cent in knowledge of α.

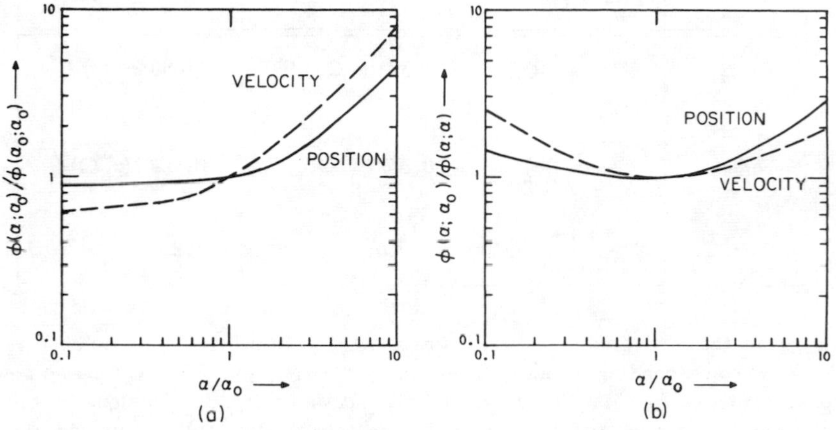

Fig. 9. Sensitivity of rms error to wrong choice of acceleration bound. (a) Ratio of realized performance to performance predicted on basis of incorrect acceleration bound. (b) Ratio of realized performance to performance obtainable if true acceleration bound were known.

10. SUMMARY AND DISCUSSION OF RESULTS

Optimal Design

The optimal minimax estimator for position filtering, and its performance, have been obtained as a function of available observation time T. A graph of the maximum rms error for this estimator vs T is shown in Fig. 2. Graphs of the filter impulse response function for different values of T are shown in Figs. 3a-f. The impulse response function is found to terminate with a maximum observation time $T = T_{max}$. Thus the impulse response function for $T \geq T_{max}$ is the same as that for $T = T_{max}$. A sketch of the "limiting" response function for $T \geq T_{max}$ is shown in Fig. 3f. The optimal "least favorable" target acceleration for each of the filters of Figs. 3a-f, is also shown. For $T \geq T_{max}$, this solution is a chatter solution with a limit point at $T = T_{max}$. The equation defining the position filter impulse response function is the first of eqs. (40).

Optimal estimators have also been obtained for cases of position smoothing, velocity filtering, and velocity smoothing, in the limit of infinite observation time: $T \longrightarrow \infty$. Sketches of the impulse response functions for these estimators are shown in Figs. 5, 6, and 7, respectively. The performances of the three estimators, along with that of the infinite time position filter, are summarized in Table 5.

Suboptimal Design

It is found that the rms performance of the optimal (infinite time) position filter can be realized to within one part in 10^4 using a "suboptimal" filter, de-

TABLE 5.
PERFORMANCE INDEX FOR POSITION AND VELOCITY ESTIMATORS
— MAXIMUM RMS ERROR — ϕ

	Observation Interval	Position	Velocity
Filtering:	$(-\infty, 0)$	$1.321\,(\alpha Q^2)^{1/5}$	$1.458\,(\alpha^3 Q)^{1/5}$
Smoothing:	$(-\infty, \infty)$	$0.6572\,(\alpha Q^2)^{1/5}$	$0.8089\,(\alpha^3 Q)^{1/5}$
Ratios:	$\dfrac{\phi \text{ Filtering}}{\phi \text{ Smoothing}}$	2.010	1.803

signed for the restricted observation interval $(-T_1, 0)$, where T_1 is the observation time corresponding to the parameterization $[\zeta, N] = [0, 1]$. The impulse response function for this filter is graphically shown in Fig. 3c. Designs for other suboptimal filters, especially adapted to digital computer applications and to realization with lumped circuit elements, will be found in reference 14.

Sensitivity

Curves showing the sensitivity of the minimax filter to changes in the choice of design parameters α and Q are shown in Fig. 8. The effect of errors in the designer's knowledge of the acceleration bound α is shown in Fig. 9. These curves are important because the bound is usually chosen subjectively, hence an accurate value cannot be obtained. The right-hand side of Fig. 9 shows that the minimum of the sensitivity curve with respect to knowledge of α is quite broad. Hence, the performance of the minimax filter is relatively insensitive to the choice of bound.

APPENDIX A: ANALYSIS OF OVERLAP IN $[\zeta, N]$ PARAMETERIZATION

Tables 1 and 2 reveal an apparent overlap in the $[\zeta, N]$ parameterization such that the pairs $[0, N]$ and $[\infty, N+1]$ correspond to identical values for the performance index, ϕ, and observation time, T. It is the purpose of this appendix to show analytically that the performance index and observation time corresponding to these two parameterizations are, in fact, equal, and that the corresponding fil ters are identical.

Let us begin with the solution for the parameterization $[\zeta, N+1]$, and denote the corresponding normalized characteristic function by $\tilde{\rho}_{N+1}(\tau)$. To fix ideas, a rough sketch of the last three oscillations of $\tilde{\rho}_{N+1}(\tau)$ is shown in the upper part of Fig. 10. Let us perform a *renormalization* of $\tilde{\rho}_{N+1}(\tau)$ to bring its Nth oscillation down into the unit interval $(-1, 0)$ in such a manner that the Nth oscillation satisfies the standard requirements (46), (50), and (52). This renormalized func-

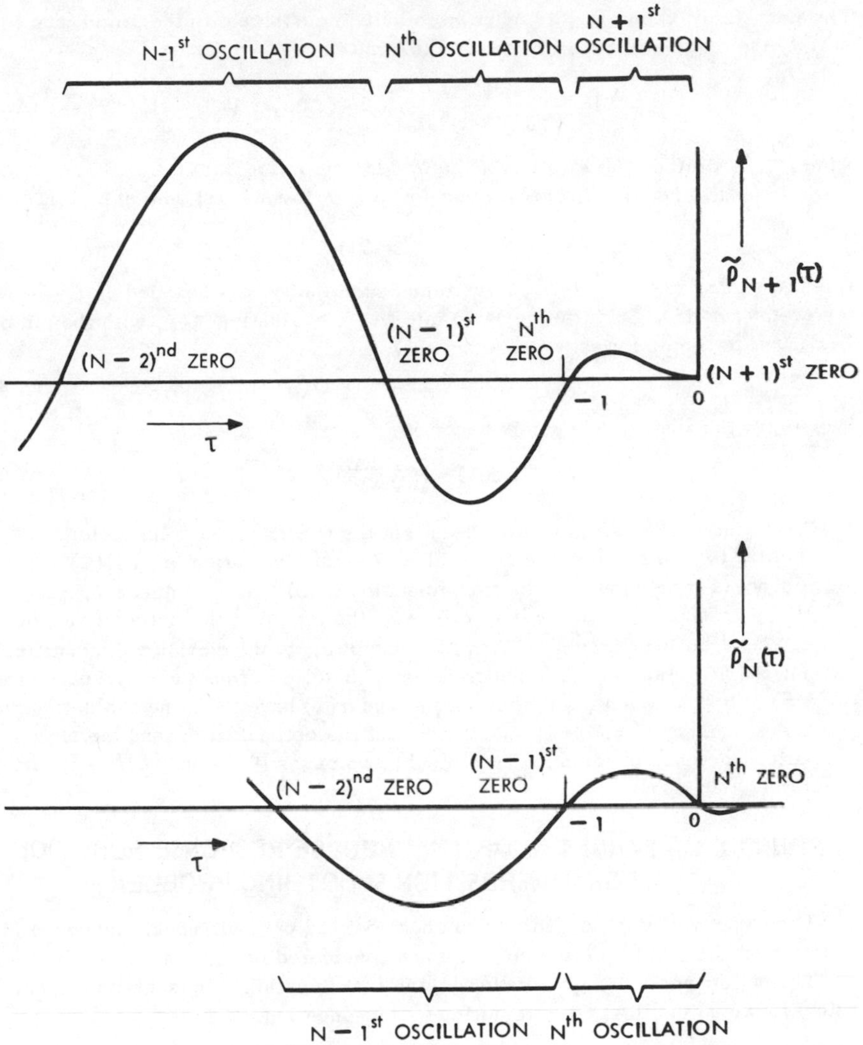

Fig. 10. Renormalization of the solution $[\zeta, N+1]$.

tion will be denoted by $\widetilde{\rho}_N(\tau)$ and is sketched in the lower part of Fig. 10. The renormalization is performed as follows:

The $N+1$st oscillation of $\widetilde{\rho}_{N+1}(\tau)$ is given by eq. (53). The expression for the Nth oscillation of $\widetilde{\rho}_{N+1}(\tau)$ is obtained by expanding (53) in powers of $\tau+1$ (i.e., about the point $\tau = -1$), and reversing the sign of the coefficient on $(\tau+1)^4$. Thus

$$\widetilde{\rho}_{N+1}(\tau) = \frac{1}{24}[(\zeta+1)(\tau+1) - (2\zeta+3)(\tau+1)^2 + (\zeta+3)(\tau+1)^3 + (\tau+1)^4]. \quad \text{(A.1)}$$

The normalization on $\widetilde{\rho}_{N+1}(\tau)$ required to shift the Nth zero to the origin, and to satisfy the requirements (46), (50), and (52), is

$$\widetilde{\rho}_N(\tau) = \frac{-1}{(\tau_{N-1}+1)^4}\, \widetilde{\rho}_{N+1}\,[-(\tau_{N-1}+1)\,\tau - 1], \tag{A.2}$$

where τ_{N-1} defines the location of the $N-1$st zero of $\widetilde{\rho}_{N+1}(\tau)$.

It is readily verified from (A.1) that for large ζ the $N-1$st zero of $\widetilde{\rho}_{N+1}(\tau)$ is

$$\tau_{N-1} = -\zeta + O(1), \tag{A.3}$$

where the remainder $y = O(x)$ denotes terms such that y/x is bounded as $\zeta \longrightarrow \infty$ (see reference 15). Substituting (A.1) into (A.2), evaluating τ_{N-1} with the aid of (A.3), and retaining lowest-order terms only, yields

$$\widetilde{\rho}_N(\tau) = -\tfrac{1}{24}\,\tau^3(1+\tau) + O(\zeta^{-1}). \tag{A.4}$$

Passing to the limit $\zeta \longrightarrow \infty$ this becomes,

$$\lim_{\zeta\to\infty} \widetilde{\rho}_N(\tau) = -\tfrac{1}{24}\,\tau^3(1+\tau). \tag{A.5}$$

Comparing (A.5) with (53), it is seen that the renormalized solution for $\zeta = \infty$ is *identical* to (53) for the case $\zeta = 0$. The $N+1$st oscillation of $\widetilde{\rho}_{N+1}(\tau)$, on the other hand, is transformed by the transformation (A.2) into the interval $\tau = (0, \zeta^{-1} + O(\zeta^{-2}))$. In the limit $\zeta \longrightarrow \infty$, the length of this interval vanishes and the contribution of the $N+1$st oscillation of $\widetilde{\rho}_N$ to the normalized quantities $\widetilde{\nu}_0$, $\widetilde{\mu}_0$, and $\widetilde{h}(\tau)$ [see eq. (55)] becomes zero. It follows from the correspondence of (A.5) with (53), when $\zeta = 0$, that $\widetilde{\nu}_0$, $\widetilde{\mu}_0$, and $\widetilde{h}(\tau)$ have the same evaluations in the cases $[0, N]$ and $[\infty, N+1]$, and hence that the optimal filter, and therefore its performance and observation time for the two cases $[0, N]$ and $[\infty, N+1]$, are identical.

APPENDIX B: SYMMETRY OF THE IMPULSE RESPONSE FUNCTION FOR THE POSITION SMOOTHING PROBLEM

The purpose of this appendix is to show that the optimal impulse response function for the position smoothing problem considered in Section 8 is symmetric.

The performance of a given filter design $h(t)$ is obtained by substituting eq. (20A) for $\ddot{x}(-t)$ in (10A). The resulting performance index is

$$\phi^2\{h\} = \alpha^2 \left[\int_{-T}^{T} |\rho(\tau)|\, d\tau\right]^2 + Q \int_{-T}^{T} [h(\tau)]^2\, d\tau, \tag{B.1}$$

where $\rho(\tau)$ is defined in terms of $h(\tau)$ by eq. (11A).

The proof is by contradiction. Let us assume that the optimal impulse response function $h^*(t)$ is nonsymmetric:

$$h^*(t) \neq h^*(-t); \quad \text{over a region of nonzero measure.} \tag{B.2}$$

Let us then define the new filter

$$h(t) = \tfrac{1}{2}\,[h^*(t) + h^*(-t)]. \tag{B.3}$$

It is readily verified that if $h^*(t)$ satisfies the constraints (12A), then $h(t)$ does also. In addition, it can be shown [from eq. (11A)] that the characteristic function corresponding to $h(t)$ can be written in terms of the characteristic function for $h^*(t)$ according to

$$\rho(t) = \frac{1}{2}[\rho^*(t) + \rho^*(-t)]. \tag{B.4}$$

Substituting (B.3)–(B.4) into (B.1) and using the relations

$$|a + b| \leq |a| + |b|$$
$$(A + B)^2 = 2(A^2 + B^2) - (A - B)^2, \tag{B.5}$$

yields

$$\phi^2\{h\} = \frac{\alpha^2}{4}\left[\int_{-T}^{T} |\rho^*(\tau) + \rho^*(-\tau)|\, d\tau\right]^2 + \frac{Q}{4}\int_{-T}^{T} [h^*(\tau) + h^*(-\tau)]^2\, d\tau$$

$$\leq \frac{\alpha^2}{4}\left[\int_{-T}^{T} |\rho^*(\tau)|\, d\tau + \int_{-T}^{T} |\rho^*(-\tau)|\, d\tau\right]^2$$

$$+ \frac{Q}{2}\int_{-T}^{T} [h^*(\tau)^2 + h^*(-\tau)^2]\, d\tau - \frac{Q}{4}\int_{-T}^{T} [h^*(\tau) - h^*(-\tau)]^2\, d\tau$$

$$= \alpha^2\left[\int_{-T}^{T} |\rho^*(\tau)|\, d\tau\right]^2 + Q\int_{-T}^{T} [h^*(\tau)]^2\, d\tau$$

$$- \frac{Q}{4}\int_{-T}^{T} [h^*(\tau) - h^*(-\tau)]^2\, d\tau$$

$$= \phi^2\{h^*\} - \frac{Q}{4}\int_{-T}^{T} [h^*(\tau) - h^*(-\tau)]^2\, d\tau. \tag{B.6}$$

According to (B.2), the last integral in (B.6) is non-zero. It follows that strict inequality holds:

$$\phi^2\{h\} < \phi^2\{h^*\}, \tag{B.7}$$

and that, contrary to assumption, the nonsymmetric filter $h^*(t)$ cannot be optimum.

ACKNOWLEDGMENTS

The author wishes to express his appreciation to colleagues at the Sylvania Applied Research Laboratory for their patience and helpful criticisms during course of the work reported here. Special thanks are owed to Dr. Walter H. Ku for discussions and comments through much of the formulative stages of the analysis, and to Professors Arthur E. Bryson, Jr., and Y. C. Ho, of Harvard University, for pointing out several simplifications and corrections in the final manuscript.

REFERENCES

1. J. H. Laning and R. H. Battin, *Random Processes in Automatic Control* (New York: McGraw-Hill, 1956).

2. F. W. Nesline, Jr., "Polynomial Filtering of Signals," *Proc. Conv. on Military Electronics*, 1961, pp. 531–542.

3. R. E. Kalman and R. S. Bucy, "New Results in Linear Filtering and Prediction Theory," *ASME Trans., J. Basic Engineering*, **83D**, pp. 95–108 (March 1961).

4. D. E. Johansen, "Solution of a Linear Mean Square Estimation Problem When Process Statistics are Undefined," *Proc. 1965 Joint Automatic Control Conf.*, Troy, N.Y., June 22–25, 1965, pp. 64–75.

5. L. A. Zadeh, "General Filters for Separation of Signal and Noise," *Proc. Symp. on Information Networks* (Brooklyn, New York: Polytechnic Press, Polytechnic Institute of Brooklyn, 1954), pp. 31–49.

6. D. Middleton, *Introduction to Statistical Communication Theory* (New York: McGraw-Hill, 1960).

7. M. C. Yovits and J. L. Jackson, "Linear Filter Optimization with Game Theory Considerations," *IRE National Convention Record*, Part 4, 1955, pp. 193–199.

8. A. G. Carlton and J. W. Follin, Jr., "Recent Developments in Fixed and Adaptive Filtering," *Second Guided Missile Seminar*, Venice, Italy, Sept. 1956, *AGARDograph 21*, p. 285–300, Advisory Group for Aeronautical Research and Development, Paris.

9. S. Zahl, "The Linear Prediction of Deterministic Signals," *IEEE Trans. on Information Theory*, **IT-10**, pp. 222–226 (July 1964).

10. R. Isaacs, *Differential Games* (New York: Wiley, 1965).

11. J. VonNeumann, and O. Morgenstern, *Theory of Games and Economic Behavior* (Princeton, N.J.: Princeton University Press, 1955), pp. 95–96.

12. C. A. Desoer, "The 'Bang-Bang' Servo Problem Treated by Variational Techniques," *Information and Control*, **2**, pp. 333–348 (December 1959).

13. Bliss, G. A., *Lectures on the Calculus of Variations* (Chicago: University of Chicago Press, 1961) p. 189.

14. D. E. Johansen and W. H. Ku, "On the Design of Optimal Filters for Separating Signal from Noise," Research Report No. 437, Applied Research Laboratory, Sylvania Electronic Systems, Waltham, Massachusetts, 1965, (in preparation).

15. A. Erdelyi, *Asymptotic Expansions* (New York: Dover Publications, 1956) p. 5.

SYSTEM ENGINEERING

John G. Truxal
Department of Electrical Engineering
Polytechnic Institute of Brooklyn, Brooklyn, N. Y.

Model formulation and evaluation, encompassing selection of system performance measures, is the focus of both defense-space and industrial engineering applications of modern system theory. Meaningful modelling techniques reflect both process dynamics (including signal characteristics) and the constraints imposed by system design procedures and computer capabilities. Specifically, global design approaches rest upon such factors as the applicability of stability and sensitivity theories to the system model. The extension of direct digital control by broadening the scope included within the process requires corresponding simplification of the component dynamical models. Applications to both defense-space and traffic-control systems illustrate the current system design limitation.

If engineering is concerned with the understanding and design of artifacts, one might wonder why a paper on *system engineering* would be included in a symposium on system theory—why the symposium co-chairmen, Professors Drenick and Shaw, would have listed the present author in the program. Possibly this situation is related to the happenstance of our temporary, relative positions in the admininstrative system of the Polytechnic Institute. Hopefully, however, it is because system theory, as it evolves in the future, must be guided and structured by real problems—by the basic objective of understanding these artifacts which are the results of modern engineering and the systems which have evolved in nature and in our sociological structure. If the fundamental purpose of the symposium is to influence the system theory of the future, the objective of these comments is to indicate a few of the significant problems which should guide the development of this theory.

In the following paragraphs, therefore, we will discuss briefly two general, systems-type engineering problems and indicate certain significant elements of these problems. The paper concludes with a discussion of certain basic components of system engineering, as those components are illuminated by the two illustrative problems. Hopefully, from these comments will emerge a definition of system engineering and an indication of the relationship between system engineering and the system theory discussed in the preceding papers.

Example 1

The first example is a system which is now thoroughly familiar: the X-15 aircraft.[1] Discussion and planning of the X-15 dates from 1952; in 1954 studies in depth were undertaken; the development-test program began in 1959. During the past six years, 92 per cent of the flights have been successful; research and de-

Presented at the Symposium on System Theory
Polytechnic Institute of Brooklyn, April 20, 21, 22, 1965

velopment work are continuing at this time, with regular reports to industry and the engineering community and frequent additions to the scope of the research program.

The X-15, the first hypersonic airplane, was designed to investigate the aerodynamic flight corridor to speeds of Mach 7 and the characteristics of space-equivalent flight at altitudes well above the flight corridor. Hypersonic flight, in general, refers to speeds in the region where the friction of air flowing along a surface raises the air temperature to very high values (e.g., greater than 2500°F). It is the region of multiple shock waves and interference effects, where analysis involves both aerodynamics and thermodynamics.

The successful design of the X-15 *system* required the interdependent studies of a number of major subsystems. The complexity of the system-engineering problem in this case is apparent if we consider just a few of these elements of the over-all system problems. Before citing these, however, we should emphasize that the most interesting characteristic of the following list is the interlocking feature: the fact that the separate elements cannot in reality be easily separated, that design decisions in each facet markedly influence the nature and complexity of other facets. We cite here only ten of the many system elements.

1. *Flight dynamics.* Over the flight regime of the X-15, there are radical changes in the environment. System parameters were largely unknown at the outset of the program, and uncertainty existed as to the possibility of extrapolating experimental results obtained from the very small, high-speed wind tunnels. In the flights of the X-15, transient behavior is of prime importance because of the rapidity of environmental changes, yet the largest body of knowledge on flight dynamics was concerned with steady-state conditions. The X-15 is still unstable under certain operating conditions, although a major result of the test program has been the determination of various stability boundaries.

2. *Stability and control problem.* The achievement of pilot control of the aircraft under all g conditions and the successful utilization of the self-adaptive autopilot are the contributions of the X-15 program which are most familiar to the control and systems engineer.

3. *Flight simulator and centrifuge.* The manned-flight simulation program of NASA, as a whole, is among the most impressive of the experimental efforts, with over $40 million already invested in simulators for research (entirely apart from the Gemini and Apollo program facilities), and with the simulators in several cases tied in with extensive digital computing equipment for representation of flight dynamics and control system characteristics. The X-15 program has been characterized by a similar extensive and extremely elegant simulation, with the centrifuge coupled to the simulator for the investigation of pilot controllability under a $5g$ field. The pilots spend up to ten hours on the simulator in preparation for each flight.

4. *Aerothermoelasticity properties.* The characteristics of the three preceding paragraphs are directly influenced by the flutter problems and the distortion of the aircraft surfaces resulting from thermal expansion.

5. *Instrumentation.* The development of the X-15 created a host of fundamental, novel instrumentation problems. Because of the desire to operate the aircraft in a near-vacuum environment, an inertial system was selected for determination of speed, altitude, and rate of altitude change, as well as roll, pitch, and yaw relative to the earth. The system is aligned and stabilized before the launch of the X-15 from the B-52. For control, the pilot requires an indication of angle of attack and yaw. As one example of instrumentation development: in order to measure angle of attack at very low and very high pressures and at air temperatures up to 2500°F, the X-15 utilizes a novel scheme. A 6.5-inch-diameter sphere in the airplane nose has orifices aligned by a high-gain servo system so that the sphere is rotated into the face of the entering air.

6. *Pilot ejection and safety system.* Although ejection is not possible at the extreme of the flight regime, the system is provided for rapid and safe ejection under all other circumstances. The efficacy of this portion of the complete system is confirmed by the pilot safety record, in spite of several mishaps during flight and landing.

7. *Landing system.* The complexity of the landing problem is apparent from the nature of the descent glide, which involves a rate of altitude change of 30,000 feet/minute.

8. *Pressure suits.* A major research and development program was required before pressure suits were available with sufficient mobility to permit pilot functioning throughout the flight regime.

9. *Biomedical aspects.* In the public eye, the biomedical aspects of the X-15 program have been dwarfed by the results of the Gemini program, but the X-15 provided important results (albeit of short duration) on man's behavior in the zero-*g* and high-*g* environments. The program yielded certain unanticipated results as well: e.g., during flight the heart rates were never below 145, and rose as high as 185. Found to be largely the result of psychological factors, such heart rates are now accepted as normal.

10. *Data analysis.* Finally, each flight results in more than four miles of taped data.

The preceding paragraphs indicate the breadth of the over-all system problem, as well as several significant facets of the system-development task. In the sense of most of the preceding papers, only items (1), (2), (3), (5), and (10) directly involve the dynamical modelling which has become such an important element of system theory. The other facets, however, significantly affect both the parameters of the models which are constructed, and the manner in which these models are utilized in analysis and design.

Example 2

As a second and quite different example of system engineering, we can consider an elementary problem drawn from the field of traffic control. Those of us

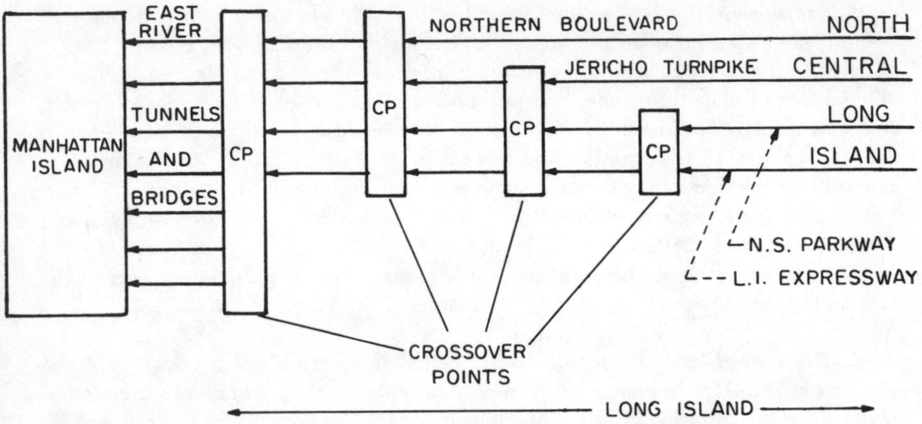

Fig. 1. Highly simplified model of the Manhattan-bound traffic arteries from north shore of Long Island.

who drove from northern Long Island into New York for this symposium encountered the situation depicted very roughly in Fig. 1. The four primary arteries toward the city are indicated. At several locations, the city-bound driver is confronted with the opportunity to switch arteries without loss of time. Unfortunately, each decision of this nature must be made by the driver with practically no useful information as to traffic flow conditions to the next switchover point. The only bases available for guiding the decision are the driver's observation of the traffic around him, his knowledge (if any) of probable flow patterns from the experience of previous days, and occasionally semivaluable observations from a broadcasting helicopter pilot.

The inability of the driver to make an intelligent decision (or even a hopeful guess) is coupled with the absence of any external control. The two failures are made even more poignant by the critical nature of traffic flow on the main arteries in an urban area. We have all learned from sad experience that the stability situation in traffic flow is a very critical one: as soon as the density of cars reaches a critical value the rate of flow drops very rapidly. Alternatively, the departure of very few cars from an expressway can yield an increase in average speed from 25 to 50 miles per hour.

The stability situation has been recognized and the system engineering modified accordingly by the Port Authority in New York at the Holland Tunnel, where traffic lights at the tunnel entrance (after the toll gate) limit the maximum number of cars in the tunnel (regardless of whether there is congestion at the input point). The result is a marked increase in the average car-handling capability of the tunnel. An analogous application of system engineering to our arterial-highway problem would control at the expressway access points and at the decision points of Fig. 1. The implementation of such control would clearly have to be preceded by a study of the effects on side roads through controlled experiments, and by an education program to achieve public acceptance, but the results could be major improvements in traffic flow and highway utilization with minimal equipment investments.

The above example is merely one instance of system engineering, and certainly the single case does not give a picture of the breadth of current research in traffic control, the attempts to apply system theory to traffic control problems,[2,3] or the complexity of most significant systems in this field of technology.

ELEMENTS OF SYSTEM ENGINEERING

From the two preceding examples, we can recognize three primary parts of system engineering: the modelling of physical situations and artifacts, the devices and components essential to the accomplishment of the system objectives, and the system design—or the interconnection of these elements in such a way as to meet performance specifications.

The *modelling* feature is perhaps the primary analytical and conceptual tool of the engineer. In our X-15 example, modelling governed the dynamical studies, the design of the simulator, the development of the adaptive controller, and the analysis of experimental data. In the field of traffic control, digital simulation models provide the guides to design, the bases for experiment development, and the rapid study of a variety of complex situations.

Throughout system engineering today, two fundamental problems in modelling seem to arise again and again. First is the problem of modelling the human operator: a key difficulty in the development of any man-machine system or any system which is to operate in contact with human beings. While rather astonishing success has been achieved in the modelling of human beings in the simple tracking task[4] which is directly relevant to aircraft control, comparatively little quantitative information is as yet available for other tracking modes, let alone for other control and communication tasks.

The second major problem in modelling is that of dynamical-model simplification. For example, an electric generating station (boiler and turbogenerators) may be described by an 8×8 matrix of transfer functions, each element of the matrix varying with the load demands. Even this relatively simple case represents a complexity beyond the scope of modern system engineering, and simplified models must be used in analysis, simulation, and design. Multilevel control becomes a necessity, just because of the limits on human circumspection.

The *devices* and *components* constitute the second important part of system engineering, as already indicated by the mention above of the instrumentation equipment in the X-15 aircraft or the role implied for sensors in a traffic control system. The solution of modern system engineering problems frequently rests on the application of theory and modelling in the development of an entirely new component.

For example, there has been interest in developing a device which will permit an astronaut to maneuver outside his vehicle, but will still leave his hands free for docking manipulations, and so forth[5]. Consideration has been given to the possibility of actuating the attitude control system by tongue motion, eye motion, breath impulses, musical tones, head motion, and voice commands. Because of the desire to utilize a system in which the commands would be easy for the astronaut under stress to remember, the voice-command system was selected for detailed investigation. The engineering of the device requires the development of pattern recognition equipment, and the selection of a vocabulary of allowable voice commands which would be easily remembered and recognized and which could be corrected in case of errors.

The importance of the role of device and component development in system engineering is the basis for the common opinion that the accomplishments of engineering are bounded not by theory, but by components.

The third and final part of system engineering is system design. Here we recognize four components of widespread significance in modern system engineering.

1. *Stability.* A wide variety of modern control systems are designed primarily on the basis of achieving absolute stability over the operating regime. This philosophy of "design for stability" is a primary contribution of modern system theory. The problem of the balancing of one or more inverted pendula, the control of a satellite rotating in space to realize an artificial gravity field, and the control of complex vibrational systems can frequently be achieved by selection of a Lyapunov function which assures asymptotic stability; the controller program is then determined in direct synthesis from this Lyapunov function and the process model.

2. *Relative stability.* Frequently, system engineering devolves to a compromise between relative stability and performance. The X-15 re-entry at high angle of attack provides one example,* but a more familiar example is the sailboat designed for racing. In the latter case, if high speed is sacrificed, we can design with excessive relative stability; if, on the other hand, stability is of secondary interest, high speed can be realized. The system engineering involves determination of the desirable compromise—and investigation of techniques for achieving a system which approaches the maximum, theoretical figure of merit. In this area of system design, the engineer looks to the system theorist for the derivation of fundamental figures of merit and bounds on composite system characteristics.

3. *Performance specifications.* The establishment of system performance specifications in a form meaningful to system objectives and compatible with design techniques is a key part of the design portion of system engineering. The Appollo communication system[6] provides one example: here one of numerous objectives is to measure the position of an active object (the Apollo vehicle) at a distance of 200,000 miles and with sufficient accuracy to permit guidance decisions from the earth. The transponder in the vehicle is controlled by the signal transmitted from the earthbound control station. In this system, the desired accuracy in distance measurement of 1.05 meters is achieved in two steps: a pseudo-random code is used to modulate an rf signal at a 1-μsec pulse rate to give 150-meter accuracy. An rf doppler counter then yields the required system accuracy.

*For example, the force on the lower vertical tail which stabilizes the airplane also tends to roll the aircraft; this effect tends to complicate radically the pilot's control problem. (The problem is alleviated in the X-15 by jettisoning this part of the tail before landing.)

A second example is the heart pacemaker: a bioelectronic system which is one of the signal achievements of biomedical engineering. For patients with heart block, the pacemaker is an electronic oscillator which supplies to the heart the electrical pulses required to give regular heart beating at the desired rate. Only eight years ago, the standard system was an oscillator carried externally by the patient, with wires through the skin to the heart. Today, more than 4000 patients carrying pacemakers implanted under the skin of the stomach attest to the system engineering effort—to the mercury-batteries and electronic circuits developed in the American space and military programs. In this system, determination of performance specifications required physiological studies (to decide, for example, on 3.7-volt, 65-microjoule pulses), as well as extensive experiments on the effect on plastic materials of body acids. Present system engineering is focussed on providing patients with external control of pulse rate by a circuit inductively coupled to the pacemaker; when this is accomplished, the patient will be able to vary the pulse rate from 75–120 pulses/minute so that he can participate in such mild activities as bowling, hiking, and so forth.

4. Optimization. Finally, system engineering includes optimization (or sub-optimization) of system characteristics: optimization based upon the models of process components, on the devices available for sensing and control, and on the stability analysis and the performance specifications.

CONCLUSION

Thus, system engineering is structured from three elements: modelling, components, and system design. The three components are intimately interdependent; the system engineer must be familiar with all three aspects, and must make decisions on the compromises which are inevitable in the practice of engineering. The system theory (the central theme of this symposium) provides, first, the limitations on physical achievement, second, the techniques for modelling and simulation, and finally, the approaches to system design.

REFERENCES

1. W. H. Stillwell, "X-15 Research Results," NASA SP-60, Washington, D. C., 1965.

2. D. C. Gazis, "Control Problems in Automobile Traffic," IBM Research Paper RC-1362, Symposium on Control Theory and Applications, IBM Research Center, January 27, 1965.

3. D. C. Gazis, "Optimum Control of a System of Oversaturated Interactions," *Operations Research*, Vol. 12, No. 6, pp. 815-831 (November–December, 1964).

4. R. W. Obermayer and F. A. Muckler, "On the Inverse Optimal Control Problem in Manual Control Systems," NASA CR-208, April 1965, Washington, D. C.

5. W. E. Drissel, R. L. Haines, R. J. Kell, D. N. Lovinger, and D. M. Moses, "Study of an Attitude Control System for the Astronaut Maneuvering Unit," NASA CR-198, Washington, D. C., March 1965.

6. J. H. Painter and G. Hondros, "Unified s-band Telecommunications Techniques for Apollo," NASA TN D-2208, Vol. 1, March 1965, Washington, D. C.

A FEEDBACK REALIZATION OF A CONTINUOUS-TIME OPTIMAL FILTER

Samuel L. Fagin
Inertial Division, Sperry Gyroscope Co., Division of Sperry Rand Corp., Great Neck, N. Y.

Another derivation of a continuous-time optimal linear filter is presented. Using this result as a point of departure, a feedback version of this continuous filter is postulated and shown to be optimal in the limit as the "feedback gain" becomes infinite. It is then demonstrated that the need for this infinite feedback gain can frequently be eliminated. This feedback realization of the continuous optimal filter has application to the problem of optimally mixing two or more redundant signals, each contaminated by random noise. The feedback configuration has the advantages of simplicity and the bounding of otherwise troublesome, very large errors. A simple example is given of the mixing of two (velocity) references, each having exponentially correlated error.

1. INTRODUCTION

Kalman and Bucy[1,2] have derived a continuous optimal filter for the case where the measurement is contaminated by white noise. Bryson and Johansen[3] have extended these results by showing that the colored noise case can be reduced to that of white noise. By adopting a model which admits only colored noise (white noise can be approximated as closely as desired) the author has arrived at equivalent results in different form. If not simpler, these results were arrived at differently and should add to the understanding of continuous filters. These results are used as a point of departure for a continuous feedback realization of the optimal filter.

The need for a feedback realization of the continuous optimal filter arises quite naturally in the problem of optimally and continuously mixing two (or more) redundant signals, each contaminated by random noise. If the signal level is much larger than the noise levels, it is apparent that the best (minimum variance) estimate for the signal level can be obtained from the best estimate for the noises, which in turn should involve only the differences between the redundant sources. It is seen (see simple example, Section 8) that the problem of estimating the errors reduces down to the continuous optimal filtering or estimation problem of the type mentioned above. However, this procedure of estimating the errors and subtracting them from the system outputs does not provide a convenient means of bounding the error levels which in some cases (inertial navigator vertical errors, for example) would grow quite troublesomely. Thus, a "feedback" configuration is sought which will continuously drive the errors in at least some of the signal sources to zero and yet retain the accuracy of the continuous optimal filter.

Presented at the Symposium on System Theory
Polytechnic Institute of Brooklyn, April 20, 21, 22, 1965

In Sections 5 and 6, such a configuration, called a "Continuous Feedback Optimal Filter" is postulated and shown to approach the optimal as the feedback gain becomes infinite. (These configurations involve only the error propagation model. It is assumed that corresponding feedbacks on the actual system are possible, such that the resulting error propagation will be identical to that of these desired feedback configurations.) In Section 7, it is shown that for a wide class of systems, the requirement for infinite feedback gain is unnecessary. A simple example is given in Section 8 of the application of this feedback filter to the problem of mixing two redundant signal sources (two velocity references), each contaminated by exponentially correlated noise.

2. SUMMARY OF PREVIOUS RESULTS

For the convenience of the reader, a short summary of previous results[1,4] pertinent to the development of the continuous optimal filter is given below. These results are for a linear continuous system where observations are available at discrete times.

Consider the wide class of continuous systems (or error propagation models thereof) which can be represented by the first order differential equations

$$\dot{X} = A(t)X + N(t) \tag{2.1}$$

where

X = a k dimensional column "state" vector;
$A(t)$ = a $k \times k$ "system feedback" matrix which may vary with time;
$N(t)$ = a k dimensional column vector of white noise inputs such that their covariance, $E[N(t_1)N^T(t_2)] = \pi\delta(t_1 - t_2)q(t_1)$ and $E[N(t)] = 0$;
δ = the Dirac delta function;
$q(t_1)$ = a $k \times k$ "noise matrix."

In the modelling adopted here, the state vector X includes "noise" states such as measurement errors and error sources. Most frequently, q is constant and diagonal, the diagonal elements being the single-ended power spectral density of the white noise necessary to create the noise state of the desired variance.

A sequence of r dimensional observations $Y(t_i)$ are made at discrete times $t_1, t_2, t_3 \ldots t_i \ldots$ defined by the equation

$$Y(t_i) = M(t_i)\,X(t_i) \tag{2.2}$$

where $M(t_i)$ is a "measurement matrix" of dimension $r \times k$ where $r < k$. $M(t_i)$ is not necessarily equal to $M(t_j)$ nor does r necessarily remain constant.

Equations (2.1) and (2.2) can be represented by the multidimensional canonical block diagram of Fig. 1. In this figure and in the sequel, double lines indicate the flow of vector quantities and matrix boxes multiply their vector inputs from the left.

The optimal filter or estimation problem is to obtain a "best" estimate for the state vector X based on these observations and any prior knowledge of the states summed up in an initial covariance matrix $P(0)$.

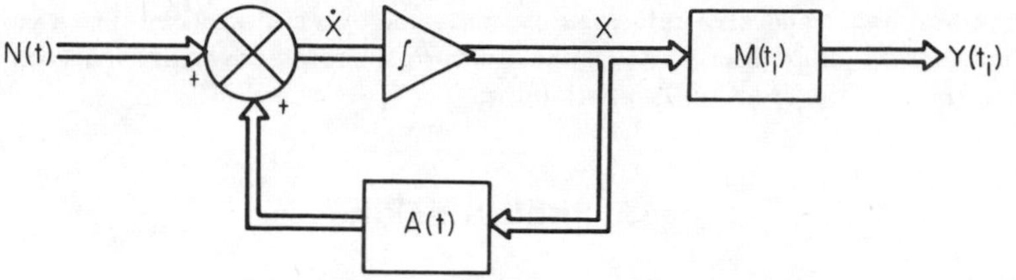

Fig. 1. The canonical model.

The solution of this optimal filter or estimation problem is given as follows: The minimum variance estimator for each of the components of X in the class of all unbiased linear estimators is given by the recursive relations:

$$\hat{X}(t_i + s) = \Phi(t_i + s;\ t_i)\,\hat{X}(t_i - 0)$$
$$+\ \Phi(t_i + s;\ t_i)P(t_i - 0)M^T(t_i)[M(t_i)P(t_i - 0)M^T(t_i)]^{-1}[Y(t_i) - M(t_i)\hat{X}(t_i - 0)] \quad (2.3)$$

$$P(t_i + s) = \Phi(t_i + s;\ t_i)P(t_i - 0)\,\Phi^T(t_i + s;\ t_i) - \Phi(t_i + s;\ t_i)P(t_i - 0)$$
$$\times\ M^T(t_i)[M(t_i)P(t_i - 0)M^T(t_i)]^{-1}M(t_i)P(t_i - 0)\Phi^T(t_i + s;\ t_i) + Q(t_i + s) \quad (2.4)$$

where

$\hat{X}(t_i + s)$ is the unbiased minimum variance estimator for $X(t_i + s)$;

$\hat{X}(t_i - 0)$ is the unbiased minimum variance estimator for X at time just prior to the measurement, $Y(t_i)$, at time t_i;

$P(t_i + s)$ is the error covariance matrix for the optimal estimate for the state vector at time $t_i + s$;

$P(t_i - 0)$ is the covariance matrix at the time just prior to the measurement, $Y(t_i)$, at time t_i;

$M(t_i)$ is the measurement matrix at time t_i;

$\Phi(t_i + s;\ t_i)$ the state transition matrix, is determined as the solution of the matrix differential equation

$$\frac{d\Phi(t_i + s;\ t_i)}{ds} = A(t_i + s)\,\Phi(t_i + s;\ t_i);\ \Phi(t_i;\ t_i) = I$$

$$Q(t_i + s) = E\{U(t_i + s)\,U^T(t_i + s)\}$$
$$= \pi\Phi(t_i + s;\ t_i)\int_0^s \Phi^{-1}(t_i + t;\ t_i)\,q(t_i + t)\,\Phi^{-1\,T}(t_i + t;\ t_i)\,dt$$
$$\Phi^T(t_i + s;\ t_i)$$

$U(t_i + s)$ is the zero initial condition response to the white noise input starting at time t_i

$q(t)$ is the "noise" covariance matrix and is defined by the relation

$$E\{N(t_1)\,N(t_2)\} = \pi\,\delta(t_1 - t_2)\,q(t_1)$$

Of course, these recursive relations are initiated by an a priori minimum variance estimate of the state vector, $X(0)$, and its corresponding covariance matrix, $P(0)$, before the first observation is available.

3. PRELIMINARIES

Before launching into a derivation of the continuous optimal filter, some immediate pertinent observations can be made. By straightforward differentiation of eqs. (2.3) and (2.4)

$$\frac{d\,\hat{X}(t_i + s)}{ds} = A(t_i + s)\,\hat{X}(t_i + s) \tag{3.1}$$

$$\frac{d\,P(t_i + s)}{ds} = A(t_i + s)\,P(t_i + s) + P(t_i + s)\,A^T(t_i + s) + \pi q(t_i + s) \tag{3.2}$$

where

$$0 < s < (t_{i+1} - t_i)$$

and the initial conditions are

$$\hat{X}(t_i + 0) = \hat{X}(t_i - 0) + P(t_i - 0)\,M^T(t_i)\,[M(t_i)\,P(t_i - 0)\,M^T(t_i)]^{-1}\,[Y(t_i) - M(t_i)\,\hat{X}(t_i - 0)] \tag{3.3}$$

$$P(t_i + 0) = P(t_i - 0) - P(t_i - 0)\,M^T(t_i)\,[M(t_i)\,P(t_i - 0)\,M^T(t_i)]^{-1}\,M(t_i)\,P(t_i - 0) \tag{3.4}$$

Further, by simply multiplying the last two relations by $M(t_i)$ there results:

$$M(t_i)\,\hat{X}(t_i + 0) = Y(t_i) \tag{3.5}$$

$$M(t_i)\,P(t_i + 0) = 0 \tag{3.6}$$

Thus, each row of $M(t_i)$ is orthogonal to each column (or row) of $P(t_i + 0)$. In addition, the inner product of a row of $M(t_i)$ with $\hat{X}(t_i + 0)$ gives a component of $Y(t_i)$. The relations (3.1), (3.2), (3.5), and (3.6) will be employed to derive the continuous optimal filter.

4. DERIVATION OF THE CONTINUOUS OPTIMAL FILTER

The continuous optimal filter is now derived from the results summarized in Section 2 (eqs. (2.3) and (2.4)) by allowing the intervals between observations to approach zero. Defining

$$\hat{X}(t_{i+1} - 0) - \hat{X}(t_i + 0) = \Delta\hat{X}_i$$

$$P(t_{i+1} - 0) - P(t_i + 0) = \Delta P_i$$

$$M(t_{i+1}) - M(t_i) = \Delta M_i$$

and substituting in eqs. (3.3) and (3.4), there results, after using eqs. (3.5) and (3.6),

$$\hat{X}(t_{i+1}+0)-\hat{X}(t_i+0)=\Delta\hat{X}_i+[\Delta P_i M^T(t_i)+P(t_i+0)\,\Delta M_i^T+\Delta P_i\,\Delta M_i^T]$$
$$\{M(t_i)\,\Delta P_i M^T(t_i)+\Delta M_i\,[P(t_i+0)+\Delta P_i]\,\Delta M_i^T\}^{-1}$$
$$\{Y(t_{i+1})-Y(t_i)-\Delta M_i\hat{X}(t_i)-M(t_i)\,\Delta\hat{X}_i-\Delta M_i\,\Delta\hat{X}_i\} \quad (4.1)$$

$$P(t_{i+1}+0)-P(t_i+0)=\Delta P_i-[\Delta P_i M^T(t_i)+P(t_i+0)\,\Delta M_i^T+\Delta P_i\,\Delta M_i^T]$$
$$\{M(t_i)\,\Delta P_i M^T(t_i)+\Delta M_i\,[P(t_i+0)+\Delta P_i]\,\Delta M_i^T\}^{-1}$$
$$\{M(t_i)\,\Delta P_i+\Delta M_i\,[P(t_i+0)+\Delta P_i]\} \quad (4.2)$$

Now,

$$\Delta\hat{X}_i=A(t_i+0)\,\hat{X}(t_i+0)\,s+0(s) \quad (4.3)$$

$$\Delta P_i=[A(t_i+0)\,P(t_i+0)+P(t_i+0)\,A^T(t_i+0)+\pi\,q(t_i+0)]\,s+0(s) \quad (4.4)$$

and assume

$$\Delta M_i=\dot{M}(t_i+0)\,s+0(s)$$

where $s=(t_{i+1}-t_i)$ and $0(s)$ represents terms which vanish to higher order than s. Substituting in eqs. (4.1) and (4.2), dividing by s and taking the limit as $s\longrightarrow 0$ there results

$$\frac{d\hat{X}}{dt}=A(t)\,\hat{X}+K(t)\left\{\frac{dY}{dt}-[\dot{M}(t)+M(t)\,A(t)]\,\hat{X}\right\} \quad (4.5)$$

$$\frac{dP}{dt}=A(t)\,P+P\,A^T(t)+\pi q(t)-K(t)\,\{M(t)\,[A(t)P+\pi q(t)]+\dot{M}(t)P\} \quad (4.6)$$

$$K(t)=\{[P\,A^T(t)+\pi\,q(t)]\,M^T(t)+P\,\dot{M}^T(t)\}\,[M(t)\,\pi\,q(t)\,M^T(t)]^{-1} \quad (4.7)$$

The inverse $[M(t)\,\pi\,q(t)\,M^T(t)]^{-1}$ must exist for the validity of these equations and, strictly speaking, dY/dt must exist for the validity of eq. (4.5). However, the fact that

$$\frac{dY}{dt}=\frac{d}{dt}\,[M(t)X]=\dot{M}(t)X+M(t)\,A(t)X+M(t)\,N(t)$$

and therefore is sometimes infinite should present no more theoretical difficulties than those in originally setting up the system model with a white noise input. Further, the derivative need never be taken* since, by the formula for integration by parts,

$$\int K(t)\,\dot{Y}\,dt=K(t)Y-\int\dot{K}(t)Y\,dt$$

and it follows:

$$\hat{X}=\int\{A(t)-K(t)\,[\dot{M}(t)+M(t)\,A(t)]\}\,\hat{X}\,dt+K(t)Y-\int\dot{K}(t)Y\,dt. \quad (4.8)$$

If these arguments are not convincing, eq. (4.8) can be reached from (4.1), employing Stieltjes integrals.

Thus, two block diagram versions of the continuous optimal filter are presented as Figs. 2 and 3 based on eqs. (4.5) and (4.8), respectively.

*First pointed out to the author by Mr. J. Wilcox of the Sperry Gyroscope Company in an internal memorandum dated June 19, 1964.

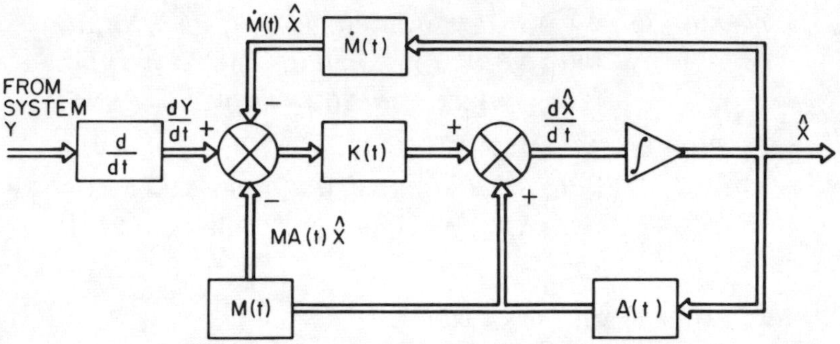

Fig. 2. Block diagram of a continuous optimal filter.

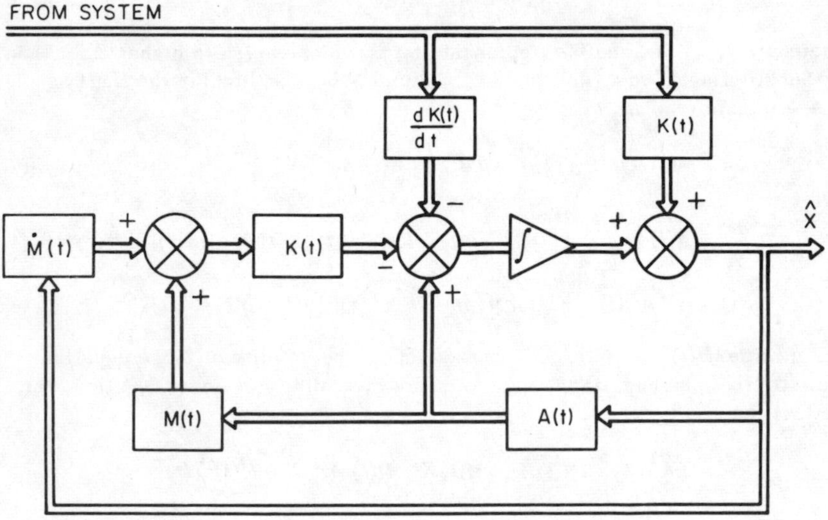

Fig. 3. Continuous optimal filter avoiding derivative.

Note that the above results apply only after the initial conditions have been imposed as determined from (3.3) and (3.4). This is a consequence of the use of (3.5) and (3.6) in the derivation. It is interesting to note that by direct evaluation

$$M(t)\frac{d\hat{X}}{dt} = \frac{dY}{dt} - \dot{M}(t)\hat{X} \tag{4.9}$$

or

$$\frac{d}{dt}[M(t)\hat{X}] = \frac{dY}{dt} = \frac{d}{dt}[M(t)X]. \tag{4.10}$$

In addition,

$$M(t)\frac{dP}{dt} = -\dot{M}(t)P \tag{4.11}$$

or

$$\frac{d[M(t)P]}{dt} = 0. \tag{4.12}$$

Furthermore, as a consequence of eqs. (3.6) and (4.12),

$$M(t)P = 0. \tag{4.13}$$

This last equation leads to a useful invariance property of the covariance matrix with respect to certain changes in the system feedback matrix $A(t)$. Consider a modified system feedback matrix:

$$A^*(t) = A(t) + D(t)\,M(t) \tag{4.14}$$

where $D(t)$ is an arbitrary, possible time-varying $k \times r$ "system transformation" matrix. It is clear from eq. (4.13) that dP/dt (eq. (4.6)), and $P(t_i + 0)$ (eq. (3.4)) is invariant with respect to this change. Thus, if the initial covariance matrix is unchanged, the covariance matrix $P(t)$ is invariant with respect to the whole class of system feedback matrix changes represented by eq. (4.14). This property is useful in proving that many of the common information mixing schemes do not affect the system potential optimal performance as represented by $P(t)$.

It has been assumed in the derivation of the equations for the continuous optimal filter ((4.5)–(4.8)) that $[M(t)\pi q(t)M^T(t)]^{-1}$ exist. However, this is not so when $M(t)\,N(t) = 0$. This reflects nothing more than that not only is the observation $Y = MX$ obtained without error† but that

$$\frac{dY}{dt} = \frac{d}{dt}(MX) = \dot{M}X + M[AX + N(t)] = [\dot{M} + MA]X \triangleq M_1(t)X \tag{4.15}$$

is, in effect, another available observation without error. If in turn $M_1(t)\,N(t) = 0$, it then follows that the second derivative is likewise an error-free observation. This can be continued until $M_n(t)\,N(t) \neq 0$. Now, since Y can be obtained from d^nY/dt^n and initial conditions by a linear operation, the use of $d^n Y/dt^n$ in place of Y and $M_n(t)$ in place of $M(t)$ is suggested.

Thus, use eqs. (4.5)–(4.8) as they stand with

$$\frac{d^n Y}{dt^n} = M_n(t)X$$

substituted for $Y = M(t)X$ in the canonical model and the following initial observations incorporated as per eqs. (3.3) and (3.4) at startup:

$$Y(0) = M(0)X$$

$$\frac{dY(0)}{dt} = M_1(0)X$$

$$\cdot \qquad \cdot$$

$$\cdot \qquad \cdot$$

$$\cdot \qquad \cdot$$

$$\frac{d^n Y(0)}{dt^n} = M_n(0)X \tag{4.16}$$

†Note, that in the modelling assumed here the observation of a signal plus noise is obtained error free. This results in some unfortunate conceptual and semantic difficulty.

The reasoning behind this goes as follows: Consider a sequence of observations

$$\frac{d^n Y(t_i)}{dt^n}$$

for discrete times t_i where $i = 1, 2, \ldots$. These, and the above initial observations are optimally incorporated on a discrete time basis as per eqs. (2.3) and (2.4). The result is optimal in the class of all linear estimates involving the observations

$$Y(0), \frac{dY(0)}{dt}, \ldots \frac{d^n Y(0)}{dt^n}, \frac{d^n Y(t_1)}{dt^n}, \frac{d^n Y(t_2)}{dt^n} \ldots .$$

But, if the interval between observations is allowed to approach zero, this class of linear estimates will include as close an approximation as is desired for

$$Y, \frac{dY}{dt}, \ldots \text{ and } \frac{d^{n-1} Y}{dt^{n-1}} .$$

Thus, in the limit, the inclusion of the latter as observations adds nothing to the class of linear estimators from which our optimal is drawn. However, in the limit as the intervals between observations approaches zero, the continuous optimal filter eqs. (4.8) and (4.9) apply provided that the proper startup is carried out using initial observations indicated in eq. (4.16).

In many cases the required derivatives of Y are readily available without carrying out a differentiation and thus the procedure outlined above makes for little hardship.

5. THE CONTINUOUS FEEDBACK OPTIMAL FILTER

In many applications (such as in the alignment of an inertial system), the state vector X of the canonical model of Fig. 1 represents error states for the system. Since the model may not be exact (or linear) for large errors, it is desirable to provide some means of correcting these outputs. Conceivably, a means of "controlling" these outputs would be logically deduced employing the techniques of Optimal Estimation and Control Theory. However, the author simply postulated a feedback filter configuration and, as will be shown below, proved that its performance could approach the optimal as the feedback gain becomes large. The form of the postulated configuration was suggested by a feedback configuration for the case where observations are obtained at discrete times.

The postulated feedback configuration which will be shown to approach the optimal is given in Figure 4. The covariance matrix $P(t)$ is as given by eq. (4.6); α is an undetermined scalar, and the (*) superscript denotes the modified outputs.

In equation form this system is described by the system of differential equations

$$\dot{X}^* = A(t)X^* + N(t) - \alpha K(t)\frac{dY^*}{dt} \tag{5.1}$$

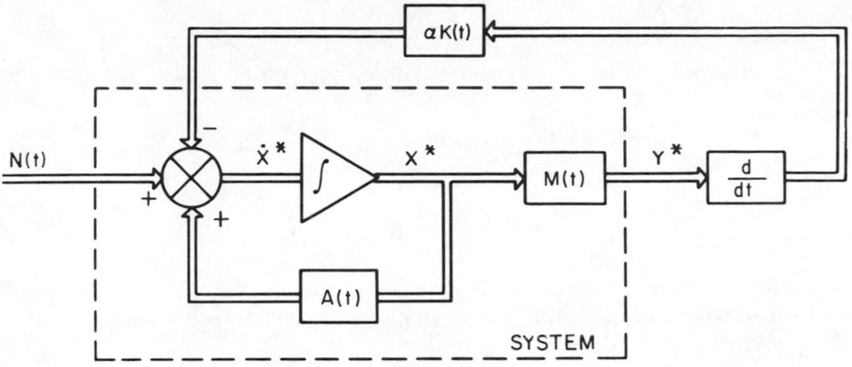

$K(t) = \{[P(t)A^T(t) + \pi q(t)]M^T(t) + P(t)\dot{M}^T(t)\}[M(t)\pi q(t)M^T(t)]^{-1}$.

Fig. 4. The continuous feedback optimal filter.

It will now be shown that the system with feedback as indicated in Fig. 4 and eq. (5.1) has an output covariance P^* which approaches P when the scalar constant $\alpha \longrightarrow \infty$.

Since $Y^* = M(t)X^*$, eq. (5.1) can be written

$$\dot{X}^* = A(t)X^* + N(t) - \alpha K(t)\,[M(t)\dot{X}^* + \dot{M}(t)X^*]$$

or

$$[I + \alpha K(t)\,M(t)]\,\dot{X}^* = [A(t) - \alpha K(t)\,\dot{M}(t)]\,X^* + N(t). \tag{5.2}$$

Employing the formula of Sherman-Morrison and the Bartlett[5],

$$[I + \alpha K(t)\,M(t)]^{-1} = I - \alpha K(t)\,[I + \alpha M(t)\,K(t)]^{-1}\,M(t). \tag{5.3}$$

Since $M(t)P$ is zero, then by straightforward matrix multiplication, $M(t)\,K(t) = I$ and eq. (5.3) becomes

$$[I + \alpha K(t)\,M(t)]^{-1} = I - \frac{\alpha}{1+\alpha}\,K(t)\,M(t). \tag{5.4}$$

Using this relation, (5.2) becomes

$$\dot{X}^* = \left[I - \frac{\alpha}{1+\alpha}\,K(t)\,M(t)\right][A(t) - \alpha K(t)\,\dot{M}(t)]\,X^* + \left[I - \frac{\alpha}{1+\alpha}K(t)M(t)\right]N(t) \tag{5.5}$$

which is a more tractable form of the differential equation for the output of the modified system.

It is well known (cf. eq. (3.2)) that if

$$\dot{X}^* = A^*X^* + N^*(t),$$

the covariance matrix for X^* is given as the solution of the system of differential equations

$$\frac{dP^*}{dt} = A^*\,P^* + P^*A^{*T} + \pi q^*(t). \tag{5.6}$$

Thus, letting

$$A^* = \left[I - \frac{\alpha}{1+\alpha} K(t)\, M(t) \right] [A(t) - \alpha K(t)\, \dot{M}(t)]$$

$$= A(t) - \frac{\alpha}{1+\alpha} K(t)\, [M(t)\, A(t) + \dot{M}(t)] \quad (5.7)$$

and

$$q^*(t) = \left[I - \frac{\alpha}{1+\alpha} K(t)\, M(t) \right] q(t) \left[I - \frac{\alpha}{1+\alpha} K(t)\, M(t) \right]^T, \qquad (5.8)$$

the covariance matrix for the modified system is specified as per the solution of (5.6). It remains to expand this expression and show that for $\alpha \longrightarrow \infty$, $P^* \longrightarrow P$.

Expanding (5.6) and (5.7) and (5.8)

$$\frac{dP^*}{dt} = \left\{ A(t) - \frac{\alpha}{1+\alpha} K(t)\, [M(t)\, A(t) + \dot{M}(t)] \right\} P^*$$

$$+ P^* \left\{ A(t) - \frac{\alpha}{1+\alpha} K(t)\, [M(t)\, A(t) + \dot{M}(t)] \right\}^T$$

$$+ \pi \left[I - \frac{\alpha}{1+\alpha} K(t)\, M(t) \right] q(t) \left[I - \frac{\alpha}{1+\alpha} K(t)\, M(t) \right]^T, \quad (5.9)$$

and, expanding further,

$$\frac{dP^*}{dt} = A(t) P^* + P^* A^T(t) + \pi q(t) - \frac{\alpha}{1+\alpha} K(t)\, \{M(t)\, [A(t) P^* + \pi q(t)] + \dot{M}(t) P^*\}$$

$$- \frac{\alpha}{1+\alpha} \{[P^* A^T(t) + \pi q(t)]\, M^T(t) + P^* \dot{M}^T(t)\}\, K^T(t)$$

$$+ \left[\frac{\alpha}{1+\alpha} \right]^2 \{[P A^T(t) + \pi q(t)]\, M^T(t) + P \dot{M}^T(t)\}\, K^T(t). \qquad (5.10)$$

If initially $P^*(0) = P(0)$, as $\alpha \longrightarrow \infty$, the last two terms will cancel out and it is clear from comparison with eq. (4.6) that $P^*(t)$ will approach $P(t)$. Thus the approach to optimal performance of the feedback configuration of Fig. 4 is confirmed.

It should be remembered that, as mentioned in Section 4, the above results do not apply to discontinuities in $M(t)$. At startup, the initial output $X^*(0)$ must be set to $X(0) - \hat{X}(0+)$ and the covariance matrix must be modified in accordance with eqs. (3.3) and (3.4).

6. ELIMINATING THE DERIVATIVE

As before, since

$$\int K(t) \frac{dY^*}{dt} dt = K(t) Y^* - \int \frac{dK(t)}{dt} Y^* \, dt$$

the Continuous Feedback Optimal Filter can be structured as in Fig. 5.

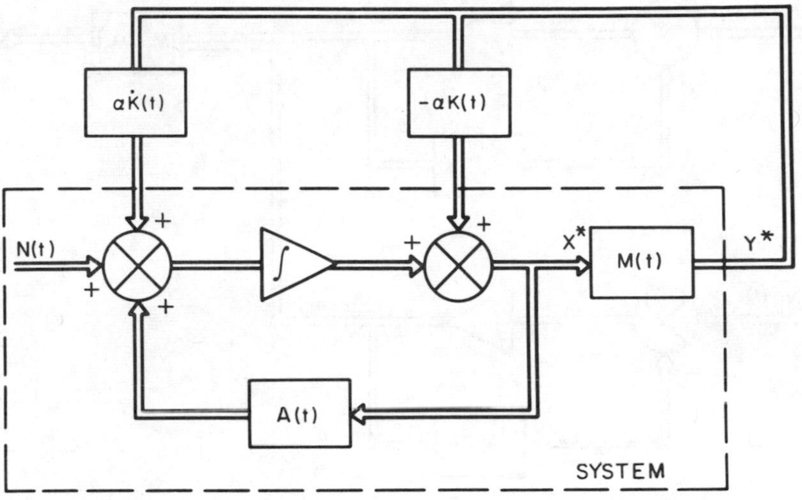

Fig. 5. The continuous feedback optimal filter (avoiding the derivative).

As before, $X^*(0)$ must be set to $X(0) - \hat{X}(0+)$ and $P(0)$ set to $P(0^+)$ in accordance with eqs. (3.3) and (3.4).

7. ELIMINATING THE REQUIREMENT FOR INFINITE GAIN, FIRST ORDER NOISE SYSTEMS

The infinite gain indicated in Figs. 4 and 5 is a troublesome and, as it turns out, a frequently unnecessary requirement.

Consider the wide class of systems describable by Fig. 6, where

$$A(t) = \begin{bmatrix} A_1 & \vdots & 0 \\ \cdots & & \cdots \\ 0 & \vdots & A_2 \end{bmatrix}, \quad X = \begin{bmatrix} X_1 \\ \cdots \\ X_2 \end{bmatrix}, \quad M(t) = [M_1 \mid M_2]$$

and

$$N(t) = \begin{bmatrix} N_1(t) \\ \cdots \\ N_2(t) \end{bmatrix}.$$

Here, X_2 can generally be regarded as the state vector of noise in the observations. In this section it is further stipulated that A_2 has the same dimension, r, as the observations. Consequently, A_2 is $r \times r$, M_2 is $r \times r$, $N_2(t)$ is $r \times 1$ and this type of system is called a "first order noise system." It is shown below that for this class of systems infinite gain is not necessary.

The evolution of the noninfinite gain optimal feedback filter from the infinite gain version of Fig. 4 is shown in Figs. 7 through 13. Figures 7 through 9 are

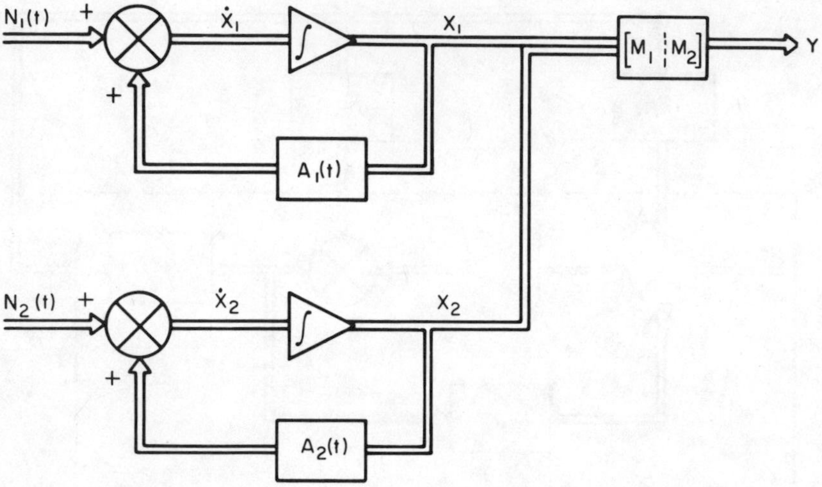

Fig. 6. Canonical model equivalent for class of systems which are susceptive to noninfinite optimal feedback.

self-explanatory.* Figure 10 follows from Fig. 9 since, because of the infinite gain,

$$Y^{\neq} = M_2 \hat{X}_2 \tag{7.1}$$

and, since

$$\dot{\hat{X}}_2 = A_2 \hat{X}_2 + K_2 Y_0, \tag{7.2}$$

substituting (7.1) in (7.2) yields

$$Y_0 = K_2^{-1} \left[\frac{d}{dt} (M_2^{-1} Y^{\neq}) - A_2 M_2^{-1} Y^{\neq} \right] \tag{7.3}$$

where it has been assumed that M_2^{-1} and K_2^{-1} exist. A straightforward application of integration by parts transforms Fig. 10 into Fig. 11, thus avoiding the derivative. The algebraic loop in Fig. 11 can be eliminated** since

$$X^{\neq} = X_0 + F_2 M(t) X^{\neq}$$

$$\left\{ I + \left[\frac{K_1}{0} \right] K_2^{-1} M_2^{-1} M(t) \right\} X^{\neq} = X_0$$

*Note that the assumption of first order noise is not necessary for the validity of Fig. 9. Thus, Fig. 9 could serve as a point of departure for eliminating the need for infinite gain in higher order noise systems. Of course, if it is assumed that all observations are contaminated by additive white noise, the need to consider higher order noise is obviated.

**Suggested by Dr. A. Graefe of the Sperry Gyroscope Company.

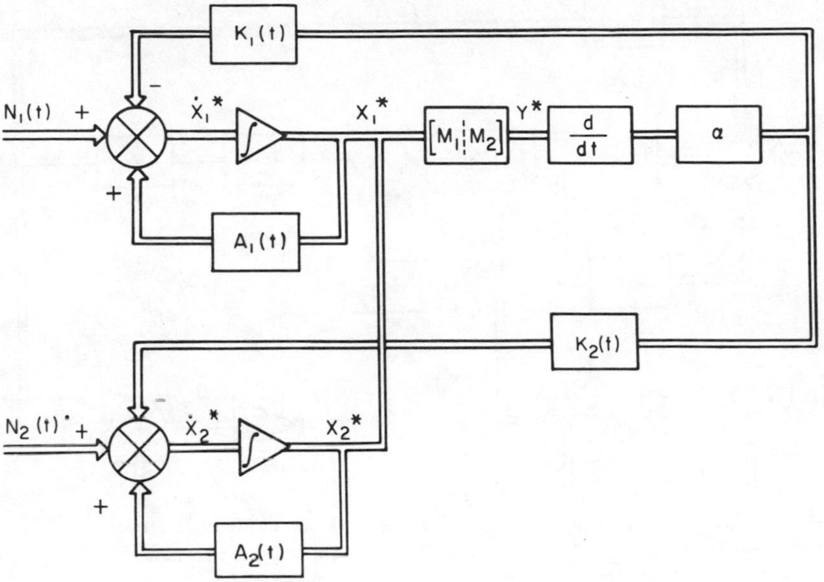

Fig. 7. Evolution of the noninfinite gain optimal feedback filter, (a), equivalent to continuous optimal feedback filter of Fig. 4.

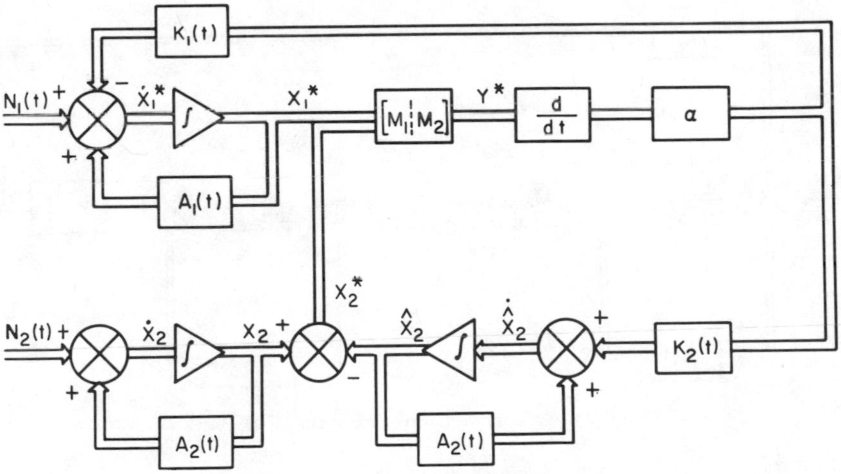

Fig. 8. Evolution of the noninfinite gain-optimal feedback filter, (b).

and, as a consequence of

$$\left\{ I + \left[\frac{K_1}{0}\right] K_2^{-1} M_2^{-1} M(t) \right\}^{-1} = \left\{ I - \left[\frac{K_1}{0}\right] M(t) \right\},$$

$$X^{\neq} = \left\{ I - \left[\frac{K_1}{0}\right] M(t) \right\} X_0 . \tag{7.4}$$

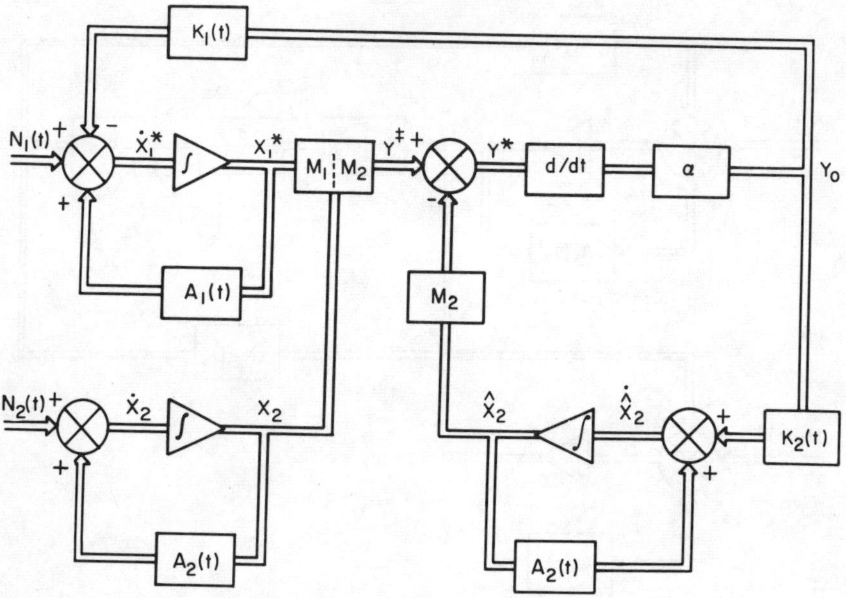

Fig. 9. Evolution of the noninfinite gain optimal feedback filter, (c).

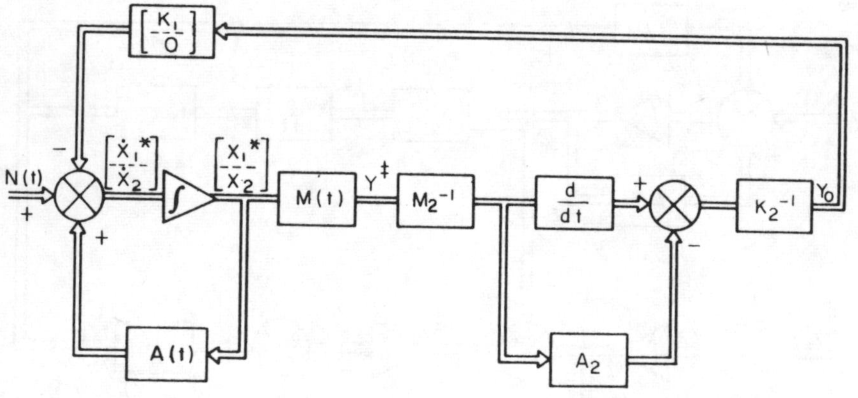

Fig. 10. Evolution of the noninfinite gain optimal feedback filter, (d).

This leads to Fig. 12. The alternate configuration of Fig. 13 arises in the following manner:

$$\dot{X}_0 = [A(t) + F_1 M(t)]\, X^{\neq} + N(t) \tag{7.5}$$

Substituting (7.4) in (7.5), there results

$$\dot{X}_0 = A(t)X_0 + \left\{F_1 - A(t)\begin{bmatrix} K_1 \\ \hline 0 \end{bmatrix} - F_1 M(t)\begin{bmatrix} K_1 \\ \hline 0 \end{bmatrix}\right\} M(t)X_0 + N(t). \tag{7.6}$$

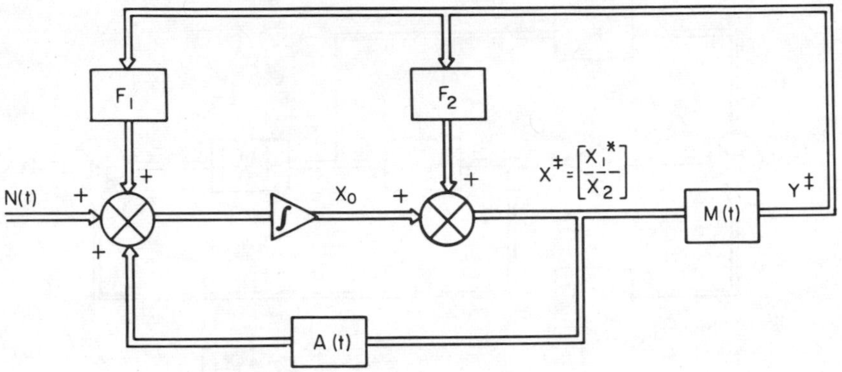

$$F_1 = \left[\begin{array}{c} K_1 K_2^{-1} A_2 + \dfrac{d}{dt}(K_1 K_2^{-1}) \\ \hline 0 \end{array}\right] M_2^{-1}, \qquad F_2 = -\left[\begin{array}{c} K_1 \\ \hline 0 \end{array}\right] K_2^{-1} M_2^{-1}.$$

Fig. 11. Evolution of the noninfinite gain optimal feedback filter, (e), avoiding the derivative.

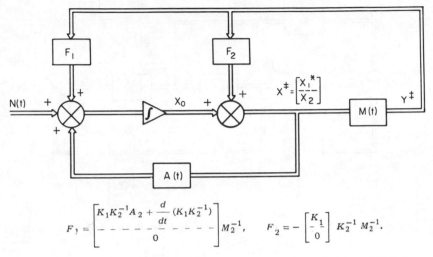

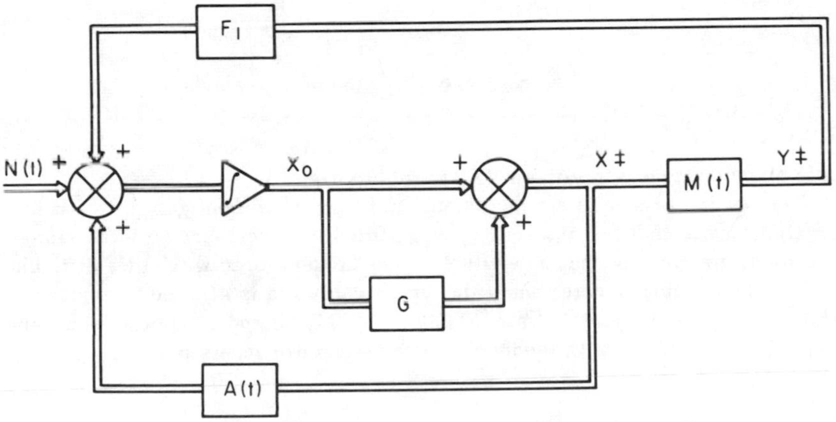

$$F_1 = \left[\begin{array}{c} K_1 K_2^{-1} A_2 + \dfrac{d}{dt}(K_1 K_2^{-1}) \\ \hline 0 \end{array}\right] M_2^{-1}, \qquad G = -\left[\begin{array}{c} K_1 \\ \hline 0 \end{array}\right] M(t).$$

Fig. 12. Evolution of the noninfinite gain optimal feedback filter, (f), eliminating an algebraic loop.

Now,

$$MK = I = M_1 K_1 + M_2 K_2$$
$$M_1 K_1 = I - M_2 K_2 .$$

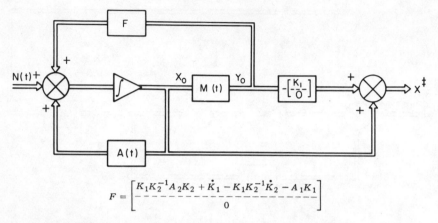

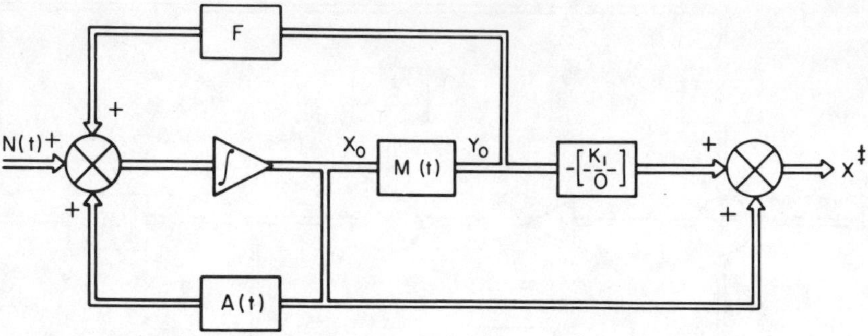

$$F = \left[\begin{array}{c} K_1 K_2^{-1} A_2 K_2 + \dot{K}_1 - K_1 K_2^{-1} \dot{K}_2 - A_1 K_1 \\ \hline 0 \end{array}\right]$$

Fig. 13. Evolution of the noninfinite gain optimal feedback filter, (g), alternate configuration.

Thus (7.6) becomes

$$\dot{X}_0 = A(t) X_0 + N(t) + \left\{ F_1 M_2 K_2 - A(t) \left[\begin{array}{c} K_1 \\ \hline 0 \end{array}\right] \right\} M(t) X_0$$

or

$$\dot{X}_0 = A(t) X_0 + N(t) + \left[\begin{array}{c} K_1 K_2^{-1} A_2 K_2 + \frac{d}{dt}(K_1 K_2^{-1}) K_2 - A_1 K_1 \\ \hline 0 \end{array}\right] M(t) X_0 . \quad (7.7)$$

This equation, together with eq. (7.4) leads to Fig. 13.

Figures 11, 12 and 13 are considered to be practical configurations. It is tacitly assumed that the system can be modified in accordance with the aforementioned diagrams or that an equivalent can be developed with little difficulty.

It is interesting to note that if the first order noise is allowed to approach white noise then K_1 goes to zero. Thus, Figs. 11, 12 and 13 become suprisingly simple configurations with feedbacks at the integrator inputs only.

8. SIMPLE EXAMPLE: THE MIXING OF TWO REDUNDANT SIGNALS, EACH HAVING EXPONENTIALLY CORRELATED ERROR

Consider the problem of how to best mix two redundant signal sources, each nominally putting out the same thing, say, velocity, but each contaminated by exponentially correlated noise with zero mean.

Thus, the two redundant signal outputs are

$$v_{R1} = v_T + \varepsilon_1$$

$$v_{R2} = v_T - \varepsilon_2$$

where v_T is true velocity and ε_1 and ε_2 are the errors in the first and second

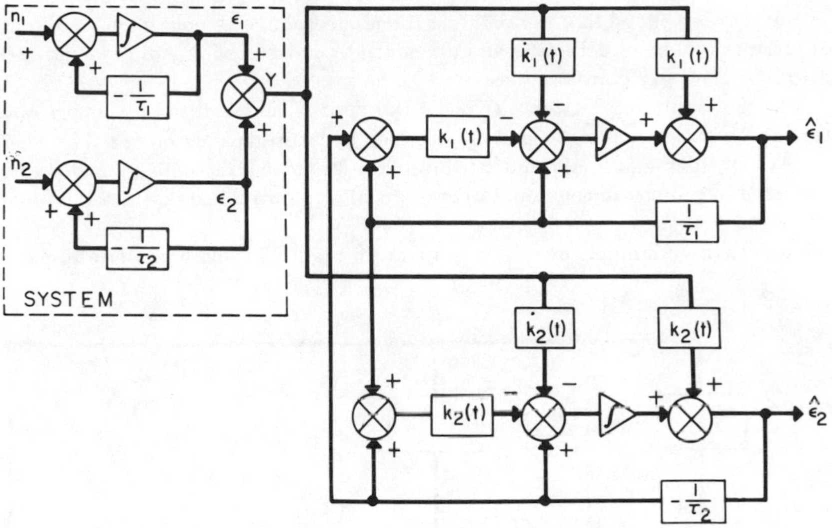

Fig. 14. Continuous optimal filter for the simple mixing problem (exponentially correlated signal embedded in exponentially correlated noise, based on Fig. 3).

reference, respectively. Further,

$$E\{\varepsilon_1\} = E\{\varepsilon_2\} = E\{\varepsilon_1\,\varepsilon_2\} = 0,$$

$$E\{\varepsilon_1(t)\,\varepsilon_1(t+\tau)\} = \sigma_1^2\, e^{-\frac{|\tau|}{\tau_1}},$$

$$E\{\varepsilon_2(t)\,\varepsilon_2(t+\tau)\} = \sigma_2^2\, e^{-\frac{|\tau|}{\tau_2}}.$$

It is clear that if the velocity levels are much greater than the errors, the best that can be done is to subtract the two outputs and use this difference to estimate ε_1 or ε_2 and correct either v_{R1} or v_{R2}. Thus the situation can be described by the left side of Fig. 14 where Y is the difference between the two velocity references. This system is recognized to be in the canonical form of Fig. 1 where

$$X = \begin{bmatrix} \varepsilon_1 \\ \varepsilon_2 \end{bmatrix}, \quad A = \begin{bmatrix} -\dfrac{1}{\tau_1} & 0 \\ 0 & -\dfrac{1}{\tau_2} \end{bmatrix}, \quad N(t) = \begin{bmatrix} n_1(t) \\ n_2(t) \end{bmatrix},$$

$$q = \begin{bmatrix} \dfrac{2}{\pi}\dfrac{\sigma_1^2}{\tau_1} & 0 \\ 0 & \dfrac{2}{\pi}\dfrac{\sigma_2^2}{\tau_2} \end{bmatrix}, \quad M = [1 \quad -1]$$

It is further recognized that the problem formulated above is equivalent to the well-known problem of detecting an exponentially correlated signal ($\mathcal{E}_1$) embedded in exponentially correlated noise ($\mathcal{E}_2$).

From the results of Section 4 (Fig. 3) the optimal nonfeedback or "open loop" filter for the estimation of $\mathcal{E}_1$ and $\mathcal{E}_2$ is given by the right side of Fig. 14. Since $\hat{\mathcal{E}}_1 + \hat{\mathcal{E}}_2 = Y$, it is easily shown that this filter for estimating both $\mathcal{E}_1$ and $\mathcal{E}_2$ can be reduced to the one-dimensional open loop filter identical to that obtained by Bryson and Johansen[3].

A feedback version of this filter is given in Figure 15 and a noninfinite gain

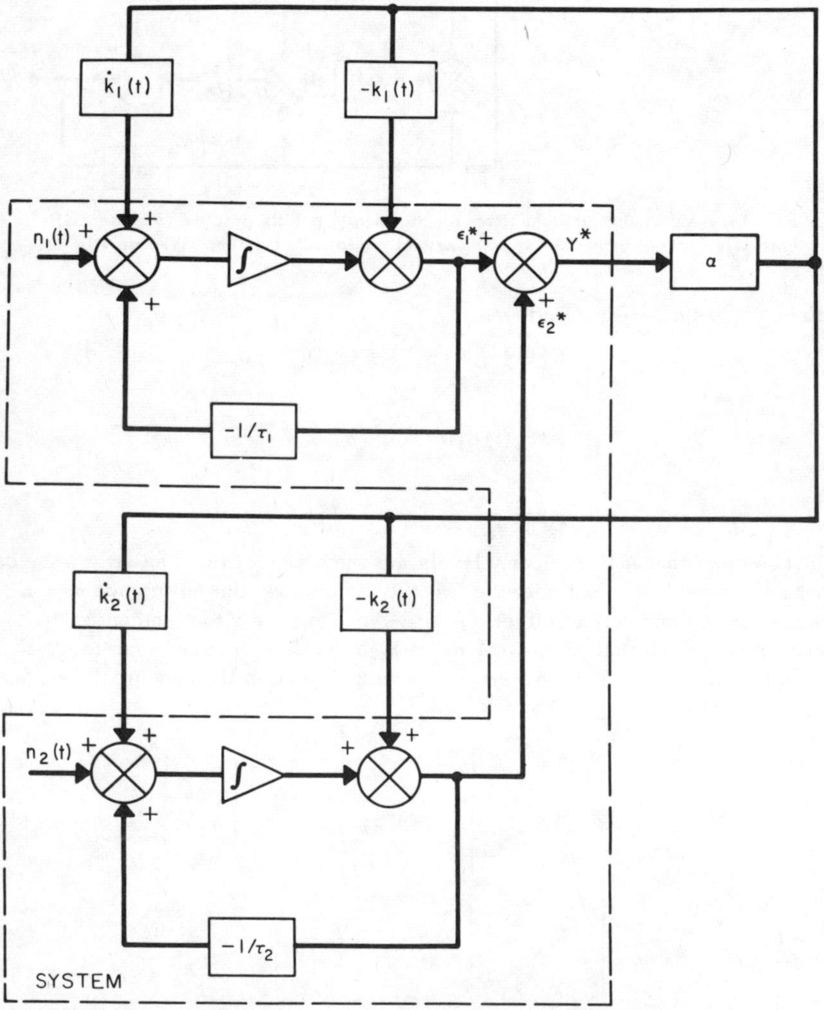

Fig. 15. Feedback optimal filter for the simple mixing problem (based on Fig. 5).

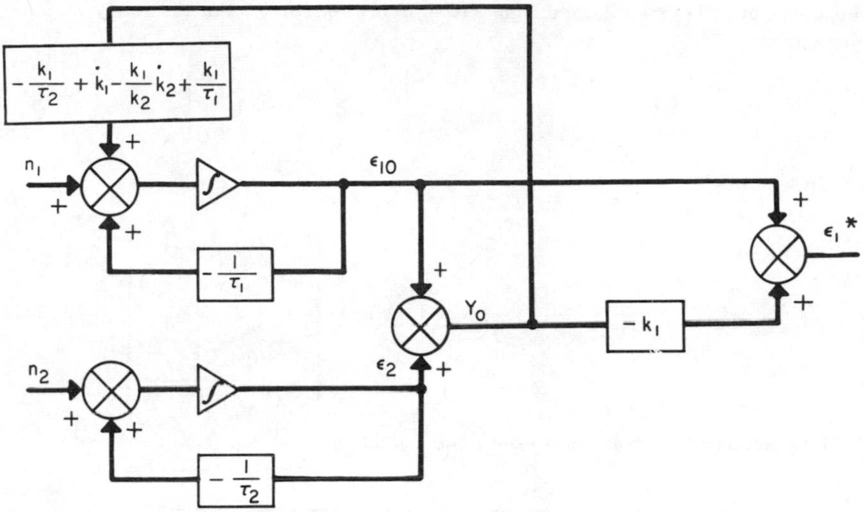

Fig. 16. Feedback optimal filter for the simple mixing problem, noninfinite gain (based on Fig. 13).

version of this feedback filter is given as Figure 16. (Note the advantage of these latter two in that less equipment is involved.)

It remains to determine the scalars k_1, k_2, $\dot{k}_1$, and $\dot{k}_2$. It follows from $Y = \varepsilon_1 + \varepsilon_2$ that

$$P(t) = \begin{bmatrix} p(t) & -p(t) \\ -p(t) & p(t) \end{bmatrix}. \tag{8.1}$$

By substitution in eq. (4.6) there results

$$\dot{p} = \frac{-(\tau_2 - \tau_1)^2 p^2 - \{4\tau_1\tau_2[\sigma^2(\varepsilon_1) + \sigma^2(\varepsilon_2)]\}p + 4\tau_1\tau_2\sigma^2(\varepsilon_2)\sigma^2(\varepsilon_1)}{2\tau_1\tau_2[\tau_2\sigma^2(\varepsilon_1) + \tau_1\sigma^2(\varepsilon_2)]} \tag{8.2}$$

which is a one-dimensional Riccati equation. Following Ince,[6]

$$p(t) = \frac{2\tau_1\tau_2[\tau_2\sigma^2(\varepsilon_1) + \tau_1\sigma^2(\varepsilon_2)]}{(\tau_2 - \tau_1)^2}\,\frac{m_1 e^{m_1 t} + C m_2 e^{m_2 t}}{e^{m_1 t} + C e^{m_2 t}} \tag{8.3}$$

where

$$\left.\begin{matrix} m_1 \\ \\ m_2 \end{matrix}\right\} = \frac{-\left[1 + \dfrac{\sigma^2(\varepsilon_1)}{\sigma^2(\varepsilon_2)}\right] \pm \sqrt{1 + \left[\dfrac{\tau_2}{\tau_1} + \dfrac{\tau_1}{\tau_2}\right]\dfrac{\sigma^2(\varepsilon_1)}{\sigma^2(\varepsilon_2)} + \dfrac{\sigma^4(\varepsilon_1)}{\sigma^4(\varepsilon_4)}}}{\tau_1 + \tau_2\dfrac{\sigma^2(\varepsilon_1)}{\sigma^2(\varepsilon_2)}} \tag{8.4}$$

and C is obtained from the initial condition

$$p(0+) = \frac{2\tau_1\tau_2[\tau_2\sigma^2(\varepsilon_1) + \tau_1\sigma^2(\varepsilon_2)]}{(\tau_2 - \tau_1)^2}\,\frac{m_1 + C m_2}{1 + C} \tag{8.5}$$

The value of $p(0+)$ is obtained from $P(0-)$ using eq. (3.4). For the fairly logical assumption

$$P(0-) = \begin{bmatrix} \sigma^2(\varepsilon_1) & 0 \\ 0 & \sigma^2(\varepsilon_2) \end{bmatrix}, \quad \text{and} \quad \hat{X}(0-) = \begin{bmatrix} 0 \\ 0 \end{bmatrix} \tag{8.6}$$

it follows that

$$p(0+) = \frac{\sigma^2(\varepsilon_1)\sigma^2(\varepsilon_2)}{\sigma^2(\varepsilon_1) + \sigma^2(\varepsilon_2)}, \quad \text{and} \quad \hat{X}(0+) = \begin{bmatrix} \dfrac{Y(0)\sigma^2(\varepsilon_1)}{\sigma^2(\varepsilon_1) + \sigma^2(\varepsilon_2)} \\[2ex] \dfrac{Y(0)\sigma^2(\varepsilon_2)}{\sigma^2(\varepsilon_1) + \sigma^2(\varepsilon_2)} \end{bmatrix} \tag{8.7}$$

The steady state solution is obtained by setting $\dot{p}$ in eq. (8.2) to zero and solving to obtain

$$p(\text{steady state}) = \frac{2\tau_1\tau_2}{(\tau_2 - \tau_1)^2}\left\{\sqrt{\sigma^4(\varepsilon_1) + \sigma^4(\varepsilon_2) + \sigma^2(\varepsilon_1)\sigma^2(\varepsilon_2)\left[\frac{\tau_2}{\tau_1} + \frac{\tau_1}{\tau_2}\right]} - [\sigma^2(\varepsilon_1) + \sigma^2(\varepsilon_2)]\right\} \tag{8.8}$$

Further,

$$K(t) \triangleq \begin{bmatrix} k_1(t) \\ k_2(t) \end{bmatrix} = \frac{1}{2[\tau_2\sigma^2(\varepsilon_1) + \tau_1\sigma^2(\varepsilon_2)]}\begin{bmatrix} 2\tau_2\sigma^2(\varepsilon_1) + (\tau_1 - \tau_2)p(t) \\ 2\tau_1\sigma^2(\varepsilon_2) + (\tau_2 - \tau_1)p(t) \end{bmatrix} \tag{8.9}$$

$$\dot{K}(t) \triangleq \begin{bmatrix} \dot{k}_1(t) \\ \dot{k}_2(t) \end{bmatrix} = \frac{\tau_1\tau_2}{\tau_1 - \tau_2}\begin{bmatrix} \dfrac{(m_1 - m_2)^2\, C e^{(m_1+m_2)t}}{(e^{m_1 t} + C e^{m_2 t})^2} \\[2ex] -\dfrac{(m_1 - m_2)^2\, C e^{(m_1+m_2)t}}{(e^{m_1 t} + C e^{m_2 t})^2} \end{bmatrix} \tag{8.10}$$

To illustrate further, take

$$\sigma^2(\varepsilon_1) = 1,$$
$$\sigma^2(\varepsilon_2) = 1,$$
$$\tau_1 = 2,$$
$$\tau_2 = 1,$$

and $P(0-)$ as per eq. (8.6). Then,

$$\left.\begin{matrix} m_1 \\ m_2 \end{matrix}\right\} = -\frac{2}{3} \pm \sqrt{\frac{1}{2}},$$

$$C = \frac{-\frac{17}{24} + \sqrt{\frac{1}{2}}}{+\frac{17}{24} + \sqrt{\frac{1}{2}}},$$

which can be substituted into eqs. (8.3), (8.9), and (8.10) to obtain k_1, k_2, $\dot{k}_1$ and $\dot{k}_2$.

In the steady state

$$p\,(\text{steady state}) = 4\sqrt{4.5} - 8 = 0.48528$$

$$K\,(\text{steady state}) = 1/3 \begin{bmatrix} 1 + 2\,(\sqrt{4.5} - 2) \\ 2 - 2\,(\sqrt{4.5} - 2) \end{bmatrix} = \begin{bmatrix} 0.41421 \\ 0.58579 \end{bmatrix}$$

and $\dot{k}_1 = \dot{k}_2 = 0$.

It is interesting to note that if the ε_2 is allowed to approach white noise, then k_1 becomes zero. This causes Fig. 16 to take the simpler form suggested in Section 7.

The reader should be reminded that at the time that observation begins, the outputs indicated in Figs. 14, 15, and 16 must be corrected for the initial estimate of errors in accordance with eqs. (3.3) and (3.4).

9. CONCLUSION

The continuous optimal filter has been derived in a manner which, it is hoped, will present fewer impediments to its utilization. Based on these results, a feedback version of the continuous optimal filter has been presented. A simple example of the mixing of two signals, each contaminated by exponentially correlated noise, was studied in detail.

The more interesting and more complicated examples (such as those that arise in inertial navigation) require, as a matter of practical necessity, the use of a computer for their solution. The Sperry Gyroscope Company has developed a digital computer program to do this as an outgrowth of the Generalized Error Analysis Program mentioned in reference 4. It is hoped that continuous optimal feedback filter configurations for the rapid alignment and damping of inertial systems will be the subject of a future paper. It is to be emphasized that these anticipated results will be time-varying feedback configurations and optimal for finite time as opposed to the Wiener solutions based on the infinite past given by Johnson,[7] Porter and Kazda.[8]

ACKNOWLEDGMENTS

The author is grateful for the many stimulating discussions with Mr. J. Caliguiri, Mrs. E. Grinoch, Dr. A. Graefe, Mr. C. SanGiovanni, and Mr. J. Wilcox, which have greatly enriched the contents of this paper.

REFERENCES

1. R. E. Kalman and R. S. Bucy, "New Results in Linear Filtering and Prediction Theory," *J. Basic Engineering* (*ASME Trans.*), **83D**, 95–108 (1961).
2. R. E. Kalman, "New Methods in Wiener Filtering," *Proc. First Symposium on Engineering Applications of Random Function Theory and Probability*, (New York: John Wiley and Sons, 1963).
3. A. E. Bryson and D. E. Johansen, "Linear Filtering for Time-Varying Systems, Using Measurements Containing Colored Noise," Sylvania Applied Research Lab., Report No. 385 (January 20, 1964).
4. S. L. Fagin, "Recursive Linear Regression Theory, Optimal Filter Theory, and Error Analyses of Optimal Systems," *1964 IEEE International Convention Record*, Vol. 12, Pt. 1.
5. A. S. Householder, *Principles of Numerical Analysis* (New York: McGraw Hill, 1953), p. 79.
6. E. L. Ince, *Ordinary Differential Equations* (New York: Dover, 1956), pp. 23–24.
7. F. Johnson, "The Synthesis of Velocity Inertial Navigation Systems," *Proc. Natl. Electronics Conf.* (1959), pp. 784–793.
8. W. A. Porter and L. F. Kazda, "Optimization of a Generalized Velocity-Inertial System," *IRE Trans. on Aerospace and Navigational Electronics* (June 1961).

CERTAIN PROBLEMS IN THE APPLICATION OF MATHEMATICAL ECONOMICS*

M. D. Godfrey
Department of Economics, Princeton University, Princeton, N. J.

This paper will divide the problems in the application of mathematical economics into two arbitrary categories: (1) we will discuss the problems concerning the meaning and accuracy of the empirical information with which economists must deal; and (2) we will present some of the theoretical problems inherent in a view of economic mechanisms as sets of interdependent stochastic relationships.

When we investigate the first problem area, we find that the idea of operationalism which we might adopt from engineering and the physical sciences can be applied only with some difficulty. In many experimental situations in engineering and experimental science, the operational significance of a measurement procedure can be fairly simply described and incorporated into the conclusions which may validly be drawn from the experiment. However, in economics we find that our empirical evidence comes about in some very complex and indirect ways. A full assessment of the operational significance of procedures as complex as the national census requires a level of knowledge and analysis which has simply not been attained in economic science.

Regarding the second problem category, we find that new techniques are required to investigate satisfactorily many of our hypotheses about economic reality. As soon as we admit the factors of interdependence and growth (both in a physical sense and in an organizational and intellectual sense), we find that much of classical statistical methodology is inappropriate for our problems. If we add to our difficulties the very reasonable hypothesis that many aspects of the economic system may purposefully attempt to hide information from statistical discovery, then we are faced with problems which are of the greatest importance but are also far from resolution.

In conclusion, we simply point out that, since the problems of applied mathematical economics are so severe, the scope for solutions of major importance is immense.

1. INTRODUCTION

There is a certain amount of opinion both within and outside economics which holds that economics is, or ought to be, a nonmathematical if not nonscientific subject. While I would not agree with this view categorically, some of the arguments in its support cannot be lightly dismissed. The strongest argument that the nonmathematical school can put forward is that the uncritical application of mathematical techniques which were developed for, and found useful in, other sciences will probably not be successful in economics. This argument is supported on the basis of the unique nature of economic problems. This and other arguments pointing to the difficulties attendent upon the mathematization of economics have been discussed to some extent in the literature. Of particular interest are the works of Oskar Morgenstern.[1,2]

*The research described here was performed at the Econometric Research Program, Princeton University, and was supported by National Science Foundation Grant NSF-GS 551.

Presented at the Symposium on System Theory
Polytechnic Institute of Brooklyn, April 20, 21, 22, 1965

In this paper I do not want to pursue further the general question of the role of mathematics in economics. Rather, I will discuss one particular problem in economics and attempt to indicate that the application of mathematical methods which fall generally in the category of system theory, while at first sight seemingly reasonable, is in fact misleading and inappropriate to what one believes to be the economic reality. However, I will go on to argue that the incorporation of some of the ideas of system theory into a mathematical model which seems to better characterize the economic problem leads to interesting results.

For the purposes of this discussion I will subdivide mathematical methods in economics into two broad categories. The first category consists of a large class of models which reduce mathematically to sets of simultaneous differential or difference equations. The development of these models was originally stimulated by the great success of classical mechanics. The formulations are formally quite similar to those of mechanics. The first complete specification of a model of this kind, applied to an entire economy, was given in 1897 by L. Walras.[3] By about 1930, the problem of statistical estimation of the parameters of these models was being given serious attention. This activity has grown very rapidly with the introduction of general purpose digital computers of an operating simplicity such that they are readily accessible to a large number of students of economics. Today a large proportion of research in economics is concerned with the formulation and estimation of mathematical models which stem from the early adaptations of classical mechanics.

The other general category of mathematical methods comes under the heading of mathematical programming and game theory. This subject is of relatively recent origin. The first important work in this area was not undertaken until the late 1920's. The mathematical formulations that were given were intended to solve problems which had originally arisen in economics. The development of this category of mathematical analysis in economics was slowed by the fact that new understanding of combinatorial mathematics was required to solve the problems presented by these formulations. Statistical estimation in this area has hardly begun.

2. PREDICTION IN ECONOMICS

For the purposes of this paper we may outline the classical development of Wiener (linear) prediction theory for discrete time series as follows. We are given a realization of N equispaced observations of a stochastic process. The process possesses a Cramer representation of the form:

$$x_t = \int_{-\pi}^{\pi} e^{i\omega t}\, dK(\omega) \tag{2.1}$$

where:

x_t = the time series process at time t,
$K(\omega)$ = probability distribution function.

$K(\omega)$ must have independent increments for x_t to be a linear process, and must have a first derivative which is absolutely continuous on the range $-\pi$ to π in order that the process be purely nondeterministic.

The spectral density function for x_t is of course given by:

$$f(\omega) = k(\omega)k^*(\omega) \tag{2.2}$$

where $k(\omega) = dK(\omega)$, and $k^*(\omega)$ = complex conjugate of $k(\omega)$.

We may then represent x_t by:

$$x_t = \sum_{j=0}^{\infty} k_j \, \varepsilon_{t-j} \tag{2.3}$$

where:

$$\varepsilon_t = \text{white Gaussian noise.}$$

The forecast, $\hat{x}_{t+\nu}$, may be represented by:

$$\hat{x}_{t+\nu} = \sum_{j=0}^{\infty} \gamma_j \, x_{t-j} = \sum_{j=0}^{\infty} \Phi_j \, \varepsilon_{t-j} \tag{2.4}$$

Clearly,

$$\Phi(\omega) = k(\omega)\, \gamma(\omega) \tag{2.5}$$

where $\Phi(\omega)$ and $\gamma(\omega)$ are the Fourier transforms of Φ_j and γ_j, respectively.

It is usual to measure the error of the forecast by the error variance

$$\begin{aligned}\sigma_\nu^2 &= E\,[\hat{x}_{t+\nu} - x_{t+\nu}]^2 \\ &= E\left[\sum_{j=0}^{\infty} \Phi_j \, \varepsilon_{t-j} - \sum_{j=0}^{\infty} k_j \, \varepsilon_{t-\nu-j}\right]^2 \\ &= \sigma_\varepsilon^2 \left[\sum_{0}^{\nu-1} k_j^2 + \sum_{0}^{\infty} (\Phi_j - k_{j+\nu})^2\right]\end{aligned} \tag{2.6}$$

This last expression is clearly minimized by setting

$$\Phi_j = k_{j+\nu}. \tag{2.7}$$

Thus, if we can estimate the parameters k_j we can obtain either the Φ_j's or the γ_j's. Least squares estimates of the k_j may be obtained by estimation of the spectral density function and spectral factorization.

An objection to this procedure was raised in the context of systems theory to the effect that there might exist a feedback from the forecast to the input of the process. Given sufficient information to identify the feedback, this problem has been solved. It is only necessary to recognize that this kind of feedback may exist in many economic applications in order to—in principle—solve the problem.

However, the problem that I want to discuss, while involving an interaction between the forecast and the process, cannot be treated as a feedback problem. In the outline above we have considered a stationary process which is characterized by the function $k(\omega)$. We have, in some sense, assumed that the particular $k(\omega)$ which characterizes the process for which we attempt to forecast future values was randomly chosen from the set of all possible $k(\omega)$. Now we want to consider the consequences for our forecasting procedure of considering the $k(\omega)$

to have been chosen by an opponent whose interest is to maximize σ_ν^2, subject to certain costs associated with his choices. Thus the opponent controls, within limits, the function $k(\omega)$, while we have under our control the estimation procedure which we will carry out. In particular, we will assume that we have a choice of:

1. the length of the realization (N),
2. the number of parameters which we will attempt to estimate.

The opponent controls $k(\omega)$ by a choice of the coefficients in the z-transform expression for $k(\omega)$:

$$k(z) = \frac{\sum_0^m a_j z^j}{1 - \sum_1^\ell b_j z^j} \tag{2.8}$$

Since σ_ν^2 is given by:

$$\sigma_\nu^2 = \sigma_\varepsilon^2 \left[\sum_0^{\nu-1} k_j^2 + \sum_0^\infty (\Phi_j - k_{j+\nu})^2 \right] \tag{2.9}$$

the opponent will attempt to maximize the sum

$$\sum_0^{\nu-1} k_j^2 + \sum_0^\infty (\Phi_j - k_{j+\nu})^2.$$

However, the opponent does not know the estimates that we will supply for the Φ_j and thus his maximization problem depends on our choice of estimation procedure. However, when we attempt to estimate $k(\omega)$ we must implicitly use an assumption concerning the values of ℓ and m in eq. (2.8). We need this information in order to decide on the number of parameters γ_j to estimate, and the length of the realization which we will need.

We will now consider a special case of this model which involves the following further simplifications:

1. The opponent chooses only the parameter ℓ and the values of the parameters b_j of a process with z-transform representation

$$k(z) = \frac{1}{1 - \sum_1^\ell b_j z^j}. \tag{2.10}$$

Thus the γ_j's which we estimate will be estimates of the b_j's directly. Given a sufficiently long realization from the process with a given ℓ and given values of b_j we can determine ℓ and estimate the b_j with asymptotically zero error due to the consistency of the least squares estimates.

2. The game is played over a long series of consecutive realizations such that we can consider expectations over these realizations.

3. Each realization comes from a given ℓ and set of b_j. The opponent may change ℓ and b_j only between realizations.

4. We have, basically, two choices with respect to estimation of the parameters γ_j. We can estimate a set of γ_j separately for each realization or we can pool realizations.

Clearly, if the opponent changes the parameters in such a way that we can reject the null hypothesis that the parameters are the same, then we will tend to estimate separately. If we cannot reject the null hypothesis, we will tend to combine realizations.

If we now want to look for a reasonable form of optimal behavior for the two participants in this situation we are led naturally to the minimax solution of a 2-person constant sum game. Thus each player will select that strategy which minimizes the maximum loss which can result from the opponent's possible actions. The payoff of the game is naturally measured in terms of the variance of the forecast error. Thus we have a payoff matrix of the form of Table I.

TABLE I.

		predictor strategies		
		$\gamma_1(z)$	$\gamma_2(z)$	$\gamma_3(z)$---
	$k_1(z)$	$\sigma^2_{\nu,(1,1)}$	$\sigma^2_{\nu,(1,2)}$	$\sigma^2_{\nu,(1,3)}$
generator strategies	$k_2(z)$	$\sigma^2_{\nu,(2,1)}$	$\sigma^2_{\nu,(2,2)}$	$\sigma^2_{\nu,(2,3)}$
	$k_3(z)$ ⋮	$\sigma^2_{\nu,(3,1)}$	$\sigma^2_{\nu,(3,2)}$	$\sigma^2_{\nu,(3,3)}$

In Table I,

$$\sum \sigma^2_{\nu,(p,q)} = \sigma^2_{\varepsilon}\left[\sum_{1}^{\nu-1} k_j^2(p) + \sum_{0}^{\infty} (\Phi_j(q) - k_{j+\nu}(p))^2\right].$$

It is clear that this matrix does not have a saddle point and thus we are led to look for a solution in terms of mixed strategies. We define mixed strategies as:

$$Sg = (\alpha_1 k_1(z), \alpha_2 k_2(z), \alpha_3 k_3(z))$$
$$Sp = (\beta_1 \gamma_1(z), \beta_2 \gamma_2(z), \beta_3 \gamma_3(z))$$

where α_i and β_j are the probabilities of using k_i and γ_j. The payoff function is then:

$$P = \sum_p \sum_q \alpha_p \beta_q \sigma^2_{\nu,(p,q)}.$$

The solution is given by:

$$P_0 = \min_p \max_q P.$$

Note that since the payoff matrix may be transformed into a Minkowski-Leontief matrix, α_i and $\beta_j > 0$ for all i and j.

3. CONCLUSION

This paper has attempted to demonstrate one simple point: that for a specified class of models, it is impossible to apply correctly the usual procedures of linear prediction theory. The inferences which one would draw from an application of these techniques would not be correct. We derive a seemingly more reasonable solution to the problem.

The kind of formulation which has been presented may obviously be extended to the problem of estimation of transfer functions given a realization of the input and the output. Extensions such as this are currently being explored.

REFERENCES

1. O. Morgenstern, "On the Limits of the Use of Mathematics in Economics," Research Memorandum No. 49, Princeton University, Econometric Research Program (January 1963).
2. O. Morgenstern, *On the Accuracy of Economic Observations*, 2nd ed. (Princeton, N. J.: Princeton University Press, 1964).
3. L. Walras, *Elements of Pure Economics* (translated by W. Jaffe), (London: George Allen and Unwin Ltd., 1954).
4. P. Whittle, *Prediction and Regulation* (Princeton, N. J.: D. Van Nostrand Co., Inc., 1963).

SOME MATHEMATICAL TOPICS IN BIOLOGY

H. Cohen* and S. I. Rubinow

Cornell University, Graduate School of Medical Sciences, New York, N.Y., and Sloan-Kettering Institute for Cancer Research, New York, N.Y.

The appearance of quantitative data in the biological sciences has usually led to a confrontation with mathematical concepts and ideas. This is not unlike the experience in the physical sciences. However, the success of mathematics in biology has been more limited because of the absence of underlying fundamental mathematical theories, such as, say, Maxwell's equations in electricity and magnetism. The mathematical theories in biology are, by and large, mathematical models which attempt to simulate biological processes in a phenomenological manner.

A number of mathematical models of biological processes will be discussed, as illustrations of the role of mathematics in biology today. These are the following: the Hodgkin-Huxley equations which describe the formation and behavior of the action potential in the nerve membrane; compartment theory, greatly stimulated in recent years by the use of radioactive isotopes, which represents a linear synthesis of physiological processes; mathematical attempts to describe some features of the human circulatory system.

I. INTRODUCTION

The scope of what might be included in a mathematical discussion of biological systems is large, probably equal to, if not greater than, that of other physical systems that we feel we know something about. Unfortunately, a careful and useful mathematical characterization has not yet been attained in many biological systems. Historically, this does not appear to be due to a lack of interest in biology on the part of theoreticians. Many eminent mathematicians and physicists have in fact interested themselves in theoretical aspects of biological problems in the past. Specifically, mention may be made of Euler,[1] Helmholtz,[2] Volterra,[3] and, in more recent times, Fisher,[4] Schrodinger,[5] and von Neumann.[6] However, the paucity of investigators must be ascribed to the lack of quantitative data that has existed in biology. As everyone knows, the remedies for this situation are now beginning to appear with many new experimental techniques and data-gathering methods making for increased quantification of the science.

The discussion we shall present will try to deal with some portions of only two systems, the circulatory system and the nerve system, both of these from physiology. The high degree of selectivity is partly based on the fact that we

*Permanent position: IBM Thomas J. Watson Research Center, Yorktown Heights, New York

Presented at the Symposium on System Theory
Polytechnic Institute of Brooklyn, April 20, 21, 22, 1965

consider these two areas to be among the most presentable mathematically, and partly on the fact that we, ourselves, know a little about them and much less about the other biological systems. We shall also make some remarks about another kind of mathematical method used in physiological studies in which even less is known about the details of the system than in the circulatory or the nervous system. This is the method called "pool" or "compartment" theory which has come to be an important tool in using radioactive isotope data to understand physiological relationships. We would like it clearly understood how well we realize that we are speaking about an ε's worth of biology.

The two systems, circulation and nerve, have, in our view, certain very special aspects in common. One can say that they are of equal geometrical complexity and that they may be considered to be nonlinear transmission lines. However, the function of one is to transmit energy, and, of the other, information. The blood flow throughout the body has a concentrated source for its energy, the heart pump; the nerve system may be said to have a focal point of information transfer, the brain, but its energy sources are distributed along its lines. Of course, all of this is simplification since, in fact, each of these systems is intimately interconnected with the other.

Finally, although the systems we discuss are potentially susceptible to systems analysis, it will be seen that we shall not be doing a systems analysis after all and that the mathematical attention is given to certain basic elements of these systems. We believe that for the two special cases we speak of, this is appropriate and necessary at this point. When an understanding of the basic elements is not available, then it is still possible to apply the general method of compartment analysis.

II. THE NERVE SYSTEM

The nerve system consists of nodal points (cell soma and dendrites), lines (axons), and special termini (receptors and neuromuscular junctures). The wiring diagram is complex, but for the peripheral system of muscle control, for example, it is not difficult to trace out bundles of nerve fibers as they leave cell bodies, synapse with others, terminate in near contact with muscles, or follow feedback routes from muscles through synapses to cells that influence the originating stimuli at motor cells. The best understood part of this process at present is the conduction of the nerve impulse along a single one of the nerve fibers or axons. It has been known for a long time that the mode of conduction is a pulse, typically of 100 millivolt amplitude and 1 millisecond width that maintains its shape as it travels at fixed velocity along the nerve membrane. The membrane is the outer covering of the nerve axon. It is 100 Å (10^{-6} cm) thick whereas the diameter of the axon itself is of the order of microns (10^{-4} cm). The membrane is the conducting element of the nerve. It is permeable to the ions in the fluids outside and inside, but its permeability, in fact, becomes the central problem of the nerve conduction process.

The fluid external to the nerve membrane has a high concentration of sodium and the internal protoplasm has a high concentration of potassium. When there is no applied voltage across the membrane, the resting state before the nerve im-

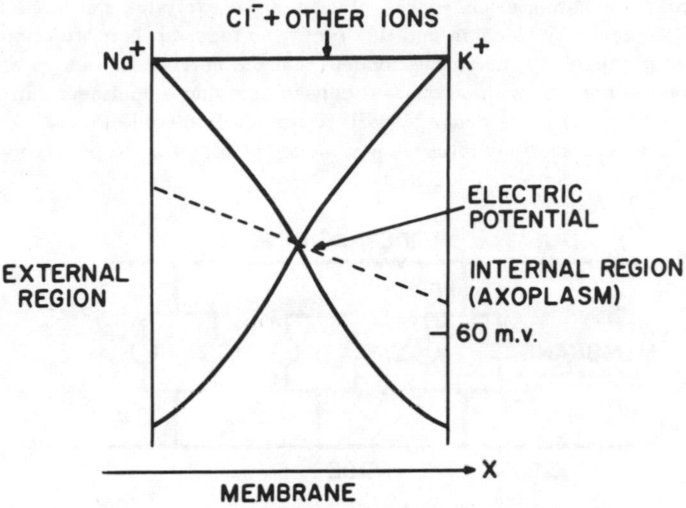

Fig. 1. Anion and cation concentrations and electric potential across a nerve membrane in the resting state.

pulses arrive, the inside is 60 millivolts negative with respect to the outside (see Fig. 1). This resting state can be represented through the Nernst-Planck equations[7] for electrolytic behavior:

$$\mu_i \left[\frac{\partial^2 C_i^{\pm}}{\partial x^2} \mp \frac{\partial\left(C_i^{\pm} \frac{\partial \psi}{\partial x}\right)}{\partial x} \right] = 0, \tag{1}$$

$$\kappa \frac{\partial^2 \psi}{\partial x^2} = \rho(x) = \sum C_i^{+} - \sum C_i^{-} . \tag{2}$$

The $C_i^{\pm}$ are the concentrations of cations and anions, ψ is the electric potential, and ρ, the total charge. We have written the equations in a normalized form to include the mobilities μ_i, which in fact play no role in the steady state, and also a coefficient κ. κ is actually a ratio of an electric relaxation time scale to a diffusion time scale. Setting $\kappa = 0$, the neutral charge condition, is a good approximation everywhere except near large changes in the potential gradient, and in this approximation the equations are easy to solve and give exponential distributions for the concentrations of the ions. However, this Nernst-Planck model is an inaccurate description of the dynamic behavior of the excitable nerve membrane. If, on the right-hand side of eq. (1), $\partial C_i/\partial t$ is added for each ion species, and the mobilities, the μ_i, are taken to have their constant aqueous values, the response time scale of a sodium-potassium system to electric field changes across the membrane is of the order of 10^{-8} seconds, not the 10^{-3} second scale of the nerve impulse (see reference 8).*

*Excitable membrane theories based on such electrolytic theories but with fixed charge distributions or convection forces added have been given by Teorell[9] and others.

A successful mathematical representation of the excitable membrane has however been achieved by Hodgkin and Huxley,[10] who focused their attention on changes in permeability, using the concept that the nerve membrane is effectively an inductance-free line with a constant capacitance and a nonlinear current flow element (see Fig. 2). The concept, derived from Kelvin cable theory, serves not only for the active sections of nerve membrane but also for the passive signal transmission that occurs in dendrites.

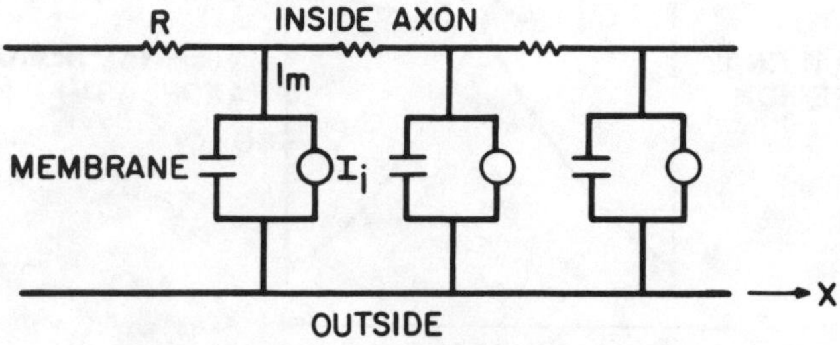

Fig. 2. Cable model of the nerve membrane.

The differential equation for I_m, the current distribution along the membrane, is

$$I_m = \frac{a}{2R}\frac{\partial^2 v}{\partial x^2} = C\frac{\partial v}{\partial t} + I_i. \tag{3}$$

Here, R is the equivalent distributed resistance due to the axoplasm; a is the axon diameter; C is the constant capacity of the membrane; and v is the voltage across the membrane. Hodgkin and Huxley contributed the careful measurement of I_i, finding that it could be represented, for the axon of the squid, by the expression

$$I_i = g_{Na}(v)(v - v_{Na}) + g_K(v)(v - v_K) + \bar{g}_\ell(v - v_\ell). \tag{4}$$

Equation (4) expresses the fact that there are separate currents associated with the sodium, potassium and leakage ions, regulated by the conductivities g_K, g_{Na}, and $\bar{g}_\ell$. The voltage v_K, and v_{Na}, and v_ℓ, are fixed characteristic voltages of this ionic current element (see Fig. 3). It was found in turn that the conductivities g_K and g_{Na} were voltage dependent and could best be presented by three new variables, m, n and h; thus,

$$g_K = \bar{g}_K n^4 \quad \text{and} \quad g_{Na} = m^3 h \bar{g}_{Na}, \tag{5}$$

where $\bar{g}_K$ and $\bar{g}_{Na}$ are constants, and the new variables satisfy the differential equations

$$\frac{dm}{dt} = \alpha_m(v)(1 - m) - \beta_m(v)\, m, \tag{6}$$

$$\frac{dn}{dt} = \alpha_n(v)(1 - n) - \beta_n(v)\, n, \tag{7}$$

$$\frac{dh}{dt} = \alpha_h(v)(1 - h) - \beta_h(v)\, h, \tag{8}$$

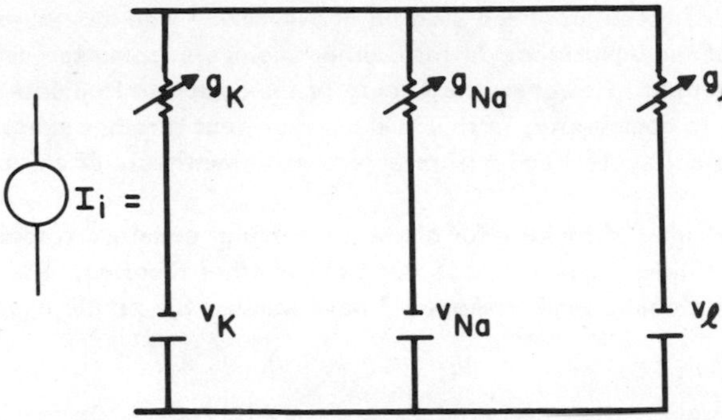

Fig. 3. The nonlinear ionic current element, I_i.

The α's and β's are experimentally determined functions of the voltage. Now, (3), (4), (6), (7), and (8) form a coupled system of partial and ordinary differential equations for the voltage $v(x, t)$ and the effective conductivities (or permeabilities) $m(x, t)$, $n(x, t)$, $h(x, t)$.

Solutions of this equation system have been obtained numerically. The knowledge that the nerve impulse has a fixed shape and a constant velocity suggests the assumption that

$$v = v(x - \theta t) = v(\xi), \quad \theta \text{ constant}, \quad \xi = x - \theta t. \tag{9}$$

The resulting system of ordinary differential equations is then solved to find a value of θ and a pulse shape that has the properties that $v(\zeta) \longrightarrow 0$ for $|\xi| \longrightarrow +\infty$.

The reason for using this complicated fifth-order system of equations is its essential biological correctness. The steady-state calculation just mentioned, when carried out numerically, provides a voltage impulse whose characteristics in amplitude, time, velocity, etc., are excellent reproductions of the experimentally measured quantities. Recently completed transient calculations[11] which do not assume the propagating wave form show that a stable wave form is attained from an initially transient state. These calculations also exhibit certain of the frequency characteristics of this model. For a given current stimulus, a hat-function for I_m at a fixed value of x, which satisfies a threshold stimulation-duration criterion, a number of pulses are produced. The number is a function of the amplitude and ranges from one to infinity. This, however, is an aspect of the equations that will require further detailed study and is also an aspect of the experimental side that will need systematic investigation.

As has been mentioned, these equations have been handled numerically, mostly by difference methods. How much information can be obtained by analytical approximations? Fitzhugh[12] has exhibited many of the geometrical properties of solutions to the nonpropagating system that are obtained when I_m is a given constant in (3). Experimentally, this "space-clamped" case is attained by forcing the current, I_m, to be a given value along a nerve axon. Fitzhugh has also proposed two different approximate systems of equations which are second order systems. One of these has been studied by Nagumo,[13] who has given a tunnel diode analog of the equations. In fact, other analogs such as the neuristor have also been presented. However, the beauty of the complete Hodgkin-Huxley theory, for all of its complexity, is that it does represent a rather exact analysis of the real biological system and not an approximate synthesis of an analogous system.

The general idea of looking for shape-preserving, constant velocity solutions to nonlinear diffusion equations has occurred in other theories. Fisher[14] and Kolmogorov, Petrovsky, and Piskunov[15] have studied the single equation

$$u_t = u_{xx} + F(u), \tag{10}$$

where $F(u)$ has properties that produce a propagating wave. In fact, in their case, which arises from a model for the propagation of a mutant gene through a population, there are an infinite number of satisfactory solutions in the steady-state analysis. The preferred solution must be chosen from an analysis of the initial value problem. Similar considerations have arisen in flame propagation studies.[16] The important property of all of these nonlinear diffusion models is that these waves are self-sustained, drawing energy from the local environment (through ion transport in the nerve case) to counteract the decay that ordinary diffusion would produce. The important question of stability that arises involves such matters as stable dependence on initial conditions as well as stability in the small perturbation case.

These remarks have had to do only with the signal conduction along an individual line of the nerve system. If one would like to consider a series of elements, one could possibly view nerve-muscle interaction in the following manner. Consider the time-distance diagram of Fig. 4. Let $x = x_0$ be effectively the locus of a motor cell body. Input signals are received from synapses at the body and its dendrites and are apparently propagated in a passive diffusion mode through the membrane of the cell body. When the summed amplitude of these signals reaches a proper threshold at the initial portion of the axon called the axon hill-

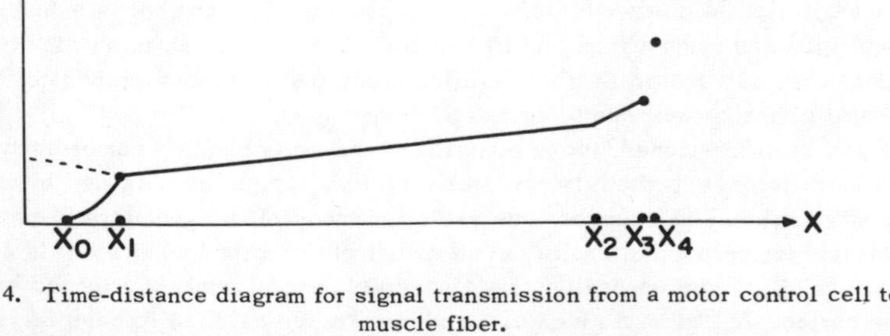

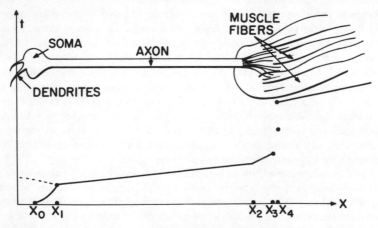

Fig. 4. Time-distance diagram for signal transmission from a motor control cell to a muscle fiber.

ock ($x = x_1$), an active propagation begins down the axon away from the cell body and also back through the cell body. The impulse travels along the axon sending out lateral signals to other cells that may return as inhibitions until, just before the muscle is reached, the nerve fiber fragments into many smaller fibers (x_2). According to the Hodgkin-Huxley theory, active impulse propagation velocity decreases with axon diameter. The fibers imbed themselves into the muscle surface, and electrical transmission of the signal is supplanted by chemical transmission across a gap (x_3–x_4) between the nerve fiber's membrane and the muscle surface. A statistical description of this process has been given by Katz and others,[17] and something is known of the frequency response of this chemical junction. A new impulse is created on the muscle side x_4 and propagates actively along the membrane of a muscle fiber, causing contractile mechanisms to be set into play.

This is the system which is yet to be developed by a thorough analysis of this series of elements. In our view, it is premature to look at this time for a kind of Kirchhoff law simplification of nerve networks. The high degree of sophistication that this electrochemical information transfer process exhibits awaits a more extensive mathematical description.

III. THE CIRCULATORY SYSTEM

The conception of the circulatory system as an electrical transmission line is an appealing one. There is an obvious analogy between pressure and potential, blood flow and electrical current, viscosity and resistance, capacitance and wall distensibility, and so forth. Furthermore, a study of the mechanics of the circulatory system has the advantage, rare in biology, that the underlying physical principles are well understood. In this case these principles are the equations of motion of deformable media. Schematically, the circulatory system appears to have a simple structure: a periodic source, the heart, distributes blood through a system of elastic tubes. A surprising feature of the system is that while the source strength is oscillating (ac), the object is to provide a steady flow at the periphery (dc power). However, there are serious technical difficulties: the arteries and veins have a highly complex geometry, detailed anatomical knowledge of it is rather sparse, and it is variable from individual to individual. Mammalian blood exhibits anomalous properties because it is a suspension, made up largely of red blood corpuscles at high concentration. The flow may not always be laminar. There is evidence that the walls of arteries are slightly viscoelastic rather than being purely elastic. There are active muscle fibers in the walls of some vessels which introduce thereby a nonlinear element in their behavior. At the capillary level, diffusion through the walls and the multiple connectivity of the vessels makes the usefulness of the concept of tube flow open to question. Not until very recently have there been some more or less empirical attempts to synthesize the entire circulatory system in a detailed manner. Grodins[18] has examined the self-regulatory and feedback aspects of the system especially with regard to cardiac operation. In these studies, however, the essentially passive elements, the arteries and the veins, have been treated as lumped parameter elements, empirically determined. Only one very recent study of the pulmonary circulatory system has considered the arteries and veins as distributed elements whose characteristics are determined by theory.[19] The theory utilized is that due to Womersley,[20] who has made an extensive investigation of the pulse transmission in arteries. Similar considerations have been made by others[21] to a greater or lesser extent. We shall present here a somewhat more elaborate version of this theory.[22]

The basic point of view is that the heart provides a known periodic pressure disturbance, which may be Fourier analysed. It will consist of a fundamental frequency, the heart beat, and higher harmonics. With each harmonic, there is associated a progressing wave. We wish to investigate the subsequent propagation of such waves throughout the arterial and venous system. We may assume that this system is made up of a sequence of branched segments. Of course, it is necessary to know what happens at a junction, but the fundamental problem is the determination of the propagation characteristics in a single segment.

The flow of blood in a single blood vessel is represented by the flow of a viscous incompressible fluid through an elastic cylindrical tube of radius a and of finite thickness h (see Fig. 5). The tube is assumed to be infinitely long, for simplicity. The fluid obeys the linearized Navier-Stokes equations and the equation of continuity,

$$\left.\begin{aligned} \rho_0 \frac{\partial u}{\partial t} &= -\frac{\partial p}{\partial r} + \mu\left[\frac{\partial^2 u}{\partial r^2} + \frac{1}{r}\frac{\partial u}{\partial r} - \frac{u}{r^2} + \frac{\partial^2 u}{\partial z^2}\right], && (11)\\ \rho_0 \frac{\partial w}{\partial t} &= -\frac{\partial p}{\partial z} + \mu\left[\frac{\partial^2 w}{\partial r^2} + \frac{1}{r}\frac{\partial w}{\partial r} + \frac{\partial^2 w}{\partial z^2}\right], && (12)\\ &\frac{\partial u}{\partial r} + \frac{u}{r} + \frac{\partial w}{\partial z} = 0. && (13) \end{aligned}\right\} 0 \leq r < a$$

In these equations, u is the radial velocity component, w the longitudinal velocity component, p the pressure, ρ_0 the fluid density, and μ the coefficient of viscosity.

The fluid, as well as the tube motion, is assumed to be radially symmetric. The tube motion is governed by the linearized equations of elasticity,

$$\left.\begin{aligned} \rho\frac{\partial^2 \xi}{\partial t^2} &= \frac{E}{2(1+\sigma)}\left[\frac{\partial^2 \xi}{\partial r^2} + \frac{1}{r}\frac{\partial \xi}{\partial r} - \frac{\xi}{r^2} + \frac{\partial^2 \xi}{\partial z^2}\right]\\ &\quad + \frac{E}{2(1+\sigma)(1-2\sigma)}\left[\frac{\partial^2 \xi}{\partial r^2} + \frac{1}{r}\frac{\partial \xi}{\partial r} - \frac{\xi}{r^2} + \frac{\partial^2 \eta}{\partial z\,\partial r}\right], && (14)\\ \rho\frac{\partial^2 \eta}{\partial t^2} &= \frac{E}{2(1+\sigma)}\left[\frac{\partial^2 \eta}{\partial r^2} + \frac{1}{r}\frac{\partial \eta}{\partial r} + \frac{\partial^2 \eta}{\partial z^2}\right]\\ &\quad + \frac{E}{2(1+\sigma)(1-2\sigma)}\left[\frac{\partial^2 \eta}{\partial z^2} + \frac{\partial^2 \xi}{\partial z\,\partial r} + \frac{1}{r}\frac{\partial \xi}{\partial z}\right], && (15) \end{aligned}\right\} a < r \leq a + h.$$

Here, ξ is the radial displacement, η the longitudinal displacement, ρ the density, E the elastic modulus and σ the Poisson ratio of the elastic medium.

At the fluid-wall interface, matching conditions must be obeyed. The velocity is continuous, and the radial and tangential components of the stress are continu-

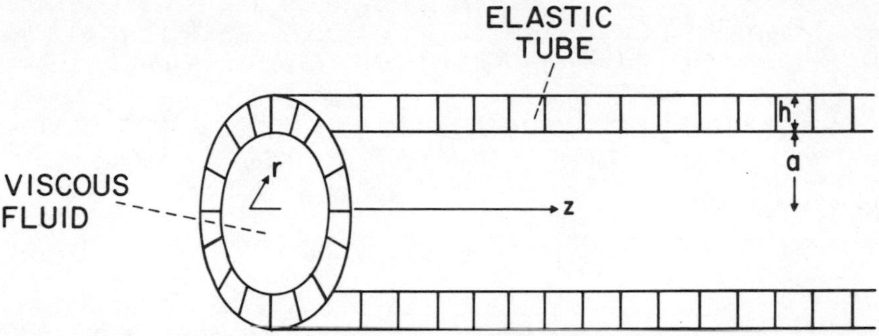

Fig. 5. Viscous fluid flowing through an elastic cylindrical tube.

ous. Thus,

$$\left.\begin{aligned} u &= \frac{\partial \xi}{\partial t}, &(16)\\ w &= \frac{\partial \eta}{\partial t}, &(17)\\ -p + 2\mu \frac{\partial u}{\partial r} &= \frac{E}{(1+\sigma)(1-2\sigma)}\left[(1-\sigma)\frac{\partial \xi}{\partial r} + \sigma\left(\frac{\partial \eta}{\partial z} + \frac{\xi}{r}\right)\right], &(18)\\ \mu\left[\frac{\partial u}{\partial z} + \frac{\partial w}{\partial r}\right] &= \frac{E}{2(1+\sigma)}\left[\frac{\partial \xi}{\partial z} + \frac{\partial \eta}{\partial r}\right], &(19) \end{aligned}\right\} r = a.$$

The tube is assumed to be "free," so that the stress components at the outer boundary of the tube must vanish,

$$\left.\begin{aligned} 0 &= \frac{E}{(1+\sigma)(1-2\sigma)}\left[(1-\sigma)\frac{\partial \xi}{\partial r} + \sigma\left(\frac{\partial \eta}{\partial z} + \frac{\xi}{r}\right)\right], &(20)\\ 0 &= \frac{E}{2(1+\sigma)}\left[\frac{\partial \xi}{\partial z} + \frac{\partial \eta}{\partial r}\right], &(21) \end{aligned}\right\} r = a + h.$$

Let us seek a solution which is harmonic in time and in the longitudinal space direction, that is, let

$$[p, u, w, \xi, \eta] = [p(r), u(r), w(r), \xi(r), \eta(r)] \exp i(kz - \omega t). \tag{22}$$

Substituting (22) into eqs. (11)-(15), there result equations for the radial parts of (22) whose solutions are known:

$$p(r) = p_0 \frac{I_0(kr)}{I_0(k)}, \tag{23}$$

$$u(r) = u_0 \frac{I_1(\sqrt{k^2 - i\alpha}\, r)}{I_0(\sqrt{k^2 - i\alpha})} - p_0 \frac{ik}{\alpha}\frac{I_1(kr)}{I_0(k)}, \tag{24}$$

$$w(r) = w_0 \frac{I_0(\sqrt{k^2 - i\alpha}\, r)}{I_0(\sqrt{k^2 - i\alpha})} + p_0 \frac{k}{\alpha}\frac{I_0(kr)}{I_0(k)}, \tag{25}$$

$$\xi(r) = \ell\left[A\,\frac{J_1(\ell r)}{J_0(\ell)} + B\,\frac{N_1(\ell r)}{N_0(\ell)}\right] + k\left[C\,\frac{J_1(pr)}{J_0(p)} + D\,\frac{N_1(pr)}{N_0(p)}\right], \tag{26}$$

$$\eta(r) = -ik\left[A\,\frac{J_0(\ell r)}{J_0(\ell)} + B\,\frac{N_0(\ell r)}{N_0(\ell)}\right] + ip\left[C\,\frac{J_0(pr)}{J_0(p)} + D\,\frac{N_0(pr)}{N_0(p)}\right]. \tag{27}$$

In these equations

$$\left.\begin{aligned} \alpha &= \frac{\rho_0\, a^2\, \omega\omega_0}{\mu}, \\ \omega_0 &= \sqrt{\frac{E}{\rho a^2}}, \\ \ell^2 &= \frac{(1+\sigma)(1-2\sigma)}{(1-\sigma)}\,\omega^2 - k^2, \\ p^2 &= 2(1+\sigma)\,\omega^2 - k^2, \end{aligned}\right\} \tag{28}$$

and ω and k are measured in units of ω_0 and $1/a$, respectively. J_ν and N_ν are Bessel and Neumann functions, respectively; I_ν are the Bessel functions of imaginary argument; and p_0, u_0, w_0, A, B, C, and D are constants to be determined.

If we impose on the solutions (23)–(27) the equation of continuity, (13), the matching conditions at the fluid wall interface ((16)–(19)), and the boundary conditions at the outer wall ((20)–(21)), there result six simultaneous linear homogeneous equations for the unknown constants, p_0, w_0, A, B, C, and D. The necessity for a nontrivial solution makes the determinant of the coefficient matrix vanish, as exhibited in eq. (29).
In eq. (29),

$$\left.\begin{aligned} F(k) &= \frac{I_1(k)}{kI_0(k)}, \\ \Delta_1(\ell) &= N_1(\ell)J_1\left(\ell + \frac{\ell h}{a}\right) - J_1(\ell)N_1\left(\ell + \frac{\ell h}{a}\right), \\ \Delta_2(\ell) &= N_0(\ell)J_1\left(\ell + \frac{\ell h}{a}\right) - J_0(\ell)N_1\left(\ell + \frac{\ell h}{a}\right), \\ \Delta_3(\ell) &= N_1(\ell)J_0\left(\ell + \frac{\ell h}{a}\right) - J_1(\ell)N_0\left(\ell + \frac{\ell h}{a}\right), \\ \Delta_4(\ell) &= N_0(\ell)J_0\left(\ell + \frac{\ell h}{a}\right) - J_0(\ell)N_0\left(\ell + \frac{\ell h}{a}\right). \end{aligned}\right\} \tag{30}$$

This is the dispersion relation which determines the allowed values of the wave number k as a function of the frequency ω and the nondimensional parameters ρ/ρ_0, h/a, σ, and α/ω. It can be considerably simplified if it is assumed that the tube thickness approaches zero, $h/a \longrightarrow 0$, but the tube mass is kept finite

$$
\begin{vmatrix}
\frac{\omega}{\alpha}(2k^2 - i\alpha)F(\sqrt{k^2 - i\alpha}) & 2\omega \frac{k^3}{\alpha^2} F(k) & 0 & \frac{i\rho k \ell^2}{\rho_o(1+\sigma)} & 0 & -\frac{i\rho(p^2 - k^2)}{2\rho_o(1+\sigma)} \\
-i2\omega \frac{k}{\alpha}\left[1 - F(\sqrt{k^2 - i\alpha})\right] & -\frac{\omega}{\alpha}\left\{1 + \frac{i2k}{\alpha}\left[1 - F(k)\right]\right\} & \frac{\rho}{\rho_o(1+\sigma)}\,\frac{p^2 - k^2}{2} & -\frac{\rho \ell^2}{\rho_o(1+\sigma)} & \frac{\rho k}{\rho_o(1+\sigma)} & -\frac{\rho k}{\rho_o(1+\sigma)} \\
kF(\sqrt{k^2 - i\alpha}) & \frac{k^2}{\alpha} F(k) & 0 & \omega \ell^2 & 0 & \omega k \\
1 & \frac{k}{\alpha} & -\omega k & 0 & \omega & 0 \\
0 & 0 & -\frac{i\rho k \ell^2}{\rho_o(1+\sigma)}\Delta_1(\ell) & \frac{i\rho k \ell^3}{\rho_o(1+\sigma)}\Delta_2(\ell) & \frac{i\rho(p^2 - k^2)}{2\rho_o(1+\sigma)}\Delta_1(p) & -\frac{i\rho(p^2 - k^2)p}{2\rho_o(1+\sigma)}\Delta_2(p) \\
0 & 0 & \begin{matrix} -\frac{\rho(p^2 - k^2)\ell}{2\rho_o(1+\sigma)}\Delta_3(\ell) \\ +\frac{\rho \ell^2}{\rho_c(1+\sigma)}\frac{a}{a+h}\Delta_1(\ell) \end{matrix} & \begin{matrix} \frac{\rho \ell^2(p^2 - k^2)}{2\rho_o(1+\sigma)}\Delta_4(\ell) \\ -\frac{\rho \ell^3}{\rho_o(1+\sigma)}\frac{a}{a+h}\Delta_2(\ell) \end{matrix} & \begin{matrix} -\frac{\rho k p}{\rho_o(1+\sigma)}\Delta_3(p) \\ +\frac{\rho k}{\rho_o(1+\sigma)}\frac{a}{a+h}\Delta_1(p) \end{matrix} & \begin{matrix} \frac{\rho k p^2}{\rho_o(1+\sigma)}\Delta_4(p) \\ -\frac{\rho k p}{\rho_o(1+\sigma)}\frac{a}{a+h}\Delta_2(p) \end{matrix}
\end{vmatrix} = 0
$$

Equation (29)

so that

$$\lim \frac{\rho\, 2\pi h a}{\rho_0 \pi a^2} \equiv \varepsilon.$$

In that case, we may replace the Δ's appearing in the last two rows of the determinant as follows:

$$\left.\begin{aligned} \frac{\pi}{2}\,\Delta_1(x) &= -\frac{h}{a} + \ldots, \\ \frac{\pi}{2}\,x\,\Delta_2(x) &= 1 - \frac{h}{a} + \ldots, \\ \frac{\pi}{2}\,x\,\Delta_3(x) &= -1 + \ldots, \\ \frac{\pi}{2}\,\Delta_4(x) &= -\frac{h}{a} + \ldots, \end{aligned}\right\} \tag{31}$$

In order to display some explicit features of the solution analytically, we shall also assume here that the fluid is inviscid. With these assumptions, the dispersion relation becomes

$$\left(\frac{\omega}{k}\right)^4 [2 + \varepsilon k^2 F(k)]\,(1 - \sigma^2) - \left(\frac{\omega}{k}\right)^2 [2 + \varepsilon\,(1 + k^2) F(k)] + \varepsilon F(k) = 0 \tag{32}$$

It is more convenient, in looking for a real solution for the wave number, to consider it an equation for the frequency determined by specified values of k, σ, and the mass ratio ε. It is then a quadratic equation in ω^2 which yields two roots. Conversely, there are two real solutions for k. In other words, there are two real propagation constants, and waves can propagate without attenuation at two velocities. There exist a denumerable infinity of other characteristic values of k, but all these are complex and represent strongly attenuated modes. Of course, with the presence of viscosity, even the propagating modes are attenuated to some extent.

At very low frequencies, and for small values of ε compared with unity, the expressions for the velocities of the propagating modes take a particularly simple form,

$$c_+ = \sqrt{\frac{E}{\rho\,(1 - \sigma^2)}}, \tag{33}$$

$$c_- = \sqrt{\frac{Eh}{2\rho_0 a}}. \tag{34}$$

The root c_+ is actually unchanged for all values of the frequency. This is not surprising, because the mode associated with this velocity is characteristic of the tube and has very little fluid motion associated with it. The velocity in fact depends only on the tube characteristics. The velocity c_-, on the other hand, depends on both the tube and fluid properties and is the velocity that is generally observed in measurements of the pulse velocity in mammalian arteries. If we investigate the dependence of this root with increasing frequency, it is found that it cuts off, that is to say, c_- becomes zero when $\omega = 1$. Beyond $\omega = 1$, the mode associated with c_- is attenuated. The extent to which the dispersive properties of c_- affect the propagation of the mammalian pulse wave has not yet been investigated, and must await a complete numerical investigation of the dispersion relation.

The above problem of flow in a single tube is the basic element out of which, hopefully, a successful model of the arterial and venous parts of the circulatory system will be formulated.

IV. COMPARTMENT ANALYSIS

The two preceding topics have obviously had the great advantage of dealing with physical processes such as electrical conduction and fluid flow, which have possessed for a long time a successful mathematical characterization. In addition, many aspects of the nervous and circulatory systems are accessible to measurement and control. The mathematical method known in biology as compartment theory has its greatest use when the biological mechanism does not have an obvious mathematical representation, may not be accessible for measurement, or may not even be distinguished or identified. Such is the experimental situation when radioactive isotopes or dyes are used to trace materials in physiological systems. This technique is well known in many areas of physics and chemistry. It corresponds, in fact, to the input-"black box"-output technique that emanated from electrical engineering and has reached out as far as economic theory.

The breadth of application of the technique in biology and medicine is large. The functions of organs such as the thyroid, liver and kidney have been examined. Blood circulation, metabolic processes and respiration cycles have all been studied by tracer methods.[23] As a hypothetical example, suppose one is interested in how a particular substance, say sodium, is distributed in a gland, the blood and the kidneys. Sodium is transportable from the gland to the blood and back, and from the blood to the kidney and back. We might suppose that the gland and the kidneys also interact with each other directly in an additional manner. We represent the gland, the blood and the kidneys as compartments, labeled 1, 2, and 3, respectively, and let c_i be the concentrations of radioactive labeled sodium in each compartment. (The absolute amount of labeled sodium in each compartment could equally well be introduced as variables). The c_i are assumed to be time-dependent and obey the compartment equations

$$\frac{dc_i}{dt} = \sum_{j=1}^{3} k_{ij} c_j \quad i = 1, 2, 3. \tag{35}$$

The coefficients k_{ij} are called transport coefficients and are assumed to be constant. Schematically, the system is represented as in Fig. 6.

Obviously, this is a familiar system of equations. In electrical circuit theory, this would be a lumped parameter linear network, and an electrical circuit analog could be readily constructed. There is little point here in discussing the solutions to such a system. Matrix and transform methods have been more or less thoroughly exploited.[24]

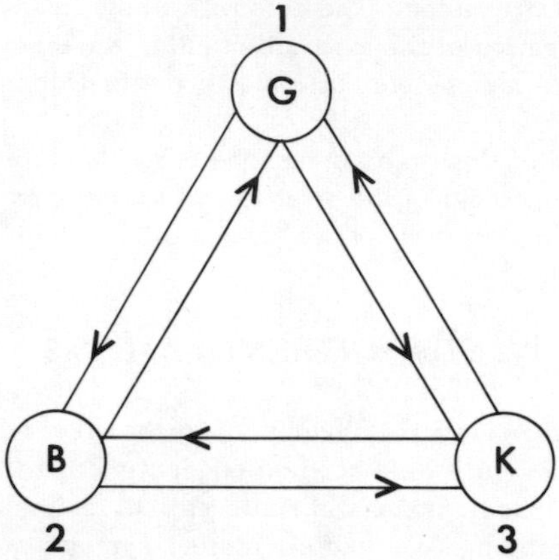

Fig. 6. Schematic representation of sodium transport through a gland (G), the blood (B), and the kidney (K).

Experimentally, the appearance and disappearance of the isotope is observed following its injection into one of the compartments. In some experiments only some of the compartments are accessible to observation. Thus it is the solution, or only part of the solution, that is obtained. From this data, an identification of the values of the rate constants k_{ij} is sought. In addition, one might seek to confirm whether a three-compartment model is in fact a suitable model of the system. This is accomplished by seeing whether the curve of the observed sodium concentration in any compartment is fitted "reasonably well" as a sum of three exponentials (or n exponentials for an n-compartment model).

We see from this example that, typically, it is the "inverse problem" that needs to be solved: given some experimental information about the solutions, to construct the appropriate compartment model. In spite of the lack of mathematical sophistication of the treatment, this approach has proven to be of considerable value in finding functional relations between elements of complex biological systems and in giving them an initial quantitative characterization.

Compartment equations have the same form regardless of what the true underlying physical mechanisms are. These mechanisms may involve diffusion, convection, electrical and thermal conduction, chemical reactions, etc. In order to understand better the nature of the approximation that is made in utilizing compartment equations, we shall analyse here a physical system for which the fundamental equations and solutions are known. We shall then show how a transition can be made from these equations to the compartment equations, and what assumptions are required to do this.

The particular physical system we shall investigate is a sequence of regions in one dimension, in each of which diffusion is the underlying phenomenon. Each region or compartment has a characteristic size, concentration c_i, and diffusion constant k_i. Each compartment is separated from its neighbor by a narrow region (representing, say, a membrane) in which diffusion is also the dominant mecha-

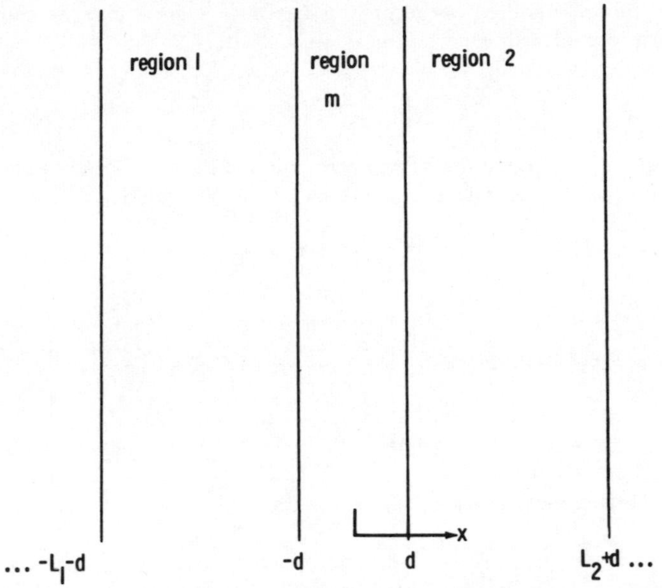

Fig. 7. A sequence of one-dimensional diffusion regions. The middle region represents a membrane connecting two compartments labeled 1 and 2.

nism (see Fig. 7). In each region we need to solve the diffusion equation

$$k_i \frac{\partial^2 c_i}{\partial x^2} = \frac{\partial c_i}{\partial t} \qquad i = 1,\ m,\ 2. \tag{36}$$

At the compartment-membrane interfaces, $x = \pm d$, we require continuity of concentration and flux. Thus,

$$\left.\begin{aligned} c_1(-d) &= c_m(-d), \\ c_m(d) &= c_2(d), \end{aligned}\right\} \tag{37}$$

and

$$\left.\begin{aligned} k_1 \frac{\partial c_1(-d)}{\partial x} &= k_m \frac{\partial c_m(-d)}{\partial x}, \\ k_m \frac{\partial c_m(d)}{\partial x} &= k_2 \frac{\partial c_2(d)}{\partial x}, \end{aligned}\right\} \tag{38}$$

Boundary conditions are also required at the outer boundaries, and we shall suppose that

$$\frac{\partial c_1(-L_1 - d)}{\partial x} = \frac{\partial c_2(L_2 + d)}{\partial x} = 0. \tag{39}$$

This problem could be solved exactly, and it is not very difficult to do so. Rather, we are interested in seeing how it becomes compartment theory. To this end, we consider the limit $k_i \longrightarrow \infty$, $k_2 \longrightarrow \infty$, $k_m \longrightarrow 0$, $d \longrightarrow 0$, but

$k_m/d \longrightarrow$ finite. Another way of saying this is to assume that the characteristic time associated with each region is very small:

$$\frac{L_1^2}{k_1} \ll 1, \quad \frac{L_2^2}{k_2} \ll 1, \quad \frac{d^2}{k_m} \ll 1. \tag{40}$$

Now let us investigate the asymptotic solution of eqs. (36) under these conditions. We readily find that the solutions may be written as:

$$\left.\begin{aligned} c_1(x, t) &= \bar{c}_1(t) + \frac{(x + d + L_1)^2}{2k_1} \frac{d\bar{c}_1(t)}{dt} + 0\left(\frac{L_1^4}{k_1^2}\right), \\ c_2(x, t) &= \bar{c}_2(t) + \frac{(x - d - L_2)^2}{2k_2} \frac{d\bar{c}_2(t)}{dt} + 0\left(\frac{L_2^4}{k_2^2}\right), \\ c_m(x, t) &= \frac{d - x}{2d} \bar{c}_1(t) + \frac{d + x}{2d} \bar{c}_2(t) + 0\left(\frac{d^2}{k_m}\right). \end{aligned}\right\} \tag{41}$$

Applying the flux requirements (38) we obtain

$$\left.\begin{aligned} L_1 \frac{d\bar{c}_1}{dt} &= k(\bar{c}_2 - \bar{c}_1), \\ L_2 \frac{d\bar{c}_2}{dt} &= k(\bar{c}_1 - \bar{c}_2), \end{aligned}\right\} \tag{42}$$

where the rate constant $k \equiv k_m/2d$. These are the compartment equations for a simple two-compartment system. It should be noted that their derivation imposes the following characterization of the physical system: the concentrations in the compartments are homogeneous in space and the rate constant is purely a property of the membrane. Furthermore, if we compared the solution to the above equations with the exact solution of the original equations expressed as an eigenfunction expansion, we would see that we are essentially representing the solution approximately by its slowest time-constant modes.

The system above would be represented schematically as in Fig. 8. We could apply our result additively to form an n-compartment system. If the nth compartment was re-entrant with the first compartment, the compartment equations would take the form

$$L_i \frac{d\bar{c}_i}{dt} = \sum_{j=i}^{n} k_{ij} \bar{c}_j \quad i = 1, 2, 3 \ldots n \tag{43}$$

where $k_{ij} = k_{ji}$.

It would perhaps be profitable to examine some biological systems along the lines of the simple method sketched here with a view toward relating compartment

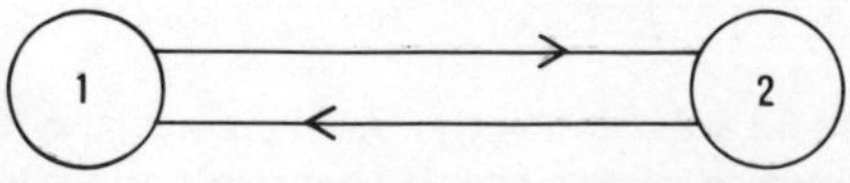

Fig. 8. Schematic representation of the two compartment equations.

theory with more concrete underlying physical theories. In this manner one would hope to gain a deeper understanding of biological mechanisms.

REFERENCES

1. L. Euler, "Principia pro motu sanguinis per arterias determinando," *Opera Posthuma II* (Petropoli, 1862), p. 814.
2. H. Helmholtz, *Treatise on Physiological Optics* (The Optical Society of America, 1924).
3. V. Volterra, *Lecons sur la Theorie Mathematique de la Lutte pour la Vie*, (Paris: Gauthiers-Villars, 1931).
4. R. A. Fisher, *The Genetical Theory of Natural Selection* (Oxford, England: Oxford University Press, 1930; New York: Dover Publications, 1958).
5. E. Schrodinger, *What is Life*, (Cambridge, England: Cambridge University Press, 1944; New York: Doubleday, 1956).
6. J. von Neumann, "The General and Logical Theory of Automata," *Collected Works*, Vol. 5 (New York: MacMillan, 1963), p. 288.
7. M. Planck, *Ann. Phys. u. Chem.*, **39**, N.F., 161 (1890); **40**, N.F., 561 (1890).
8. H. Cohen and J. W. Cooley, *Biophys. J.*, **5**, 145 (1965).
9. T. Teorell, *J. Gen. Physiol.*, **42**, 831 (1959).
10. A. L. Hodgkin and A. F. Huxley, *J. Physiol.*, **117**, 500 (1954).
11. F. Dodge, J. W. Cooley, Paper presented at the Biophysical Society Meeting, February 1965; paper in preparation.
12. R. Fitzhugh, *J. Gen. Physiol.*, **43**, 867 (1960).
13. J. Nagumo, *Proc. IRE*, **50**, 2061 (1962).
14. R. A. Fisher, *Annals of Eugenics*, **7**, Pt. 4, 355 (1957).
15. A. Kolmogorov, I. Petrovsky, and N. Piskunov, *Moscow Univ. Bull. Math.*, Serie Internationale, Sect. A., Math. et Mec., **1**, 6, 1 (1937).
16. Y. B. Zeldovich, NACA T.M. 1282, Washington, D.C. (June 1951).
17. J. Del Castillo and B. Katz, *Progress in Biophysics*, **6** (New York: Pergamon Press, 1956), p. 121.
18. F. S. Grodins, *Quart. Rev. of Biology*, **34**, 93 (1959).
19. Fred Weiner, "The Mechanics of the Pulmonary Circulation," Doctoral Dissertation, Columbia University (1964).
20. John R. Womersley, *Phil. Mag.*, **46**, 199 (1955); WADC Technical Report TR 56–614, "An Elastic Tube Theory of Pulse Transmission and Oscillatory Flow in Mammalian Arteries" (1957).
21. H. Lamb, *Manchester Memoirs*, **42**, 9 (1898); K. Witzig, "Uber erzwungene Wellenbewegungen zaher, inkompressibler Flussigkeiten in elastichen Rohren," Inaug. Diss. Bern., Wyss, Bern. (1914); G. W. Morgan and J. P. Kiely, *J. Acoust. Soc. Amer.*, **26**, 323 (1954).
22. Joseph B. Keller and S. I. Rubinow, unpublished.
23. See bibliography in J. S. Robertson, *Physiological Reviews*, **37**, 133 (1957), and C. W. Sheppard, *Basic Principles of the Tracer Method* (New York: John Wiley and Sons, 1962).
24. R. L. Schoenfeld and M. Berman, *1957 IRE Convention Record*, Pt. 4, p. 84; M. Berman, M. F. Weiss and E. Shahn, *Biophys. J.*, **2**, 289 (1962).

INDEX TO CONTRIBUTORS

CUMULATIVE INDEX TO CONTRIBUTORS TO THE PROCEEDINGS VOLUMES I - XV, 1952 - 1965

This continuing series of annual international symposia is organized by the Polytechnic Institute of Brooklyn under the aegis of its Microwave Research Institute. The series is cosponsored by the Air Force Office of Scientific Research, the Office of Naval Research and the Army Research Office, and has been held in cooperation with appropriate professional groups of the Institute of Electrical and Electronics Engineers (IEEE Groups on Antennas and Propagation, Automatic Control, Circuit Theory, Electron Devices, Electronic Computers, Information Theory, Microwave Theory and Techniques, Nuclear Science, and Sonics and Ultrasonics), and on occasion with the American Institute of Aeronautics and Astronautics, the Optical Society of America and the Society for Industrial and Applied Mathematics.

Where known to the editors, this index gives the authors' affiliations current in 1965, rather than those at time of presentation.